D1060109

McGRAW-HILL PUBLICATIONS IN THE
BOTANICAL SCIENCES

EDMUND W. SINNOTT, *Consulting Editor*

PLANT MORPHOLOGY

McGRAW-HILL PUBLICATIONS IN THE BOTANICAL SCIENCES

EDMUND W. SINNOTT, *Consulting Editor*

ARNOLD—An Introduction to Paleobotany
AVERY ET AL.—Hormones and Horticulture
BABCOCK AND CLAUSEN—Genetics
CURTIS AND CLARK—An Introduction to Plant Physiology
EAMES—Morphology of Vascular Plants
EAMES AND MacDANIELS—An Introduction to Plant Anatomy
FITZPATRICK—The Lower Fungi
GATES—Field Manual of Plant Ecology
GÄUMANN AND DODGE—Comparative Morphology of Fungi
HAUPT—An Introduction to Botany
HAUPT—Laboratory Manual of Elementary Botany
HAUPT—Plant Morphology
HILL—Economic Botany
HILL, OVERHOLTS, AND POPP—Botany
JOHANSEN—Plant Microtechnique
KRAMER—Plant and Soil Water Relationships
LILLY AND BARNETT—Physiology of the Fungi
MAHESHWARI—An Introduction to the Embryology of Angiosperms
MILLER—Plant Physiology
POOL—Flowers and Flowering Plants
SHARP—Fundamentals of Cytology
SHARP—Introduction to Cytology
SINNOTT—Botany: Principles and Problems
SINNOTT—Laboratory Manual for Elementary Botany
SINNOTT, DUNN, AND DOBZHANSKY—Principles of Genetics
SMITH—Cryptogamic Botany
   Vol. I. Algae and Fungi
   Vol. II. Bryophytes and Pteridophytes
SMITH—The Fresh-water Algae of the United States
SWINGLE—Textbook of Systematic Botany
WEAVER—Root Development of Field Crops
WEAVER AND CLEMENTS—Plant Ecology

There are also the related series of McGraw-Hill Publications in the Zoological Sciences, of which E. J. Boell is Consulting Editor, and in the Agricultural Sciences, of which R. A. Brink is Consulting Editor.

PLANT MORPHOLOGY

ARTHUR W. HAUPT

Professor of Botany
University of California, Los Angeles

"Morphology...is one of the most interesting departments of natural history, and may almost be said to be its very soul." —Charles Darwin, *Origin of Species*.

New York   Toronto   London

McGRAW-HILL BOOK COMPANY, INC.

1953

PLANT MORPHOLOGY

THE MAPLE PRESS COMPANY, YORK, PA.

PREFACE

This book deals with the principal groups of plants from the standpoint of their structure, reproduction, and development. It presents a survey of the plant kingdom with emphasis upon relationships as revealed by basic similarity in bodily organization and life histories. It gives an account of the general course of evolution that existing groups appear to have followed. It endeavors to interpret, as far as possible, the structural and developmental complexities of the higher plants in terms of the simpler conditions prevailing among the lower plants.

The principal groups of plants are taken up in an ascending sequence based on ever-increasing structural complexity. This order of presentation does not imply direct phylogenetic relationship between successive groups, even though in some cases such relationship may exist. It merely denotes different degrees of progress from what is assumed to have been a more primitive condition. Conclusions as to the derivation of one group from another are based on substantial morphological evidence, but are always tentative and subject to confirmation by paleontological evidence. A true understanding of phylogeny can rest only on the fossil record and, with a few notable exceptions, this is very incomplete.

The system of classification used as a basis for the presentation of the principal plant groups is at once simple and conservative. The older classification, which continues to be the one most widely used, has certain limitations, but these arise mainly from uncertainties regarding the affinities of many groups, particularly the lower ones. As long as these uncertainties remain, there is little justification for abandoning an established system of classification for a newer one. A somewhat simplified classification is adopted because of its greater convenience and because more detailed schemes may be found in advanced works dealing with special plant groups. It is comprehensive enough to embrace, under almost every class, the most important orders; but it generally does not include families.

Usually the outstanding features of each order are developed through a detailed discussion of one or, more frequently, of several of its representative genera. The distinguishing characters of the order are then given in the form of a summary. Likewise the characters of each class are summarized after all its members have been considered. These are usually presented with the characters of related classes, so that a com-

v

parison can be made. General conclusions are given at the end of the account of each of the major divisions of the plant kingdom, *viz.*, algae, fungi, bryophytes, pteridophytes, and spermatophytes. Here are emphasized the evolutionary tendencies within the group, its contributions to the evolution of the plant kingdom, and the interrelationships of its classes.

This book is designed for use in a two-semester course with adequate laboratory work. It is intended to follow a course in general botany, where the student has gained a knowledge of such material as the many available elementary textbooks present. In particular, the student should understand the cytological relations involved in alternation of generations, including the behavior of the chromosomes in vegetative mitosis, fertilization, and meiosis. Much material properly belonging to the special fields of plant anatomy, cytology, and taxonomy has been omitted from the present work, especially in the treatment of the angiosperms. Emphasis is placed throughout on the evolution of the plant kingdom as revealed by a comparative study of the morphology of the main groups. At the end of the book a list of supplementary readings has been added. These will serve to introduce the student to the current literature dealing with special groups and topics.

More than two-thirds of the illustrations are original, and most of these have not hitherto been published elsewhere. Some have been taken from the author's earlier writings. Of the figures borrowed from the works of others, for which credit is given in every case, almost all have been redrawn and are designated in the legends by the word "after."

The author is indebted for many valuable suggestions to his colleague, Prof. Orda A. Plunkett, and to H. R. Bennett of Chicago, who read Chap. IV; to Prof. P. Maheshwari, University of Delhi, India, who read Chaps. VIII and IX, and to Prof. Paul D. Voth, The University of Chicago, who read the entire manuscript. The author is also grateful to his wife for making some of the slides from which illustrations have been made and for much assistance in proofreading.

ARTHUR W. HAUPT

Los ANGELES, CALIF.
   April, 1953

CONTENTS

Preface . . . . **v**

I. INTRODUCTION **1**

Classification of Plants 1
Plant Life of the Past 4

II. THALLOPHYTA: ALGAE **7**

1. Cyanophyceae 8
2. Euglenophyceae 14
3. Chrysophyceae 16
4. Dinophyceae 18
5. Xanthophyceae 18
6. Bacillariophyceae 21
7. Chlorophyceae 25
   1. Volvocales 26
   2. Chlorococcales 32
   3. Ulotrichales 38
   4. Oedogoniales 45
   5. Conjugales 48
   6. Siphonocladiales 54
   7. Siphonales 57
   Summary of Chlorophyceae 61

III. THALLOPHYTA: ALGAE (CONTINUED) **63**

8. Charophyceae 63
9. Phaeophyceae 66
   1. Ectocarpales 67
   2. Sphacelariales 69
   3. Cutleriales 70
   4. Dictyotales 72
   5. Laminariales 76
   6. Fucales 80
   Summary of Phaeophyceae 85
10. Rhodophyceae 85
Comparison of the Classes of Algae 93
General Conclusions 94

IV. THALLOPHYTA: FUNGI **100**

1. Schizomycetes 100
2. Myxomycetes 104
3. Phycomycetes 103

1. Chytridiales 108
2. Monoblepharidales 111
3. Plasmodiophorales 112
4. Saprolegniales 113
5. Peronosporales 114
6. Mucorales 117
7. Entomophthorales 120
4. Ascomycetes 121
    1. Protoascales 122
    2. Protodiscales 123
    3. Plectascales 124
    4. Perisporiales 127
    5. Pezizales 129
    6. Helvellales 133
    7. Tuberales 134
    8. Pyrenomycetales 134
    9. Laboulbeniales 140
5. Basidiomycetes 140
    1. Ustilaginales 140
    2. Uredinales 142
    3. Auriculariales 146
    4. Tremellales 146
    5. Exobasidiales 146
    6. Hymenomycetales 147
    7. Gasteromycetales 151
Fungi Imperfecti 153
Lichenes 153
Comparison of the Classes of Fungi 156
General Conclusions 157

V. BRYOPHYTA 160

1. Hepaticae 161
    1. Marchantiales 161
    2. Sphaerocarpales 173
    3. Jungermanniales 177
    4. Anthocerotales 186
2. Musci 192
    1. Sphagnales 192
    2. Andreaeales 197
    3. Bryales 198
Comparison of Liverworts and Mosses 205
General Conclusions 205

VI. PTERIDOPHYTA 209

The Vascular System 210
1. Psilophytinae 212
    1. Psilophytales 212
    2. Psilotales 214
2. Lycopodiinae 218
    1. Lycopodiales 218

2. Selaginellales 230
3. Lepidodendrales 238
4. Isoetales 241
3. Equisetinae 247
1. Hyeniales 247
2. Sphenophyllales 248
3. Equisetales 250
4. Calamitales 258

VII. PTERIDOPHYTA (CONTINUED) 260

4. Filicinae 260
1. Coenopteridales 260
2. Ophioglossales 261
3. Marattiales 270
4. Filicales 276
5. Hydropteridales 292
Comparison of the Classes of Pteridophytes 303
General Conclusions. 304

VIII. SPERMATOPHYTA 309

1. Gymnospermae 310
1. Cycadofilicales 311
2. Bennettitales 315
3. Cycadales 319
4. Cordaitales 330
5. Ginkgoales 333
6. Coniferales 340
7. Gnetales 354

IX. SPERMATOPHYTA (CONTINUED) 362

2. Angiospermae. 362
Vegetative Organs 363
The Flower 372
Chief Orders of Angiosperms 399
Comparison of Gymnosperms and Angiosperms 408
General Conclusions. 409

X. EVOLUTION OF THE PLANT KINGDOM 412

Prominent Evolutionary Tendencies 415
Evolution of Sex 417
Alternation of Generations 422

Selected References 427

Glossary 431

Index 445

CHAPTER I

INTRODUCTION

Morphology deals with the form and structure of plants. It is concerned with both gross, external features and minute, internal details. It includes a study of the development of plants throughout all their growth stages, called *ontogeny*, as well as their evolutionary development, or *phylogeny*, by means of which all existing plants have been derived from those of past ages. Morphology considers the interrelationships of the groups forming the larger units of classification, but does not deal with species, the study of which belongs to taxonomy. One of the main objectives of morphology is the determination, so far as possible, of lines of descent.

A sound knowledge of the structure and development of plants is a necessary foundation for successful specialization in any phase of botany, whether it be taxonomy, physiology, ecology, pathology, or genetics. A study of the lower plants is often neglected, since the higher ones are more familiar and, in general, more important. Many of the problems encountered in the higher plants, however, are more easily studied in the lower plants, whose structure and functions are much simpler. The logical procedure is to study simple plants before attempting to understand complex plants.

CLASSIFICATION OF PLANTS

For many years the system of classification most widely adopted by botanists has been one in which the plant kingdom is separated into four major divisions: Thallophyta, Bryophyta, Pteridophyta, and Spermatophyta. Each *division* comprises a number of *classes*. A class is made up of *orders*, an order of *families*, a family of *genera*, and a genus of *species*. Categories of intermediate rank are designated by the prefix *sub*.

At one time the two subkingdoms Cryptogamia and Phanerogamia were recognized, the former including the three lower divisions and the latter the fourth division. These names have fallen into disuse because they are inappropriate. *Cryptogam* means "fertilization concealed" and *phanerogam* means "fertilization evident." The names were given because stamens and pistils, the organs once thought to produce directly the cells which unite in fertilization, are present in seed plants but not in plants without seeds. After the true nature of fertilization was dis-

1

covered, it was found to be actually more evident in the so-called crypto-gams than in the phanerogams.

Often all plants above the level of the Thallophyta are grouped together as the Embryophyta, plants in which the zygote gives rise to an embryo that undergoes its early development within either an archego-nium or an embryo sac. A less suitable name for these plants, but one sometimes used, is Cormophyta, meaning "plants with a stem." Many bryophytes have a stem, but it is not homologous with the stem of pteridophytes and spermatophytes. Sometimes the bryophytes and pteridophytes are combined into a single group, the Archegoniatae, a name that is not distinctive because archegonia are present in nearly all gymnosperms, which form the lower class of spermatophytes. A recent tendency is to place the pteridophytes and spermatophytes together under the name of Tracheophyta, which signifies that they are vascular plants.

Classification of Thallophyta. Some botanists disapprove of the term Thallophyta on the ground that it includes a heterogeneous assemblage of plants which are not closely related. This objection is more valid when the term is applied to one of the four divisions of the plant kingdom rather than to one of two subkingdoms; for the same objection could be raised against the term Embryophyta. A partial solution of the difficulty is to consider the Thallophyta as a subkingdom and to raise the algae and fungi to the rank of divisions, as follows:

A. Thallophyta
    I. Phycophyta (Algae)
    II. Mycophyta (Fungi)
B. Embryophyta (Cormophyta)
    I. Bryophyta
    II. Pteridophyta
    III. Spermatophyta

The thallophytes comprise a number of subordinate groups. These may either be considered as classes and assigned to the algae or the fungi, or may be distributed among a larger number of divisions. The first arrangement is a convenient one, but some of the groups classified as algae or fungi have little in common with the others. Furthermore, it makes the presence or absence of chlorophyll the basis for establishing the two divisions Phycophyta and Mycophyta, a distinction which cannot be maintained among the flagellates, where both green and colorless forms occur. The flagellates were formerly regarded as constituting a distinct class of thallophytes, but are now broken up into a number of separate groups.

Some of the groups commonly included among the algae and fungi are so distinctive that their separation seems justified. These include the

Cyanophyceae, Schizomycetes, Myxomycetes, Bacillariophyceae, and possibly some of the flagellate groups. The remaining classes of algae might then be retained in one division and the remaining classes of fungi in another, or some or all of these classes might be raised to the rank of divisions. Much difference of opinion exists as to which classes should be placed together.

Two different arrangements for classifying the thallophytes are as follows:

A. THALLOPHYTA

I. Phycophyta[1]
  1. Cyanophyceae
  2. Xanthophyceae
  3. Bacillariophyceae
  4. Chlorophyceae
  5. Charophyceae
  6. Phaeophyceae
  7. Rhodophyceae
II. Mycophyta
  1. Schizomycetes
  2. Myxomycetes
  3. Phycomycetes
  4. Ascomycetes
  5. Basidiomycetes

I. Schizophyta
  1. Cyanophyceae
  2. Schizomycetes
II. Myxomycophyta (Myxomycetes)
III. Bacillariophyta (Diatomeae)
IV. Euphycophyta (Euphyceae)[1]
  1. Xanthophyceae
  2. Chlorophyceae
  3. Charophyceae
  4. Phaeophyceae
  5. Rhodophyceae
V. Eumycophyta (Eumycetes)
  1. Phycomycetes
  2. Ascomycetes
  3. Basidiomycetes

[1] Several other classes, consisting almost entirely of flagellates, are generally recognized. These are the Euglenophyceae, Chrysophyceae, Cryptophyceae, and Dinophyceae.

The elevation of a great number of classes to the rank of divisions, thus making each coordinate with the bryophytes, pteridophytes, and spermatophytes (or even with the tracheophytes, if the last two are combined), tends to conceal relationships and gives a prominent place to small, obscure groups. Moreover, when the names of all the divisions are given the termination *phyta*, in order to make them consistent throughout the plant kingdom, many lose their distinctive meanings, and we find the various groups of algae called Chlorophyta (green plants), Phaeophyta (brown plants), Rhodophyta (red plants), etc.

Classification of Embryophyta. The position of the Bryophyta as a division of the plant kingdom seems secure. Those botanists who classify the higher plants on the basis of vascular anatomy discard the names Pteridophyta and Spermatophyta and designate all vascular plants as Tracheophyta. They point out that a marked tendency toward seed formation was present in several extinct groups of pteridophytes, and that the most primitive group of seed plants, the extinct Cycadofilicales, were very fern-like. The Tracheophyta, constituting a division, are separated into four classes, the Psilopsida, Lycopsida,

Sphenopsida, and Pteropsida. The first three correspond to established classes of pteridophytes under the older classification, while the Pteropsida include the ferns (Filicinae), gymnosperms, and angiosperms.

The presence of leaf gaps in the vascular cylinder is thought to indicate a closer relationship between the ferns and seed plants than exists between the ferns and other pteridophytes. However, the basis used in distinguishing the ferns from the gymnosperms and angiosperms, when the three are grouped together as Pteropsida, is the same as when the ferns are placed in the Pteridophyta and the other two groups in the Spermatophyta. Furthermore, if the existing classes of pteridophytes represent collateral lines of descent from the psilophytes of the Devonian, a view widely accepted, their relationship to one another can better be expressed by including them in a division of their own. Certainly no greater degree of relationship is expressed by placing them in a division that also includes the gymnosperms and angiosperms.

The two different schemes of classifying the embryophytes are as follows:

B. EMBRYOPHYTA

I. Bryophyta	I. Bryophyta
1. Hepaticae	1. Hepaticae
2. Musci	2. Musci
II. Pteridophyta	II. Tracheophyta
1. Psilophytinae	1. Psilopsida
2. Lycopodiinae	2. Lycopsida
3. Equisetinae	3. Sphenopsida
4. Filicinae	4. Pteropsida
III. Spermatophyta	*a.* Filicinae
1. Gymnospermae	*b.* Gymnospermae
2. Angiospermae	*c.* Angiospermae

PLANT LIFE OF THE PAST[1]

The plants of today are the modified descendants of other plants that have lived on the earth throughout the course of geologic history. They are the products of a process of evolution that has been in operation since life first began. Our knowledge of the plants of the past has come from a study of fossil remains found embedded in the layers of rock that form the earth's crust. These remains constitute a direct record of the changes undergone by plants down through the ages. This record, incomplete as it is, helps us to follow the course of evolution and to understand the relationships that occur among the various existing plant groups.

It is not known how or when life arose on the earth. It is not even known in what form it arose, although much evidence indicates that the first living things were extremely simple and from them forms more and

[1] This subject is presented in much greater detail in Arthur W. Haupt, An Introduction to Botany, 2d ed., Chap. XX, New York, 1946.

more complex have been evolved. Some groups have made more progress than others. That is why existing groups are at different levels of development. Along with the tendency toward ever-increasing complexity, much retrogression has occurred and, as a result, some modern groups are more or less degenerate.

Paleobotany, the study of fossil plants, has made great progress because methods have been developed making it possible to study thin sections of petrified material under the microscope. Many of these sections show such an amazing wealth of structural detail that almost as much can be learned from them as from sections of living plants. Unlike petrifactions, fossils in the form of casts or impressions, made when some part of a plant falls into soft earth that later hardens into stone, show no internal structure but preserve many external features. Most fossils are of this kind.

Geologic time, whose total duration is about 2 billion years, is divided into five great eras. The Archeozoic era came first. Then followed, in order, the Proterozoic, Paleozoic, Mesozoic, and Cenozoic eras. Each era is divided into periods. The Archeozoic and Proterozoic, with an estimated duration of 800 million and 650 million years, respectively, comprise nearly three-fourths of all geologic time. Most of the evidence for the existence of life during these two great eras is indirect, consisting of extensive deposits of graphite, limestone, and iron ores, substances that are formed, at least to some extent, by organisms. The earliest plants may have been similar to certain existing bacteria and blue-green algae.

The fossil record of nonwoody plants is very fragmentary. Because of their soft and perishable nature, few have left any direct evidence of their existence. Remains are more numerous of such algae as diatoms, which have siliceous shells, and of lime-secreting seaweeds. Bryophytes have been poorly preserved and their remains are scanty. Vascular plants, on the other hand, are represented by an abundance of well-preserved fossil material, and much is known of the geologic history of many groups.

The fossil record really begins with the Paleozoic era, since so little is known of the life of the Archeozoic and Proterozoic. The periods into which the Paleozoic, Mesozoic, and Cenozoic eras are divided are given in the table on page 6. The figures in the time scale denote millions of years.

Fossil algae furnish the only record of plant life during the Cambrian and Ordovician, and the diversity of types which have been found indicates that all four of the great algal groups were represented in both periods. Silurian deposits have yielded remains of the oldest known land plants, the psilophytes, but these are scanty. During the Devonian so

much progress was made, that not only were many kinds of primitive
land plants in existence, but even such highly developed forms as large
lycopods, ferns, and primitive gymnosperms were abundant.

The Carboniferous was characterized by a wonderful display of plant
life.   Tree lycopods and horsetails, as well as fern-like and other primitive gymnosperms, formed a most luxuriant growth surpassing even the

Time scale	Periods	Eras
0	Recent	
1	Quaternary	Cenozoic
60	Tertiary	
100	Upper Cretaceous	
125	Lower Cretaceous	Mesozoic
160	Jurassic	
195	Triassic	
220	Permian	
255	Upper Carboniferous	
305	Lower Carboniferous	
355	Devonian	Paleozoic
395	Silurian	
480	Ordovician	
550	Cambrian	

densest tropical jungles of today.   The accumulated remains of the plants
that lived in the vast Carboniferous swamp forests have formed our most
extensive coal deposits.

The plant life of the Mesozoic, except during the Upper Cretaceous,
was dominated by the gymnosperms, these being of much more advanced
types than had lived during the Paleozoic.   Nearly all the large pteridophytes of the late Paleozoic, as well as the primitive gymnosperms,
became extinct early in the Mesozoic.   A striking feature of the Cretaceous was the rise of the angiosperms, as a result of which they came to
dominate the vegetation of the entire earth, a position they have maintained ever since.   With the rise of the angiosperms, the gymnosperms
have become a subordinate group.

CHAPTER II

THALLOPHYTA: ALGAE

The thallophytes comprise a large and diverse assemblage of simple plants forming the lowest division of the plant kingdom. They number about 88,000 species. The plant body may be unicellular but, where multicellular, as is generally the case, it is a *thallus*—a body without differentiation into true vegetative organs, such as characterize the higher plants. This distinction is not absolute, however, as some of the marine algae have parts that superficially resemble true vegetative organs, while some of the bryophytes have thallus bodies. A more tenable distinction is based on the structure of the reproductive organs. The sporangia of thallophytes, with only a few exceptions, are unicellular; those of the higher plants are always multicellular. The gametangia of thallophytes are prevailingly unicellular but, where multicellular, have no outer layer of sterile cells (except in the Charophyceae). In the thallophytes the zygote does not produce an embryo within the female sex organ, as it does in all the higher groups.

The Thallophyta include two main series, the algae (Phycophyta) and the fungi (Mycophyta), the former with 18,000 species and the latter with 70,000. The algae, having chlorophyll, are able to make food by photosynthesis and so are independent (*autotrophic*) plants. The fungi, lacking chlorophyll, must obtain their food from an external source and so are dependent (*heterotrophic*) plants. This distinction, being physiological, is a convenient one but does not necessarily express relationship; thus it may be without phylogenetic significance. For this reason the various classes of algae and fungi are often regarded as separate and more or less coordinate groups of thallophytes rather than as members of two different series.

Algae live in both fresh and salt water, while a few grow on moist soil, wet rocks, tree trunks, or in other terrestrial habitats. They include the pond scums, kelps and other seaweeds, and a host of less familiar forms. Many are microscopic, but some kelps reach a large size. Because of their perishable nature, algae have left few reliable records of their existence during geologic times. Most of those preserved as fossils are lime-secreting seaweeds and forms with siliceous shells (diatoms). As here presented, the algae are distributed among 10 main classes, the Cyanophyceae, Euglenophyceae, Chrysophyceae, Dinophyceae, Xanthophyceae, Bacillariophyceae, Chlorophyceae, Charophyceae, Phaeophyceae, and Rhodophyceae.

1. CYANOPHYCEAE

The Cyanophyceae,[1] or blue-green algae, are the simplest and lowest group of green plants. They are characterized by having, in addition to chlorophyll and carotinoids, a blue pigment, *phycocyanin*, the combination resulting in a blue-green color. Some of the Cyanophyceae, however, also possess a red pigment, *phycoerythrin*, the presence of which, in varying amounts, produces shades of red, brown, or purple. The Red Sea is said to have received its name from a floating species, *Trichodesmium erythraeum*, which is red and sometimes occurs in such abundance as to color the water. The Cyanophyceae are unicellular plants, the cells being nearly always grouped to form colonies of various kinds. About 1,500 species are known.

The Cyanophyceae comprise two orders: (1) the Coccogonales, whose cells are either solitary or arranged in nonfilamentous colonies; and (2) the Hormogonales, whose cells are in filamentous colonies. Some of the genera belonging to the Coccogonales are *Chroococcus, Gloeocapsa, Merismopedia, Coelosphaerium*, and *Chamaesiphon*. The main genera of the Hormogonales include *Oscillatoria, Lyngbya, Nostoc, Anabaena, Rivularia, Gloeotrichia, Tolypothrix, Scytonema*, and *Stigonema*.

Distribution and Habitat. Blue-green algae are found in all parts of the world where plants can grow. Most of them live in fresh water, some occur on moist earth, rocks, and trees, while others live in the ocean. They commonly form scums, slimy mats, or gelatinous lumps. They are especially prevalent in stagnant water, where large quantities of organic matter accumulate. Some live in hot springs at temperatures as high as 75°C. Many forms extract calcium and magnesium from the water and cause minerals, which are often brightly colored, to be deposited on rocks in the vicinity. Some species of *Nostoc* and *Anabaena* live as endophytes in the intercellular cavities of other plants, as in the thallus of *Anthoceros*, the leaves of *Azolla*, and the roots of cycads. Some blue-green algae enter into the formation of lichens.

The Cyanophyceae living in hot springs thrive under conditions that

---

[1] Sometimes called Schizophyceae or Myxophyceae. Schizophyceae means "splitting algae"; Myxophyceae means "slime algae." These names are used by some botanists in preference to Cyanophyceae, which means "blue algae," because not all the members are blue-green. But it is also true that some of them lack the slippery feel. As long as we retain the names Chlorophyceae, Phaeophyceae, and Rhodophyceae for other algal groups, we might as well retain the name Cyanophyceae for the sake of uniformity, especially since some of the Chlorophyceae are not green, some of the Phaeophyceae are not brown, and some of the Rhodophyceae are not red. The things most desired in a name are that it shall express the most prominent feature of the group and that it shall be consistent with the names of coordinate groups.

would be fatal to almost all other forms of life. For this reason, because of their simplicity in cellular organization, and because they are auto-trophic, members of this group may have lived on the earth before con-ditions were favorable for the existence of other organisms, with the possible exception of bacteria. Their great antiquity is indicated by the presence, in rocks of Proterozoic age, of what seem to be fossil Cyano-phyceae, as well as numerous calcareous deposits resembling those made by blue-green algae now living in hot springs. There is more certain

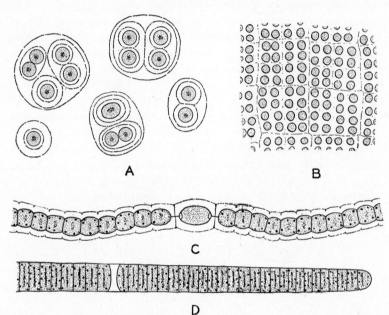

FIG. 1. Some simple colonial blue-green algae. *A, Gloeocapsa,* ×750; *B, Merismopedia,* ×750; *C, Nostoc,* ×1,000; *D, Oscillatoria,* ×600. Except in *Oscillatoria,* the cells are embedded in a mucilaginous matrix.

evidence of their existence in the Paleozoic era, particularly in the Cambrian, Silurian, and Devonian periods.

Plant Body. All the Cyanophyceae are unicellular and in nearly all of them the cells are organized to form colonies (Fig. 1). None has a truly multicellular body, although this condition is approached by the higher members of the group. In some species of *Chroococcus* the cells are solitary, while in *Gloeocapsa* they form small irregular colonies loosely held together in a gelatinous matrix. In *Merismopedia* the colonies are plate-like, the cells being arranged in regular rows. In *Coelosphaerium* the colonies are globular and hollow, in *Nostoc* they resemble a string of beads, while in *Oscillatoria* they form a compact filament. The fila-mentous type of colony is most common.

Although cilia are never present, many of the filamentous blue-green algae have the power of movement. If a mass of *Oscillatoria* growing on mud is placed in a flat dish, the filaments soon creep out in all directions. Under the microscope the filaments are seen to shift frequently their position laterally in the water. In performing these movements, the cause of which is unknown, the cells of the colony function as a unit, thus approaching a condition characteristic of multicellular plants—a cooperation of cells in the performance of their functions.

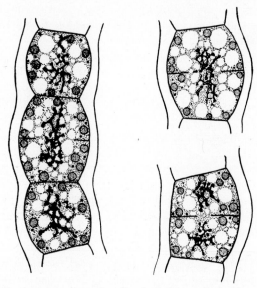

Fig. 2. Longitudinal sections through cells of *Anabaena circinalis*, some of which are dividing, ×2,750. The nuclear material is in the form of irregular masses. The spherical bodies are cyanophycin granules and represent reserve food. (*After Haupt.*)

Cell Structure. The Cyanophyceae are characterized by a very primitive cell structure. A thin cell wall, composed of cellulose and pectic compounds, seems always to be present. Generally it becomes mucilaginous and forms a matrix around the cell. The protoplast lacks the degree of organization seen in the higher plants. It consists of an outer colored portion, containing the blue and green pigments, and a central colorless portion. The latter, representing an incipient nucleus, contains a mass of scattered chromatin granules not surrounded by a membrane and without a nucleolus (Fig. 2). Plastids are not organized, the pigments being merely diffused throughout the peripheral region of the cell. Carbohydrate food is stored as glycogen, starch being absent. Reserve food often occurs also as minute oil droplets and as spherical bodies (cyanophycin granules) that are probably protein in nature.

These granules usually lie in the outer part of the cell, in many filamentous forms being commonly grouped along the cross walls.

Cell division is accomplished by a ring-like wall that develops from the outside toward the center, finally cutting the cell in half (Fig. 2). At the same time the chromatin separates into two approximately equal masses without the formation of chromosomes or other features of mitosis.

Reproduction. Because the Cyanophyceae are unicellular plants, cell division results in reproduction, a method called *fission*. The division of a cell to form two new individuals directly is the simplest method of reproduction in the plant kingdom. In most of the Cyanophyceae the cell walls break down to form abundant mucilage. Generally, as in *Gloeocapsa*, this holds together a group of cells derived from a single cell by repeated division, thus forming a colony (Fig. 1*A*). Here the mucilage surrounding the cells is in concentric layers; but in many other genera it is in a continuous mass made up of the confluent sheaths of the individual cells.

In some of the filamentous types, such as *Lyngbya*, a firm mucilaginous sheath is present around the whole colony, but in *Oscillatoria*, a related genus, the cell walls are more resistant and no sheath is formed (Fig. 1*D*). In both genera the cells are compactly arranged in the colony, each cell, except the terminal one, being shortly cylindrical. That their shape results from mutual pressure is shown by the fact that the free surface of the end cell is convex. This is also true of cells adjacent to a dead cell in the filament.

The type of colony produced depends on the way in which the cells divide. In a filament all the divisions occur in one plane. Where the cells divide in two planes, a plate or a hollow sphere one layer thick is produced. Divisions in three planes usually result in a somewhat massive type of colony.

In most of the filamentous forms, with the exception of *Oscillatoria* and its relatives, differentiated cells, called *heterocysts*, appear in the colony. They may be seen in such common genera as *Nostoc* and *Anabaena* (Fig. 1*C*). A heterocyst is an enlarged vegetative cell that becomes thick-walled and transparent. Heterocysts usually occur singly but at rather frequent intervals, thus dividing the filament into segments called *hormogonia*. These become detached and move away from one another to form new colonies. A hormogonium is merely an isolated portion of the original filament. In *Oscillatoria* and related genera hormogonia are formed by the death of unmodified cells here and there in the colony (Fig. 1*D*).

Although none of the Cyanophyceae produces zoospores or gametes, most of the filamentous members form nonmotile resting spores. One kind, called an *akinete*, arises from a vegetative cell that enlarges by the accumulation of food and develops a thick cell wall (Fig. 3*A*, *B*). These cells are very resistant to unfavorable conditions. Akinetes may be separated in the filament or several may occur together. In some forms they always appear next to a heterocyst, either at the end or in the middle of the filament. Another kind of resting cell, called an *endospore*, is developed in some genera, as in *Chamaesiphon* and in the marine genus, *Dermocarpa* (Fig. 3*C*). Endospores are small thick-walled spores that

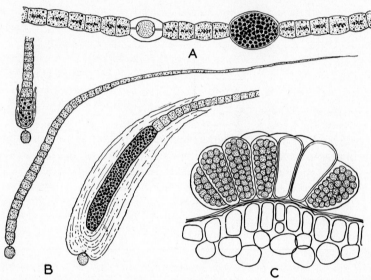

Fig. 3. Formation of resting spores in the blue-green algae. *A*, portion of filament of *Anabaena* with a heterocyst and an akinete containing many food granules, ×750; *B*, *Gloeotrichia*, showing a young filament and two stages in the development of an akinete, ×500; *C*, *Dermocarpa*, an epiphytic form, with two empty cells and others containing endospores. (*C, after Bornet and Thuret.*)

arise from a protoplast by divisions within the cell cavity and from which they later are liberated.

Rivularia is a filamentous form in which the basal cell of a filament is always a heterocyst, while the other cells become gradually smaller toward the very slender apex. A thick mucilaginous sheath, confined to the base of the filament, begins next to the heterocyst. *Gloeotrichia* is similar to *Rivularia* except that the first basal vegetative cell becomes transformed into an elongated akinete (Fig. 3*B*).

Branching. In some of the filamentous members branching occurs (Fig. 4). In *Tolypothrix* the filaments exhibit "false branching." Here the cells on one side of a heterocyst grow out beyond it to form a branch. In *Scytonema* the false branches arise laterally in pairs but usually not in connection with a heterocyst. In *Stigonema* a true branch arises as a lateral outgrowth from a single cell of the filament. This type of branching is rare in the Cyanophyceae, occurring in only a few genera.

Summary. The Cyanophyceae are an ancient group of plants showing an extremely primitive condition of structural organization. In addition to chlorophyll and carotinoids, a blue pigment (phycocyanin) is present and often a red pigment (phycoerythrin) as well. The plant body is unicellular, the cells nearly always forming colonies. The cell wall is

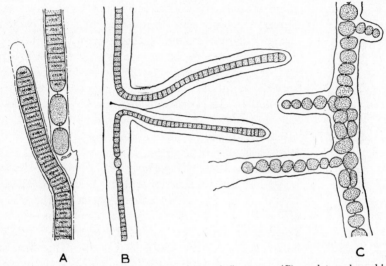

A **B** **C**

FIG. 4. False branching in *Tolypothrix* (*A*) and *Scytonema* (*B*), and true branching in *Stigonema* (*C*); *A*, ×750; *B*, ×200; *C*, ×300.

more or less unstable, usually producing abundant mucilage. The protoplast shows little organization. The pigments forming the characteristic blue-green color are diffused throughout the peripheral part of the protoplast, no plastids being present. Reserve carbohydrate food is stored as glycogen. A nucleus is represented only by scattered chromatin granules, there being no nuclear membrane or nucleolus. Reproduction occurs by fission and by nonmotile spores. It is entirely asexual. Ciliated cells are never produced. The resting cells (akinetes) are merely enlarged protoplasts with a thick wall. There is a tendency toward cellular differentiation, in some forms resulting in the establishment of a distinct apex and base. The relationships of the Cyanophyceae to the other algae are obscure. They appear to be closely related to the bacteria. In fact, the blue-green algae and bacteria are sometimes placed in the same group, the Schizophyta, and made an independent class of thallophytes.

2. EUGLENOPHYCEAE

Flagellates are unicellular organisms combining characters of both plants and animals. Zoologists regard them as one-celled animals, while botanists consider at least those with chlorophyll as plants, as well as certain colorless ones evidently derived from them. Nearly all flagellates are solitary and free-swimming, but some form loose gelatinous colonies and some are attached. Most of them live in fresh or salt water, some occur on damp earth, and some are parasitic. Formerly they were placed in a separate group, the Flagellatae, but they show so many differences among themselves that they are now distributed, so far as possible, into other groups. One of these, the Euglenophyceae, includes about 350 species of green or colorless, mainly fresh-water flagellates. The best-known genus, *Euglena*, is widely distributed and common in stagnant pools and ditches, often occurring in such abundance as to color the water a deep green.

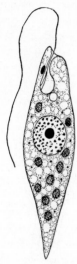

Cell Structure. *Euglena* is somewhat pear-shaped, being blunt at its anterior end and gradually tapering behind (Fig. 5). As in other flagellates, there is no cell wall, each cell consisting of a naked protoplast. In *Euglena* the outer part of the protoplast is differentiated into a thin *pellicle* that is somewhat firm but flexible enough to permit the cell to undergo frequent changes in shape. In some flagellates the pellicle is more rigid, giving the cell a constant form, while in others it is wanting. Some flagellates that lack a pellicle are amoeboid, putting out slender pseudopodia.

Flagellates are characterized by having, in the vegetative condition, one or two (rarely more) *cilia*—slender protoplasmic threads that lash back and forth in the water. Long whip-like cilia are called flagella,[1] the possession of which gives the flagellates their name. The flagella are generally borne at the anterior end of the cell and, where two are present, they are either equal or unequal in length.

Euglena has a single flagellum attached anteriorly. Near its base is a conspicuous red *eyespot*, which is thought to be sensitive to light. Although avoiding direct sunlight, the organism tends to swim toward the best-illuminated part of the water. At the anterior end of the cell

Fig. 5. *Euglena viridis*, ×750. The cell contains a large nucleus and a number of chloroplasts. At the anterior end is a long flagellum, a narrow gullet leading to the reservoir, a contractile vacuole, and an eyespot.

---

[1] If a distinction is to be made between cilia and flagella, the latter are not only longer than the cell that bears them but coarser and fewer in number. Cilium means "eyelash"; flagellum means "whip."

is a short narrow tube, called the *gullet*, that leads to a spherical cavity, the *reservoir*. The flagellum is inserted inside the reservoir and projects through the gullet. Near the reservoir is a *contractile vacuole* (more than one in some species), which alternately contracts and expands. The contractile vacuole discharges its contents into the reservoir. Contractile vacuoles, usually regarded as organs of excretion, are found in many one-celled animals, as well as in the motile cells of many algae.

Flagellates show an advance over the blue-green algae in having a definite nucleus. Moreover, their photosynthetic pigments, where present, are always confined to definite plastids. *Euglena* has many small green plastids (*chloroplasts*), but some flagellates, not belonging to the Euglenophyceae, have yellow or brown plastids. All these colored forms carry on photosynthesis. Other flagellates, some belonging to the Euglenophyceae, are colorless and live either as saprophytes, absorbing organic matter in solution through the plasma membrane, or as animals, ingesting solid particles of food either through the gullet or by means of pseudopodia. A few flagellates are parasitic on animals, one of these, *Trypanosoma*, causing a disease of man known as African sleeping sickness. Some forms with chlorophyll ingest solid food particles through the gullet. Some species of *Euglena* carry on photosynthesis in the light, but, if kept in darkness and supplied with organic matter in solution, become colorless and saprophytic. In all the Euglenophyceae food is stored as paramylon, a starch-like carbohydrate, and often as oil. The presence of paramylon granules is very characteristic, even in colorless cells. True starch is not formed. Flagellates belonging to other groups of algae differ with respect to the type of food stored.

Reproduction. As in all flagellates, reproduction in *Euglena* occurs by fission, the cell dividing longitudinally. In the presence of unfavorable conditions, encystment often occurs. The protoplasm retracts the flagellum, rounds up, secretes a thick gelatinous covering about itself, and goes into a resting stage. Although later the cyst usually produces a single motile protoplast, sometimes it divides internally into a number of smaller protoplasts that escape, develop flagella, and grow to mature size. Sexual reproduction in the Euglenophyceae is of doubtful occurrence.

Colacium, a member of the Euglenophyceae, is interesting in being an attached form lacking flagella in the vegetative condition. Its cells are surrounded by a gelatinous wall and are united into small irregular colonies. When reproduction occurs, the cell contents escape as a naked euglenoid protoplast with a flagellum.

Relationships. Flagellates are related on the one hand to various groups of algae and on the other hand to the Protozoa. The fact that they are intermediate between plants and animals strongly suggests that the earliest forms of life may have been similarly undifferentiated and that from such a common ancestry both plants and animals may have arisen.   Although the relationship of the Cyanophyceae to the flagellates, if any, is very obscure, most of the higher algal groups are thought to have been derived from flagellate ancestors.   Where intermediate forms occur, such a derivation seems almost certain.

Summary.   The Euglenophyceae are a group of flagellates with bright green chloroplasts containing only chlorophyll and its associated carotinoids, the chlorophyll predominating, as in the green algae.   Some members are colorless, these being either saprophytic or animal-like in their nutrition.   All are unicellular and uninucleate, the cells being solitary or rarely in colonies.   The cells have one or two cilia (flagella) that may be equal or unequal but are always attached anteriorly.   Except in colonial forms, the cells are motile and lack a cell wall.   Reserve food is stored as paramylon and often also as oil.   Reproduction occurs by longitudinal fission.   Resting cells (cysts) are commonly formed.   Sexual reproduction is doubtful.

3. CHRYSOPHYCEAE

The Chrysophyceae, or golden-brown algae, are a small group numbering only about 200 species and occurring mainly in fresh water.   Their plastids contain chlorophyll and an excess of yellow and brown carotinoid pigments, giving them a golden-brown color.   Most members are flagellates, being unicellular motile forms without a cell wall.   The cells are solitary or in colonies and may be either free-swimming or attached. Motile cells have one or two, rarely three, cilia (flagella) attached anteriorly.   The two cilia may be equal or unequal in length.   A few forms have a cell wall and are either filamentous or palmelloid, the latter with cells loosely held together in a gelatinous matrix.   All members are uninucleate.   Food is stored as oil or as leucosin, which is a protein-like substance of unknown composition.   Some forms are colorless, while a few, with chlorophyll, may ingest solid food.   Reproduction occurs by fission, mainly longitudinal.   A characteristic feature is the occurrence of cysts with a silicified cell wall having a small plug at one end.   Zoospores may be produced in members that are not flagellates.   Sexual reproduction is of doubtful occurrence.

Chromulina is a motile unicellular form (Fig. 6).   *Chrysamoeba* is amoeboid.   *Synura* and *Uroglena* are globular free-swimming colonies. *Dinobryon* has species in which the cells form a dendroid colony.   *Hydrurus* and *Phaeocystis* are palmelloid forms.   *Phaeothamnion* is a branched filament and represents the highest type of organization attained by the group.

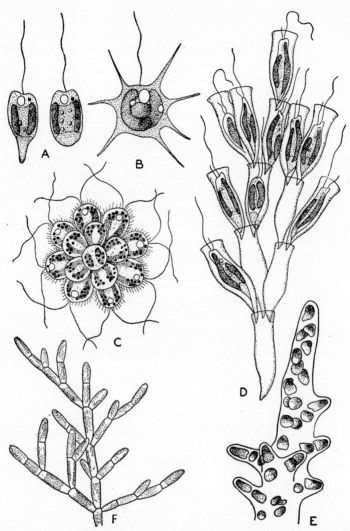

FIG. 6. Group of golden-brown algae. *A, Chromulina ovalis,* ×1,450; *B, Chrysamoeba radians,* ×960; *C, Synura uvella,* ×600; *D, Dinobryon sertularia,* ×900; *E, Hydrurus foetidus,* ×480; *F, Phaeothamnion confervicolum,* ×440. (*A* and *B, after Klebs; C, after Stein; D, after Senn; E, after Berthold; F, after G. M. Smith.*)

Another group composed almost entirely of flagellates are the Cryptophyceae, yellow-green and brown forms that store food as starch or a related substance. Motile cells have two unequal cilia (flagella). Reproduction occurs by fission. Sexual reproduction has been reported in only one species. The Cryptophyceae comprise only 30 species, mostly occurring in fresh water, and are rarely seen. In some respects they resemble the next class.

4. DINOPHYCEAE

The Dinophyceae comprise a group of nearly 1,000 species of organisms, most of which are known as dinoflagellates. Although some occur in fresh water, most of them are free-swimming marine forms. A few have naked protoplasts, but nearly all have sculptured walls of cellulose usually composed of a definite number of jointed plates (Fig. 7). All the dinoflagellates are unicellular and most of them are solitary; some occur in chain-like colonies. The cells are small and generally have a pair of laterally attached cilia (flagella). A characteristic feature is the occurrence of two grooves, one encircling the cell transversely and the other extending longitudinally along one side. The cilia arise at the point of intersection of the grooves. One lies in the transverse groove and the other is directed backward.

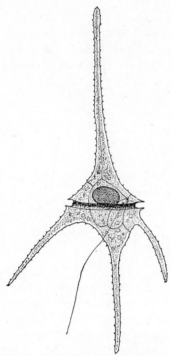

Fig. 7. *Ceratium hirudinella,* a fresh-water dinoflagellate, ×400.

The dinoflagellates have a definite nucleus and usually a number of brownish yellow plastids, in which there is a predominance of carotinoids over the chlorophyll. Some are colorless. The colorless forms live either as saprophytes or as animals, the latter ingesting solid food particles. Some are parasitic. Reserve food occurs either as starch or as oil. Many of the dinoflagellates are phosphorescent. The prevailing method of reproduction is by fission, but some members produce zoospores. As in the other flagellates, cysts are often formed. Sexual reproduction has been reported in only one member of the class.

In addition to the dinoflagellates, the Dinophyceae include a few forms with a higher type of cellular organization, such as *Gloeodinium,* a palmelloid form, and *Dinothrix* and *Dinocladium,* both of which are filamentous.

5. XANTHOPHYCEAE

The Xanthophyceae,[1] or yellow-green algae, are a small but distinct group of only about 200 species characterized by having an excess of

---

[1] Also called Heterocontae.

yellow pigments, especially carotin, in their plastids. *Xanthophyll* and *carotin* are the two carotinoid pigments associated with chlorophyll in other green plants, but here their proportions are different. Although a few are marine, most yellow-green algae are found in fresh water. They are either unicellular or multicellular. Many are flagellates. The group was formerly classified with the Chlorophyceae, but seems to have had an independent origin from a flagellate ancestry and to have followed a line of evolution parallel to that of the green algae. Three representative genera are *Chlorochromonas*, *Tribonema*, and *Botrydium*.

Chlorochromonas. This is a naked unicellular flagellate with two yellow-green plastids (Fig. 8). It has two cilia (flagella) of unequal length attached anteriorly, a contractile vacuole, and a central nucleus. It stores food as leucosin and probably also as oil. A leucosin granule, contained in a vacuole, lies at the posterior end of the cell. Reproduction takes place by fission. From such a form as *Chlorochromonas*, the other Xanthophyceae appear to have evolved.

Fig. 8. *Chlorochromonas minuta*, ×2,000. (*After Lewis.*)

Tribonema. This is a filamentous alga, widely distributed in fresh-water pools (Fig. 9). The filaments are unbranched and composed of elongated cylindrical cells. The walls are made up of two overlapping pieces that appear H-shaped in a longitudinal section. The cells contain a nucleus and a number of yellow-green plastids. Asexual reproduction occurs by the formation of aplanospores, akinetes, or zoospores. *Aplanospores* are nonmotile spores with a wall distinct from the wall of the parent cell. *Akinetes* are also nonmotile but are derived from an entire vegetative cell whose wall becomes the wall of the spore. *Zoospores* are ciliated and naked. In *Tribonema* one or more aplanospores may be produced within a cell, while the zoospores are usually formed singly. Sexual reproduction, which is rare, takes place by the fusion of isogametes formed in ordinary cells. Usually one gamete settles down before the other unites with it. The motile cells have two cilia of unequal length, attached anteriorly, and the reserve food is stored as oil or leucosin, never as starch.

Botrydium. *Botrydium* is a terrestrial alga often found on wet muddy flats. The vegetative body is unicellular and multinucleate, consisting of a balloon-shaped bladder about 1 to 2 mm. in diameter (Fig. 10). It is fastened to the soil by means of branched colorless rhizoids. The cytoplasm, containing many nuclei and, in the aerial portion, numerous yellow-green plastids, forms a thin layer lining the cell wall and enclosing a large central vacuole.   Such a multinucleate body, without any cross walls, is called a *coenocyte*.   Food is stored as oil or leucosin.

Asexual reproduction may occur either by zoospores or aplanospores. When covered with water, the entire aerial portion may release numerous uninucleate zoospores through a terminal pore.   The zoospores have two

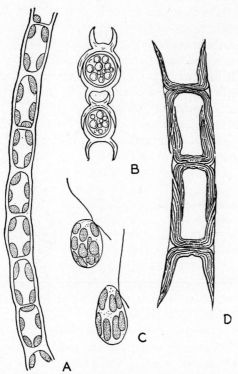

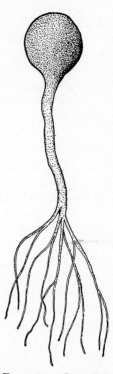

Fig. 9.   *Tribonema bombycinum*, a yellow-green alga.   *A*, portion of vegetative filament; *B*, aplanospores; *C*, zoospores; *D*, structure of cell wall, as revealed by special treatment. (*A, B, C, after Gay; D, after Bohlin.*)

Fig.   10.   *Botrydium granulatum*, showing balloon-shaped aerial portion and branched subterranean portion, ×20.

cilia of unequal length, attached anteriorly.   They may either germinate immediately or form a wall and go into a resting stage.   In the absence of sufficient moisture, the aerial portion may give rise to aplanospores or all the cytoplasm may move into the rhizoidal portion and there produce aplanospores.   The aplanospores of *Botrydium* may be either uninucleate or multinucleate and, after a dormant period, may give rise either to zoospores or to new plants directly.   Sexual reproduction is accomplished by small biciliate isogametes, each with a single nucleus, that fuse to form thick-walled zygotes. These germinate immediately, giving rise directly to a new vegetative body. Sometimes the gametes conjugate before being liberated.

6. BACILLARIOPHYCEAE

The Bacillariophyceae,[1] or diatoms, constitute an isolated group whose relationships to the other algae are very uncertain. They include over 5,000 species of unicellular plants occurring almost universally in fresh and salt water, as well as on damp soil. Some of the more common genera are *Melosira, Coscinodiscus, Biddulphia, Pinnularia, Surirella, Cocconeis, Navicula,* and *Pleurosigma.* Diatoms may be either free-floating or attached. Frequently they form slimy brown coatings on mud at the bottom of shallow bodies of water, as well as on sticks, stones, shells, other aquatic plants, etc. That they were more numerous in geologic times is shown by the great accumulations of diatomaceous earth found in various parts of the world. This consists of the shells (cell walls) of dead diatoms. Deposits of diatomaceous earth were formed mainly during the Tertiary, but the fossil record of diatoms extends as far back as the Jurassic.

Although most diatoms are solitary, some form colonies of diverse types, the individuals being held together by a sheath of mucilage. Their color, usually a golden brown, is due to the presence of chlorophyll in association with an excess of carotinoids, particularly carotin and several brown xanthophyll pigments. Diatoms are distinguished from other algae by their silicified cell wall. This consists

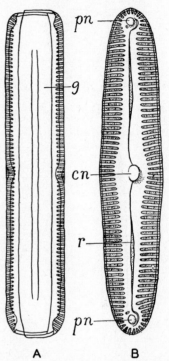

A   **B**

FIG. 11. Two views of the shell of *Pinnularia viridis. A,* girdle view; *B,* valve view; *g,* girdle; *pn,* polar nodule, *cn,* central nodule; *r,* raphe. (*After Pfitzer.*)

of two valves, one overlapping the other like the lid and bottom of a pillbox (Fig. 11). The place where the valves overlap is called the *girdle.* The cell wall is composed mainly of pectin impregnated with a large amount of silica. It is variously marked with numerous fine transverse lines that form regular and elaborate patterns. These make diatoms among the most striking and beautiful objects to be seen under the

[1] Also called Diatomeae.

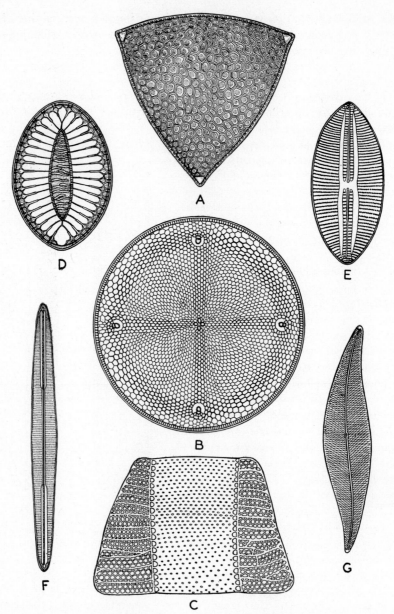

FIG. 12. Group of common diatoms. *A, Triceratium; B, Aulacodiscus; C, Isthmia; D, Surirella, E, Navicula; F, Amphipleura; G, Pleurosigma. (Adapted from a Turtox classroom chart.)*

microscope.   A good microscope will show that the striations on the silicified cell wall generally consist of rows of very minute pores.   They appear
as lines because the pores are very close together.[1]

Two views of a diatom are possible—girdle (side) view and valve
(top) view (Fig. 11).   Many diatoms possess a *raphe*, which is a longitudinal slit extending down the center of the valve.   Such forms have the
power of locomotion, movement apparently being accomplished by a
streaming of protoplasm along the raphe.

The Bacillariophyceae comprise two orders: (1) the Centrales, which
are radially symmetrical in valve view, often circular, and have no raphe

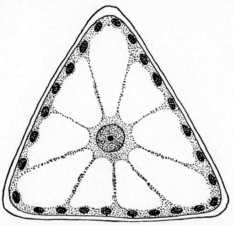

Fig. 13.   *Triceratium*, a large marine diatom, as seen in optical section, ×400.   The
nucleus lies in the center of the cell, while numerous small plastids lie just inside the cell wall.

(Fig. 12*A–C*) and (2) the Pennales, which are usually bilaterally symmetrical, not circular, and generally have a raphe (Fig. 12*D–G*).   The
difference in symmetry is clearly shown by the pattern of markings on
the valves, being radial in the Centrales and bilateral in the Pennales.

In most diatoms the nucleus is suspended in the center of the cell by
slender strands or by a broad transverse band of cytoplasm connected
with a thin layer lying next to the cell wall (Figs. 13 and 14*A*).   Embedded in the peripheral layer are one or more plastids that are usually
brown, frequently yellow, or rarely green.   In the Centrales the plastids
are small and numerous.   In the Pennales they are large and few in
number; commonly there are two.   The plastids of diatoms vary greatly
in shape, being often irregular and sometimes elaborately lobed.   The
cell contains no starch, food being stored mainly as oil.

[1] Some diatoms have striae so fine that they are used as test objects in determining
the efficiency of microscope lenses.   A good oil immersion objective will resolve markings that are as fine as five striae to the micron.

Reproduction occurs chiefly by fission, the cell always dividing in the plane of the valves (Fig. 14). The two valves separate and each daughter protoplast forms a new wall on its naked side, the new wall fitting inside the old one. One of the cells is always as large as the parent cell,

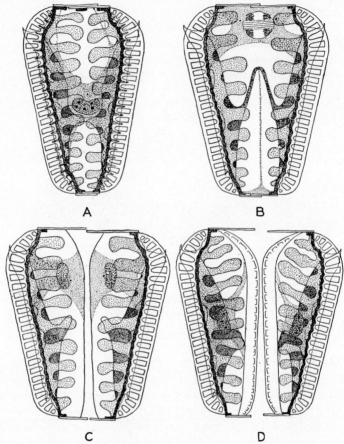

FIG. 14. Cell division in *Surirella calcarata*, ×275. *A* to *D*, successive stages. (*After Lauterborn.*)

but the other is smaller. Thus, as cell divisions continue, some of the individuals become constantly smaller. After a minimum size for the species has been reached, the original size is regained through the formation of *auxospores*.

In the Centrales an auxospore is formed by the escape from its cell wall of a protoplast that soon grows to the original size and develops a new cell wall. An auxospore may directly become a new individual or may form two new individuals by dividing in half. In most of the

Pennales auxospore formation is due to a fusion of cells. In some forms two vegetative protoplasts escape and conjugate to produce a single auxospore (Fig. 15). In other forms two diatoms unite to produce two auxospores. Here the two fusing cells lie within a gelatinous matrix and each produces two gametes. Then each of the gametes derived from one cell conjugates with one of those derived from the other cell. It is apparent that an "auxospore" formed by sexual fusion is really a zygote.

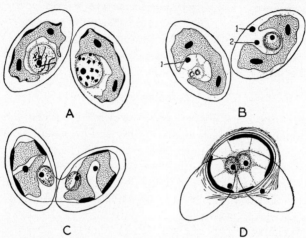

Fig. 15. Conjugation in *Cocconeis placentula*, ×1,500. *A* and *B*, meiosis in conjugating cells; *C*, fusion of protoplasts; *D*, zygote with sexual nuclei not yet fused. (*After Geitler.*)

Just previous to conjugation the nucleus of each of the pairing protoplasts undergoes a reduction of chromosomes, giving rise to four haploid nuclei. Some of these degenerate.

In some of the Centrales many small biciliate protoplasts arise within a vegetative cell and later escape into the water. These have been called "microspores." Some observers think that they function as zoospores, while others regard them as gametes, claiming that they fuse in pairs. The occurrence of these ciliated cells in the Bacillariophyceae suggests that the group may have been derived from flagellates with brown plastids. The connection, however, is a remote one.

7. CHLOROPHYCEAE

The Chlorophyceae, or green algae, are predominantly fresh-water forms whose plastids contain a preponderance of chlorophyll over its associated carotinoids, the green and yellow pigments occurring in approximately the same proportions as in the groups above the thallophyte level.[1] Only a comparatively few members are marine, but

[1] In a few members accessory pigments in the cell sap may mask the green color of the chloroplasts.

some of these are widely distributed and often abundant. Some green algae grow as scums on the surface of quiet water, while others are attached to various objects beneath the surface. A few forms grow on moist soil, rocks, or tree trunks. Most of the green algae are multicellular but some are unicellular, these occurring either as isolated cells or as colonies. The Chlorophyceae are generally regarded as the group of algae from which the bryophytes and other higher groups of green plants have been derived. Lime-secreting forms are known as fossils as far back as the Ordovician. The Chlorophyceae number over 5,000 species, nearly all of which are included in seven principal orders: Volvocales, Chlorococcales, Ulotrichales, Oedogoniales, Conjugales, Siphonocladiales, and Siphonales.

1. Volvocales

The Volvocales are a distinct group of primitive green algae that are widely distributed in fresh water. Only a few members are marine. They appear to have been derived from green flagellates, which they resemble in many ways, and to have given rise, in turn, to the other groups of Chlorophyceae. The Volvocales include about 50 genera and 300 species. The main genera are *Chlamydomonas, Sphaerella, Gonium, Pandorina, Eudorina,* and *Volvox.*

Chlamydomonas. This is a unicellular alga that does not form permanent colonies. It is widely distributed in pools and ditches and on damp ground. The vegetative cell, which is free-swimming, is generally spherical or egg-shaped (Fig. 16*A*). A cell wall is always present. At the anterior end are a pair of cilia, equal in length, a red eyespot, and two (rarely more) small contractile vacuoles. Surrounding the nucleus is a small mass of colorless cytoplasm lying in the depression of a large cup-shaped chloroplast. Embedded in the chloroplast is a conspicuous spherical *pyrenoid*. Pyrenoids are protein bodies that function as centers of starch formation. Although occurring in some members of certain other algal groups, they are especially characteristic of the Chlorophyceae.

Chlamydomonas reproduces asexually by means of *zoospores*. The vegetative cell becomes quiescent by retraction of the cilia and then its protoplast divides internally to form two, four, or eight daughter protoplasts, each of which, after enlarging slightly, forms a new cell wall and a pair of cilia while within the parent cell (Fig. 16*B, C*). By the breaking down of the original cell wall, the small cells are set free as zoospores, each soon undergoing further enlargement to become an adult vegetative cell (Fig. 16*D*). Under conditions unfavorable for vegetative activity, *Chlamydomonas* may pass into a "palmella" stage. The daughter cells, produced by the internal division of a vegetative cell, increase in number but, instead of escaping, become surrounded by abundant mucilage derived from the cell walls (Fig. 16*E*). Later, when favorable conditions return, the cells develop cilia and swim out of the mucilaginous matrix.

Sexual reproduction in *Chlamydomonas* occurs by the union of similar *gametes*. These arise from a quiescent vegetative cell by division of its protoplast into 16 or 32 daughter protoplasts (Fig. 16*F*). The gametes are smaller than the zoospores and are usually without a cell wall, but

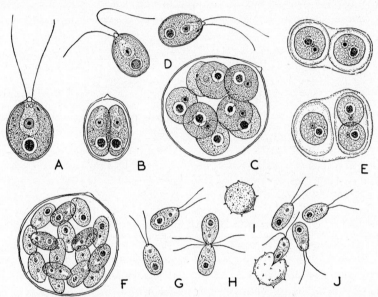

FIG. 16. *Chlamydomonas*, a free-swimming, unicellular green alga, ×1,000. *A*, vegetative cell, showing large cup-like chloroplast with embedded pyrenoid, nucleus, eyespot, two contractile vacuoles, and two cilia; *B* and *C*, formation of zoospores within parent cell wall; *D*, two escaped zoospores; *E*, "palmella" stage; *F*, formation of gametes; *G*, two escaped gametes; *H*, gametes fusing; *I*, zygote; *J*, four zoospores escaping from zygote.

otherwise have the same structural features. They escape and swim about in the water. Finally, they come together in pairs and fuse, each pair forming a zygote (Fig. 16*G*, *H*). The zygote soon loses its cilia, secretes a heavy wall about itself, and goes into a resting stage (Fig. 16*I*). While the wall is forming, the two nuclei inside the zygote unite. Upon germination, the protoplast of the zygote divides internally to form four zoospores that escape and enlarge to become new vegetative cells (Fig. 16*J*). The reduction in chromosome number from the diploid to the haploid state occurs in connection with the formation of the four zoospores from the zygote. Because, in most species, the pairing gametes are alike in size, *Chlamydomonas* is said to be *isogamous*. The fusing of similar gametes (*isogametes*) is known as *conjugation*.

In *Chlamydomonas eugametos* there are two sexually differentiated strains, designated as plus and minus. A zygote may be formed only by the union of a plus gamete with a minus gamete. Of the four zoo-spores arising from the zygote, two belong to the plus strain and two to the minus. These strains may soon undergo another sexual fusion or may be perpetuated asexually for an indefinite period. In *Chlamydomonas braunii* and a few other species the gametes of the plus strain are slightly larger than those of the minus strain, and so here a visible as well as a physiological sexual differentiation exists. Such species show that *Chlamydomonas* displays a slight tendency toward heterogamy.

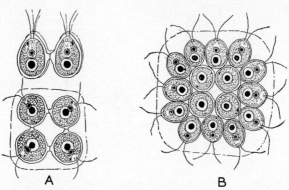

A   B

Fig. 17. Two species of *Gonium*, ×900.   *A*, side and top views of four-celled colony of *Gonium sociale*; *B*, top view of sixteen-celled colony of *Gonium pectorale*.

In *Sphaerella*, a close relative of *Chlamydomonas* and common in rain-water pools, the inner portion of the cell wall is gelatinous and thick and is traversed by many delicate cytoplasmic strands. Generally it con-tains a bright red pigment, *haematochrome*, that masks the chlorophyll. This is present in the cell sap.

Gonium.   This is a colonial form, each colony consisting of a flat plate of cells numbering either four or sixteen, according to the species (Fig. 17). The cells are regularly arranged and held together by a mucilaginous matrix derived from their cell walls.   Each cell is biciliate and otherwise similar to an adult *Chlamydomonas*.   By division of its protoplast, any cell may form a new colony that escapes from the parent cell.   Sexual reproduction occurs by the fusion of similar gametes (isogametes), the two coming from separate colonies.   The number of gametes formed in a cell corresponds to the number of cells in the colony.   They escape separately.   The zygote becomes thick-walled and dormant.   Later it produces four biciliate zoospores.   In the four-celled species these usu-ally remain together as a colony; in the sixteen-celled species they separate and each forms a new colony.

Pandorina.   This form is similar to *Gonium* except that the colony is spherical or nearly so and consists usually of 16 biciliate cells crowded together within a mucilaginous matrix and surrounding a small central cavity (Fig. 18*A*). Sometimes the colony consists of only 8 cells or, less frequently, of 32 cells. Each cell resembles that of *Chlamydomonas*. In asexual reproduction each cell divides simultaneously to produce a group of as many daughter cells as were in the parent colony (Fig. 18*B*). Each group then escapes as a new colony. In sexual reproduction each vegetative cell similarly produces a group of daughter cells as numerous as the cells in the colony, the groups separate, and the daughter cells escape individually as biciliate gametes. Although *Pandorina* is isogamous, one

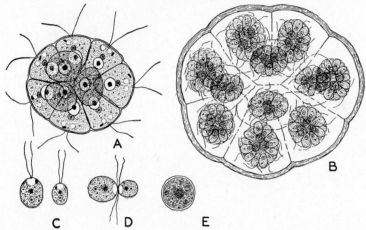

Fig. 18. *Pandorina morum*, ×750. *A*, free-swimming vegetative colony of 16 cells, those lying below not shown; *B*, colony undergoing asexual reproduction; *C*, a large and a small gamete; *D*, gametic union; *E*, a zygote.

of the fusing gametes is slightly larger and less active than the other, thus showing a tendency toward heterogamy (Fig. 18*C, D*). The zygote remains motile for a while, finally settling down and secreting a cell wall (Fig. 18*E*). Upon germination the zygote divides internally into four protoplasts, but generally only one becomes a zoospore. The zoospore produces a new colony.

Eudorina. *Eudorina* is a spherical colony usually consisting of 16, 32, or 64 biciliate cells, each like a cell of *Chlamydomonas*. The cells are loosely arranged in a single layer near the surface of a mucilaginous matrix. As in the preceding genera, any cell may give rise to a new colony by internal division of its protoplast, but an advance is seen in sexual reproduction (Fig. 19). Some of the cells divide to form groups of *sperms*, as many as 64 usually arising from a single vegetative cell. The other cells enlarge slightly by the accumulation of food and become *eggs*. Although both male and female gametes are biciliate, only the sperms escape from the colony and become free-swimming. At first the sperms hang together as a plate, but finally separate and fuse with the eggs. The union of a sperm and egg, called *fertilization*, results in the formation of a thick-walled resting zygote. Upon germination, the zygote produces four biciliate zoospores but only one functions, the other three degenerating inside the zygote. Because the pairing gametes are differentiated into sperms and eggs and are therefore unlike, *Eudorina*

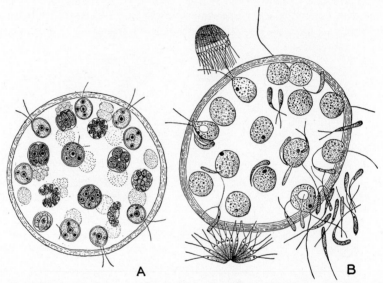

A   B

Fig. 19. *Eudorina elegans.* *A*, colony of 32 cells, many of which are dividing to form daughter colonies, ×500; *B*, a female colony surrounded by numerous sperms, two groups of which are still intact, while others, having separated, are uniting with the eggs. (*After Goebel.*)

is *heterogamous.* Some species show a further degree of sexual differentiation in being *dioecious.* Here all the cells in the male colony give rise to sperms, while all those in the female colony become eggs.

Volvox. This is the most highly developed member of the Volvocales. It lives in quiet bodies of fresh water, especially pools, ponds, and lakes. It consists of a hollow globular colony composed of hundreds or sometimes thousands of biciliate cells embedded in mucilage and arranged in a single layer (Fig. 20*A*). Often the colony reaches a diameter of nearly 2 mm. It is free-swimming, as in other members of the order. Each cell is like an adult *Chlamydomonas*, with two cilia, an eyespot, contractile vacuoles, a nucleus, and a single chloroplast with a pyrenoid. In most species the cells are connected by very fine protoplasmic strands, and thus the colony approaches the multicellular condition of organization. This is also shown by the fact that most of the cells function only vegetatively during the entire life of the colony, while others become reproductive cells. Such a "division of labor" is not seen in lower members of the order.

Volvox reproduces asexually by the formation of new colonies inside the old one. A few of the vegetative cells, seldom over 10 or 12, retract

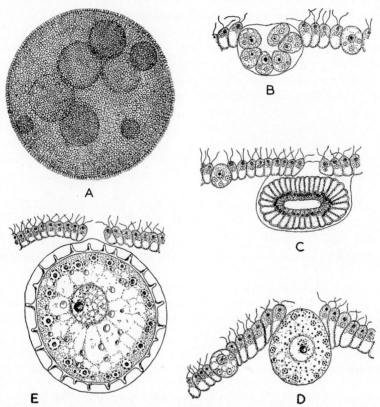

FIG. 20. *Volvox.* *A*, mature colony with young colonies inside; *B*, young colony in rim of mature colony; at the right, a vegetative cell has lost its cilia and is starting to form a new colony; *C*, a group of sperms derived from a single vegetative cell, one of which, to the left, has lost its cilia and is enlarging; *D*, an egg shortly before fertilization and, to the left, an egg beginning to develop from a vegetative cell; *E*, a mature zygote; *A*, ×170; *B* to *E*, ×780. (*After Chamberlain.*)

their cilia and increase slightly in size. Each divides to form a small group of cells that enter the colony and give rise to a new colony, remaining inside until the old colony dies (Fig. 20*B*).

In sexual reproduction, *Volvox* is heterogamous. Any cell may retract its cilia, enlarge by the accumulation of food, and become an egg (Fig. 20*D*). Another cell may enlarge and, at the same time, divide to form many small biciliate sperms (Fig. 20*C*). These arise as a hollow sphere or plate of cells that later separate. The sperms and eggs escape into the colony and there fertilization occurs. The zygote becomes heavy-walled and remains dormant for several months (Fig. 20E). In some species it then gives rise to a single biciliate zoospore, while in others it forms a new colony directly. In connection with the germination of the zygote, the number of chromosomes is reduced one-half. As is *Eudorina*, some species of *Volvox* are monoecious, others dioecious.

Summary. The Volvocales are distinguished from the other Chlorophyceae by the fact that their vegetative cells are ciliated and motile. They exhibit a range of development from single isolated cells to complex globular colonies. Each cell has one nucleus and generally one chloroplast. Asexual reproduction occurs by zoospores and by the formation of a new colony from a single parent cell. The number of cells in the colony is definite and is determined during early development. It is not subsequently increased by vegetative cell divisions. Sexual reproduction shows an advance from isogamy to heterogamy, while dioecism is attained by some species of *Eudorina* and *Volvox*.

2. Chlorococcales

The Chlorococcales constitute a large order of diverse forms that are probably not closely related. They are chiefly fresh-water algae, only a few occurring in the ocean. Some live in moist places on land. Some are endophytic in the intercellular spaces of certain seed plants, while others live symbiotically in the lower animals. Others are lichen formers. The order contains 90 genera and approximately 700 species. Some characteristic genera are *Chlorococcum*, *Chlorella*, *Scenedesmus*, *Pediastrum*, *Hydrodictyon*, and *Protosiphon*.

Chlorococcum. This simple alga grows on damp soil or rocks. It is unicellular, spherical, and nonmotile. At first it has a single nucleus and a large cup-like chloroplast with one or more pyrenoids (Fig. 21). Later the cell becomes multinucleate and the protoplast divides to form a variable number of biciliate zoospores that escape. After coming to rest, a zoospore loses its cilia, secretes a wall, and becomes a vegetative cell. Asexual reproduction may also occur by aplanospores. These arise in the same way as zoospores but have no cilia and develop a cell wall before being freed. As in *Volvox*, a "palmella" stage may develop by gelatinization of the cell walls in a group of cells. Sexual reproduction is accomplished by the production of a large number of biciliate isogametes by a vegetative cell. These escape and fuse in pairs. In general, *Chlorococcum* is like *Chlamydomonas* except that the vegetative cells have lost their motility.

Chlorella. *Chlorella* lives on the bark of trees, damp walls, and soil; also in various infusoria, the fresh-water sponge, and the green hydra. It can be grown easily in water cultures and is much used in experiments on photosynthesis. The cells are spherical and solitary. They have a single nucleus and a cup-shaped peripheral chloroplast usually without a pyrenoid. *Chlorella* resembles *Chlorococcum* except that it produces only aplanospores, no motile cells of any kind. A protoplast divides to form as many as 16 daughter protoplasts, each of which, before escaping, secretes a cell wall. Gametes are unknown.

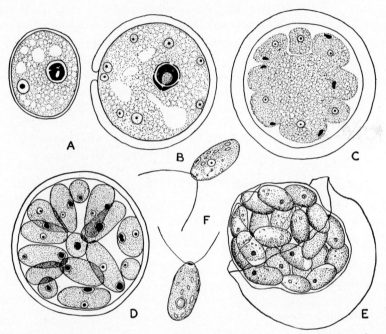

Fig. 21. *Chlorococcum infusionum.* *A*, section of vegetative cell with single nucleus and pyrenoid; *B*, multinucleate stage; *C*, appearance of cleavage furrows, isolating uninucleate protoplasts with a pyrenoid fragment; *D*, section of nearly mature sporangium; *E*, escape of zoospores in a gelatinous vesicle; *F*, two zoospores; *A*, ×2,000; others, ×2,700. (*After Bold.*)

Scenedesmus. This alga is common and widely distributed in fresh water. It is a colonial form with generally four or eight cells arranged in a short row (Fig. 22). The end cells often bear conspicuous spine-like projections. Each cell contains a single nucleus, a large peripheral chloroplast, and a pyrenoid. In reproduction, a protoplast divides within its own cell wall to form a new colony that escapes as a whole. Neither zoospores nor gametes are produced.

Pediastrum. *Pediastrum* is a free-floating form widely distributed in fresh water. It consists of a colony of cells symmetrically arranged in a flat plate (Fig. 23). The number of cells may be 2, 4, 8, etc., up to 128, but is most commonly 16 or 32. The cells are nearly all alike, except that the peripheral ones often bear short spine-like projections.

In young colonies the cells are uninucleate but later become multi-nucleate (coenocytic), as many as eight nuclei being present. Young cells have a single peripheral chloroplast with one pyrenoid, while older cells have several pyrenoids, the chloroplast becoming diffuse.

In asexual reproduction a protoplast divides generally into as many daughter protoplasts as there are cells in the colony, but often into twice as many. These become biciliate zoospores that escape as a group enclosed in a common membrane (Fig. 24A). The zoospores then come together and form a new colony within the membrane (Fig. 24B, C).

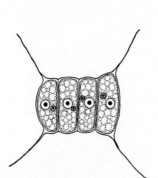

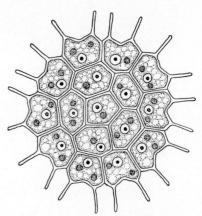

Fig. 22. Four-celled colony of *Scenedesmus*, ×750. Each cell contains a small nucleus and a large peripheral chloroplast with a pyrenoid.

Fig. 23. Young colony of *Pediastrum boryanum*, its cells forming a plate, ×750. Some of the cells have become binucleate. Each has a peripheral chloroplast and a pyrenoid.

Sexual reproduction also takes place, *Pediastrum* being isogamous. Division of a vegetative protoplast results in the formation of many biciliate gametes. These escape separately and fuse in pairs to form zygotes. After increasing in size, the zygote gives rise to a group of zoospores. These escape into the water, swim freely and, after coming to rest, develop into thick-walled polyhedral cells (Fig. 24D). The polyhedrons enlarge and divide internally to form a group of zoospores that escape in a common membrane, within which they construct a new colony by coming together without further division (Fig. 24E–G).

Hydrodictyon. This remarkable alga, common in fresh water, is a free-floating colony having the form of a large hollow net, the polygonal meshes of which are made up of elongated cylindrical cells arranged end to end (Fig. 25A). Each mesh consists usually, but by no means always, of six cells. A single colony may reach a length of 20 to 30 cm. At first each cell contains a single nucleus and a chloroplast with one pyrenoid, but later there are many nuclei and a large number of pyrenoids, the chloroplast becoming reticulate and diffuse (Fig. 25*B*). Mature cells have a peripheral layer of cytoplasm surrounding a large central vacuole. In asexual reproduction as many as 7,000 to 20,000 biciliate zoospores may arise from a single vegetative cell by progressive cleavage of its protoplast. These do not escape but swim around within the parent cell, finally coming together to form a new net (Fig. 25*C*). Later the cell walls of the old net dissolve and the young colonies are set free. These grow to the adult size without any cell division.

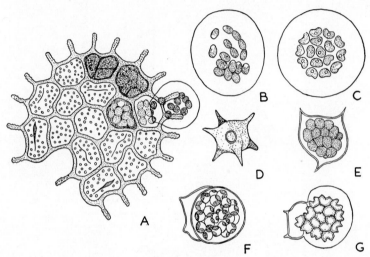

Fig. 24. *Pediastrum boryanum.* *A*, formation of zoospores and escape of one group in a common vesicle; *B* and *C*, zoospores forming a new colony; *D*, a thick-walled resting cell (polyhedron); *E, F, G*, zoospores within a polyhedron forming a new colony. (*A, B, C*, after *A. Braun; D to G, after Askenasy*.)

In sexual reproduction a single protoplast may give rise to as many as 30,000 to 100,000 biciliate isogametes. These escape from the parent cell through a small pore and fuse in pairs to form thin-walled zygotes (Fig. 25*D–F*). After undergoing a short resting period, the zygote turns green and increases in size. It then produces four large zoospores and, in connection with their formation, the number of chromosomes is reduced one-half (Fig. 25*G, H*). As in *Pediastrum*, the zoospores escape into the water, settle down, and become large heavy-walled polyhedrons (Fig. 25*I*). These remain dormant until the following spring and represent the real resting stage. Upon germination, a polyhedron produces 200 to 300 small zoospores that escape enclosed in a membrane, where they arrange themselves to form a new net (Fig. 25*J*). These nets are much smaller than the ones developed later by the zoospores arising within the vegetative cells of the colony.

Protosiphon. *Protosiphon* is a unicellular coenocytic alga occurring on damp earth. It shows a striking resemblance to *Botrydium*, one of the Xanthophyceae, and often grows with it in the same habitat. The plant has a green aerial portion that is tubular or bladder-like and a

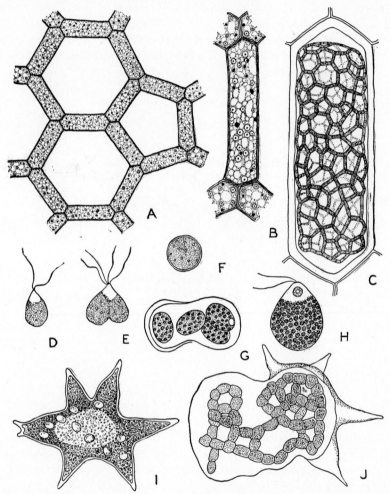

Fig. 25. *Hydrodictyon reticulatum.* *A*, portion of colony, ×150; *B*, single cell with many nuclei and pyrenoids, ×350; *C*, young net formed within a parent cell; *D*, a gamete; *E*, gametes fusing; *F*, zygote; *G*, four zoospores escaping from zygote; *H*, a zoospore escaped from zygote; *I*, polyhedron formed by a zoospore; *J*, young net escaping from polyhedron. (*C* to *F*, *after Klebs*; *G* to *J*, *after Pringsheim.*)

colorless underground portion that resembles a rhizoid (Fig. 26*A*). It is entirely without cross walls. The cytoplasm, in a thin layer surrounding a large central vacuole, contains numerous scattered nuclei (Fig. 26*B*). When young, the cell has a large reticulate chloroplast with many pyrenoids; later there may be several chloroplasts. Reserve food occurs chiefly as starch. The aerial portion may bud off new plants that later become detached. When covered with water, the protoplast may give rise to a number of biciliate zoospores or isogametes that escape

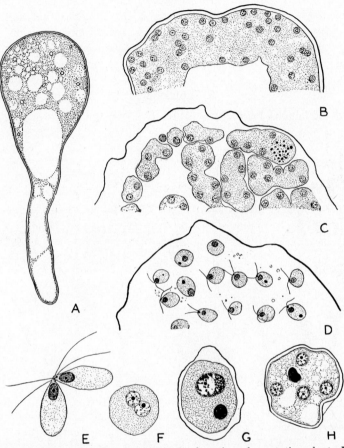

FIG. 26. *Protosiphon botryoides.* *A*, longitudinal section of vegetative plant; *B*, upper portion, showing scattered nuclei; *C*, an older stage, the cytoplasm undergoing progressive cleavage; *D*, formation of zoospores; *E* and *F*, gametic union; *G*, a zygote; *H*, germinating zygote with four nuclei. (*After Bold*.)

through an apical pore (Fig. 26*C–H*). Gametes from the same plant may pair and fuse. The zygote, which becomes thick-walled and dormant, produces a new plant directly. If the soil becomes dry, the vegetative protoplast may form aplanospores by progressive cleavage of the cytoplasm. These may be either small and uninucleate or larger and multinucleate. The latter, upon germination, usually give rise to zoospores or isogametes, but may develop into a new vegetative plant directly.

Summary. The Chlorococcales range from simple isolated cells to complex colonies. In this and succeeding orders nonmotility is the permanent condition of the vegetative cells. Although usually uninucleate, frequently these are multinucleate and often contain more than one chloroplast. Colonies are formed by the coming together of free cells (usually zoospores) derived from a single parent cell and there is no subsequent division of vegetative cells. Cell division occurs only in connection with the formation of reproductive cells. Reproduction is accomplished by zoospores, aplanospores, or akinetes, and usually also by isogametes.

3. Ulotrichales

The Ulotrichales have been called the representative group of the Chlorophyceae. Most of them live in fresh water but some are marine.

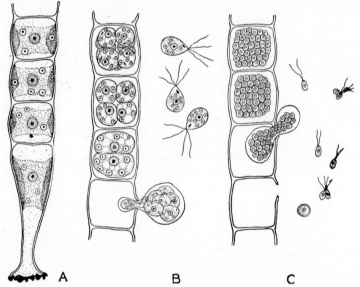

Fig. 27. *Ulothrix zonata*, vegetative and reproductive stages, ×700. *A*, basal portion of filament, showing holdfast cell and three vegetative cells, each with a single nucleus and a peripheral band-like chloroplast with many pyrenoids; *B*, formation and escape of zoospores; *C*, formation and escape of gametes, some of which are pairing.

A few live in damp places on land. *Trichophilus* grows inside the hair of the South American sloth. To this order belong 85 genera and approximately 500 species, the principal genera being *Ulothrix, Chaetophora, Draparnaldia, Stigeoclonium, Protococcus, Ulva,* and *Coleochaete*.

Ulothrix. This alga is of widespread occurrence in streams, lakes, and ponds, where it grows attached to objects in the water. A few of its species are marine. The plant body is multicellular, consisting of a simple unbranched filament (Fig. 27*A*). The basal cell is elongated and modified to serve as a holdfast, but all the other cells are alike, being shortly cylindrical. Each contains a central nucleus and a peripheral band-like chloroplast usually with many pyrenoids. The chloroplast may form either a complete or a partial band. Any cell in the filament, except the basal one, may divide by the formation of a cross wall between two daughter protoplasts, thus resulting in growth of the filament.

In asexual reproduction, the contents of any vegetative cell, except the holdfast, may divide to form mostly 2, 4, 8, or 16 zoospores (Fig. 27*B*). These escape through a pore in the cell wall and swim by means of four equal cilia attached apically. When discharged, the zoospores are enclosed in a common membrane that soon disappears. As in the vegetative cells of the Volvocales, each zoospore has a red eyespot and a contractile vacuole. After a period of free swimming, a zoospore comes to rest, withdraws its cilia, and secretes a cell wall. It then gives rise to a new filament by repeated cell divisions. Sometimes aplanospores are formed instead of zoospores. They frequently germinate within the parent cell.

Sexual reproduction takes place in *Ulothrix* by the conjugation of isogametes (Fig. 27*C*). These originate from the vegetative cells in the same way as the zoospores do, but are smaller, more numerous (usually 32 or 64 in a cell), and have only two cilia. They escape through a pore in the cell wall, enclosed in a common membrane that soon breaks down. Following pairing and fusing of the gametes, the resulting zygotes secrete a heavy wall and generally do not germinate until the following spring. Then each produces 4 to 16 zoospores (or sometimes aplanospores) that, in turn, give rise to new vegetative filaments. The zygote is the only diploid cell in the life history. When its nucleus divides, the chromosome number is reduced one-half. Although isogamous, *Ulothrix* shows some degree of sexual differentiation in that the gametes of one filament fuse only with those of another.

Chaetophora. Some of the Ulotrichales are branching filaments, often with cells showing a differentiation in size. One such member is *Chaetophora*, frequently found in standing water attached to submerged objects. The cells of the branches become progressively smaller and end in hair-like appendages that taper to a point. In a closely related form, *Draparnaldia*, common in clear, cool streams, the cells of the main filament are much larger than those of the branches (Fig. 28). Cell structure and reproduction in both genera are much the same as in *Ulothrix*. *Stigeoclonium*, another relative of *Chaetophora*, is differentiated into a cushion-like basal portion from which arise a number of sparingly branched upright filaments. When exposed to dry conditions, the cells round off and separate, giving rise to a "palmella" stage. These cells are thick-walled and divide in any plane.   They may remain in groups or become separate.   With the return of favorable conditions, they produce a new filamentous body.

Protococcus.   One of the commonest and most widely distributed of the green algae is *Protococcus*,[1] a terrestrial form growing on the shaded side of damp tree trunks, moist rocks, walls, etc.   It is a unicellular alga,

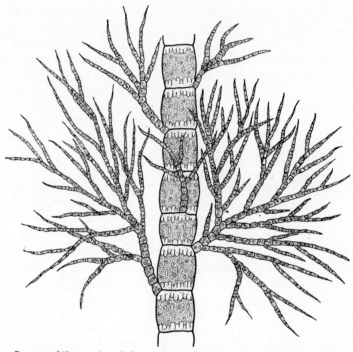

FIG. 28.   *Draparnaldia*, portion of plant, a branching filament with a marked differentiation in size of vegetative cells, ×200.   Each cell has a central nucleus obscured by the peripheral band-like chloroplast with many pyrenoids.

consisting of a spherical protoplast enclosed by a cell wall (Fig. 29). It has a small nucleus and a large, peripheral, irregularly lobed chloroplast usually without pyrenoids.   Reproduction occurs entirely by cell division, spores and gametes being unknown.   Permanent colonies are not formed but, instead of separating immediately, the cells usually hang together temporarily in small groups.   In the presence of excessive moisture, the number of cells in a group is greatly increased and sometimes some of them grow into short filaments.

In most unicellular algae the division of a cell involves the formation of a new cell wall completely around each daughter protoplast and the disintegration of the wall of the parent cell.   In *Protococcus*, however, a

[1] Often called *Pleurococcus*.

cross wall is developed across the parent cell, a method characteristic of *Ulothrix* and multicellular algae in general. If a second wall appears in one or both of the daughter cells before they separate, it comes in at right angles to the first one. Later divisions may be in the third plane. Thus there is a slight tendency in *Protococcus* toward the development of a multicellular body.

Protococcus is now generally regarded, not as a primitive form, but as one that has become reduced from more highly developed ancestors, probably as a result of its terrestrial mode of life. This is indicated by

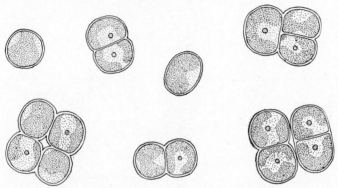

Fig. 29. *Protococcus viridis*, a unicellular green alga, ×1,000. Some of the cells have divided to form small temporary groups. Each cell has a central nucleus and a peripheral lobed chloroplast.

its advanced method of cell division combined with a failure to develop an extensive multicellular plant body like that of other Ulotrichales and by the absence of zoospores and gametes, which even such truly primitive forms as *Chlamydomonas* possess.

Ulva. This is a widely distributed marine alga commonly known as "sea lettuce." It grows along seacoasts between the high- and low-tide lines. The vegetative body consists of a plate-like thallus two layers of cells in thickness (Fig. 30). It is attached to rocks and other objects in the water by means of a basal holdfast consisting of long colorless rhizoids. The thallus may reach a length of 30 cm. or more. Each cell is uninucleate and has a single chloroplast with a pyrenoid.

Reproduction in *Ulva* closely resembles that of *Ulothrix*. Zoospores arise from ordinary vegetative cells situated along the thallus margin, four or eight zoospores being produced in each cell. They are liberated into the water through an opening in the cell wall and swim by means of four cilia. Upon germination, a zoospore gives rise to a plant that produces only gametes. These are smaller than the zoospores, more numerous (16 or 32 in a cell), and biciliate. Two similar gametes[1] coming from

[1] Although some species of *Ulva* are strictly isogamous, others produce two kinds of gametes that differ slightly in size.

separate plants unite to form a zygote. Instead of becoming a thick-walled resting cell, the zygote germinates immediately and produces a plant that bears only zoospores.

Thus *Ulva* illustrates the phenomenon of *alternation of generations*. Two separate plants, one producing gametes and the other spores, are involved in each life cycle and, although they look alike, the gamete-producing plants are haploid and the spore-producing plants are diploid.

Fig. 30. *Ulva lactuca*, the sea lettuce, about one-half natural size. The bright green thallus is only two layers of cells thick. (*After Thuret.*)

The doubling of chromosomes, resulting from the conjugation of two gametes, is carried over by the zygote to the cells of the spore-producing plant. The reduction of chromosomes takes place when the zoospores are produced. These haploid spores give rise to the gamete-producing plants. The haploid plants are called *gametophytes* and the diploid plants *sporophytes*. Because the two kinds of plants are alike vegeta-tively, *Ulva* displays an *isomorphic* alternation of generations.

Coleochaete. *Coleochaete* is a small fresh-water alga that usually grows attached to leaves and stems of aquatic seed plants, such as water lilies and cattails. Depending on the species, the vegetative body is either a branching filament, a cushion with free branches, or a circular disk with radiating rows of cells (Fig. 31*A*). When disk-like, it rarely exceeds 5 mm. in diameter. Some of the cells bear hair-like outgrowths,

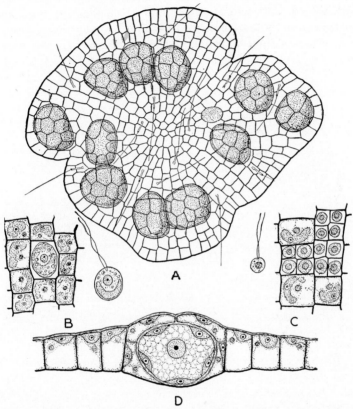

FIG. 31. *Coleochaete scutata*, a discoid species. *A*, a small vegetative plant with numerous zygotes overgrown by the surrounding cells, ✕150; *B*, a small group of vegetative cells, one of which is giving rise to a zoospore, and an escaped zoospore, ✕500; *C*, vegetative cells giving rise to antheridia, and an escaped sperm, ✕500; *D*, cross section of portion of thallus, showing a zygote, ✕350.

each with a sheath at its base. Each cell has a single nucleus and a chloroplast with one or sometimes two pyrenoids. Growth is always apical, in the discoid species occurring by means of a marginal meristem. Biciliate zoospores, formed singly, may arise in any vegetative cell (Fig. 31*B*). They escape through a pore in the cell wall.

In being heterogamous, *Coleochaete* makes an advance over the other Ulotrichales that have been considered. In the discoid species *antheridia* are formed by the division of a vegetative cell into smaller cells, the protoplasts of which escape into the water as biciliate *sperms* (Fig. 31*C*). An *oögonium* is formed near the margin of the thallus by the enlargement of a vegetative cell, its protoplast becoming a nonmotile *egg*. In the branched species the antheridia and oögonia are borne at the ends of separate branches. Here the oögonium has a long, slender extension (trichogyne) with a terminal opening. A few species are dioecious.

A sperm enters the oögonium and fertilizes the egg, the zygote enlarging and becoming thick-walled. At the same time adjacent vegetative cells grow up around the oögonium and form a case (Figs. 31*D* and 32*A*).

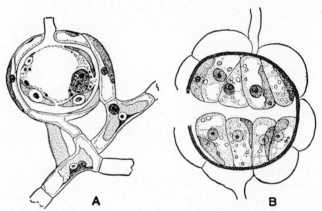

A   **B**

Fig. 32. *Coleochaete pulvinata.* *A*, section of oögonium containing a zygote and surrounded by jacket produced by adjacent vegetative cells; *B*, section of oögonium containing a group of cells derived from the zygote, each of which gives rise to a zoospore. (*After Oltmanns.*)

After undergoing a period of rest, the zygote germinates inside the oögonium and produces a spherical body consisting of 16 or 32 cells, each cell in turn producing a biciliate zoospore (Fig. 32*B*). This escapes and gives rise to a new vegetative plant. In the discoid species the zygote produces an eight-celled body. The reduction of chromosomes takes place when the zygote germinates. Consequently, the body of spore-producing cells that develops from it is haploid and so cannot be regarded as a sporophyte. Thus *Coleochaete* is without a true alternation of generations.

Summary. The plant body of the Ulotrichales is multicellular (except in *Protococcus*), being either a simple filament, a branched filament, or a flat plate-like thallus. The cells contain one nucleus and a single chloroplast. Growth occurs by division of the vegetative cells. Nearly all members produce zoospores, these being either biciliate or quadriciliate. Asexual reproduction may also occur by aplanospores or by akinetes. Sexual reproduction ranges from isogamy to heterogamy.

4. Oedogoniales

The Oedogoniales are related to the Ulotrichales and are often classified with them. They are a fresh-water group including only 3 genera and approximately 400 species. The two chief genera are *Oedogonium* and *Bulbochaete*, both occurring throughout the world.

Oedogonium. This widely distributed alga, comprising nearly 300 species, generally lives in ponds, lakes, and quiet streams, often attached to sticks, stones, and other aquatic plants. It consists of a simple unbranched filament that, when young, has a basal holdfast cell but later is usually free-floating. The cells are elongated and uninucleate. Each contains a peripheral chloroplast with many pyrenoids. The chloroplast is band-like and reticulate. Any vegetative cell except the basal one may divide.

Oedogonium has a peculiar method of cell division seen only in the other members of its order (Fig. 33). It results in the formation of distinctive "apical caps." The nucleus divides near the upper end of the cell, where simultaneously a ring-like thickening of cellulose is developed on the inside of the lateral wall above the dividing nucleus. A groove appears in this ring and the cell wall splits transversely opposite the groove. A thin cross wall now appears between the daughter nuclei and the protoplast is divided in half. The ring stretches into a cylinder as each daughter protoplast elongates, the new cross wall moving upward to the top of the parent cell, where it unites with the lateral wall very close to where the transverse split occurred. The upper cell, which has a new cell wall, continues to elongate until it reaches the size of the lower cell, which possesses the old cell wall.

Asexual reproduction occurs by the formation of large zoospores, each of which arises from the entire contents of an ordinary vegetative cell (Fig. 34*A*, *B*). This escapes as a naked protoplast that bears a crown of cilia. The liberation of the zoospore is accompanied by a transverse splitting of the cell wall at the apical end. After a period of free swimming, the zoospore comes to rest with its ciliated end downward, retracts its cilia, forms a cell wall, and gives rise by repeated divisions to a new filament. *Oedogonium* may also produce akinetes, although these are relatively uncommon. The akinetes may occur either singly or in a linear series. They germinate directly into new filaments.

Oedogonium is heterogamous. An antheridium arises as a short cell that is cut off at the apex of an ordinary vegetative cell. It may remain the only one, but generally more (from 2 to 40) are produced by continued division of the lower cell or by division of antheridia already formed (Fig. 34*C*). Each antheridium gives rise to one or, more commonly, to two sperms, either by a vertical or a transverse division of the protoplast, depending on the species. The sperms escape into the water and, like the zoospores, swim by means of a crown of cilia. An oögonium also commonly arises from the smaller upper cell produced by the division of an ordinary vegetative cell, but this cell subsequently enlarges by the accumulation of food (Fig. 34*D*). The oögonia may occur separately or

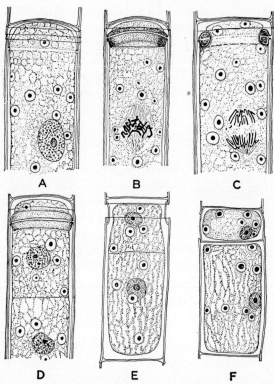

Fig. 33. Nuclear and cell division in *Oedogonium grande*, ×320. *A*, elongation of nucleus and appearance of young ring; *B*, metaphase; *C*, anaphase; *D*, formation of cross wall and separation of nuclei; *E*, broken outer layer of cell wall and stretching of ring; *F*, straightening of ring and migration of cross wall upward to unite with inner layer of cell wall. (*After Ohashi.*)

several may be cut off in a series. The entire protoplast of the oögonium becomes a large nonmotile egg.

A sperm enters an oögonium through a pore in its wall and unites with the egg. The zygote becomes a heavy-walled resting cell that later produces four zoospores (Fig. 34*E*, *F*). When liberated, these are enclosed by a common membrane that soon disappears. From each of the zoospores a new filament is developed. The reduction of chromosomes occurs in connection with the germination of the zygote, and so the four zoospores are haploid.

Some species of *Oedogonium* are monoecious, the antheridia and oögonia occurring in the same filament. Other species are dioecious, the two kinds of sex organs being borne on separate filaments. In some dioecious species the male and female filaments are approximately equal in size.

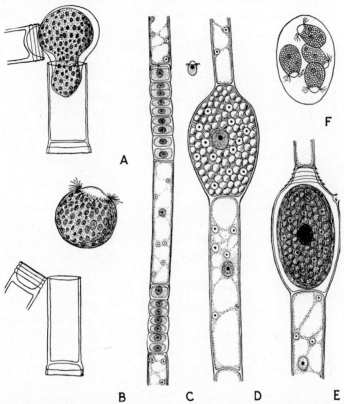

FIG. 34. Reproduction in *Oedogonium*, ✕500. *A* and *B*, the entire contents of a vegetative cell escaping as a zoospore; *C*, portion of filament with two groups of antheridia; also a single escaped sperm; *D*, portion of filament with an oögonium containing a mature egg in which are many pyrenoids and starch grains; *E*, heavy-walled zygote still within the oögonium; *F*, group of four zoospores produced by the zygote. (*A and B, after Hirn; F, after Juranyi.*)

In others the male filaments are very small, consisting of only a few cells. These dwarf filaments are produced by special small zoospores, called *androspores*, that originate singly in rows of small cells resembling antheridia. The androspores germinate on the female filaments near or on an oögonium (Fig. 35). The dwarf filament usually consists of a single vegetative cell that cuts off one or several terminal antheridia, each producing two sperms. Figure 35 shows three dwarf filaments of different ages. In the one on the right the single vegetative cell has cut off a small, undivided, antheridial cell. In the middle filament a second antheridium has been formed by the vegetative cell, while the first antheridium has produced two sperms. In the male filament on the left two sperms have escaped from the upper antheridium, but two more have been formed in the lower one.

Bulbochaete is a genus closely resembling *Oedogonium*, differing chiefly in having branches, most of the cells of which bear long one-celled hairs that are swollen at the base.

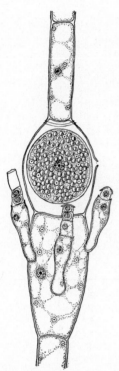

FIG. 35. A species of *Oedogonium* having dwarf male filaments, three of which have developed on the cell below the oögonium, ×300.

Summary. The Oedogoniales are a small order differing from the Ulotrichales mainly in having a peculiar method of cell division and motile reproductive cells with a crown of cilia. The vegetative body is multicellular and filamentous, the cells having one nucleus and a single chloroplast. Asexual reproduction occurs by zoospores, sometimes by akinetes. All the members are heterogamous.

5. Conjugales

The Conjugales constitute a distinct and highly specialized order of green algae that occupy an isolated position. In fact, they are sometimes removed from the Chlorophyceae and made an independent class. All of them occur in fresh water. They include 38 genera and over 2,400 species. Some representative genera are *Closterium*, *Cosmarium*, *Mougeotia*, *Spirogyra*, and *Zygnema*.

Desmids. These algae are widely distributed in bogs, ponds, and small lakes, usually becoming abundant late in the season. They number about 2,250 species. *Closterium* is a genus of nearly 200 species, while *Cosmarium* has over 800. The desmids are unicellular and the cells display a great variety of form. Like the diatoms, they have won the favor of microscopists by their great beauty.

Desmids are typically solitary, but some develop into filamentous colonies. Many desmids have the power of movement, which appears to be caused by exudation of mucilage through pores in the cell wall.

In most desmids the cell is organized into two symmetrical halves that are generally separated by a median constriction called the *isthmus* (Figs. 36 and 37). In each half there is usually one large chloroplast (sometimes two) with one or more pyrenoids. The chloroplast is often elaborately lobed. The nucleus lies in the isthmus. In *Closterium*, at each end of the cell, is a small group of calcium sulphate crystals that show Brownian movement. In some desmids, the outer surface of the cell wall displays warts, spines, ridges, or other markings, most of which show a regular arrangement.

Asexual reproduction occurs mainly by fission, rarely by aplanospores. Zoospores have never been observed. In cell division the nucleus divides

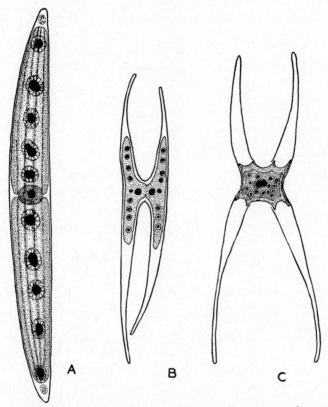

Fig. 36. *Closterium*, a common desmid. *A*, vegetative cell, showing nucleus at isthmus, a large lobed chloroplast with a row of pyrenoids in each half of the cell, and at each end a vacuole containing a few crystals, ×300; *B* and *C*, another species, showing two stages in conjugation, ×200.

first and then a cell wall is formed across the isthmus. Each of the two chloroplasts splits transversely. The daughter cells then separate and each forms a new half similar to itself. In sexual reproduction two cells come together and secrete a common mucilaginous sheath (Fig. 36*B*, *C*). Their walls generally break at the isthmus. Then the protoplasts escape and fuse to form a zygote. In a few desmids each cell sends out a short tube. These meet, become continuous, and the two protoplasts fuse in the tube. The desmids are isogamous but their gametes, each represent-

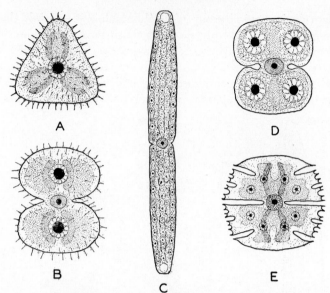

Fig. 37. Several desmids, showing variety of form. *A*, end view and *B*, front view of *Staurastrum; C, Docidium; D, Cosmarium, E, Micrasterias; C,* ×250; others, ×400.

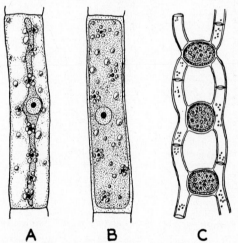

Fig. 38. Single cells of *Mougeotia*, showing the plate-like chloroplast as seen in side (*A*) and face (*B*) views, ×500; *C*, conjugating filaments, with three zygotes formed in the conjugating tubes.   (*C, after Wittrock.*)

ing an entire vegetative protoplast, are nonciliated.   The zygote becomes thick-walled and, after a period of rest, its protoplast escapes and divides generally into two daughter protoplasts, each of which becomes a new individual.   As a result of two successive divisions of the zygote nucleus, during which the reduction of chromosomes occurs, each daughter protoplast has two haploid nuclei. Then one nucleus in each protoplast degenerates.

Mougeotia. This alga consists of a delicate unbranched filament. Each cell displays a nucleus and a peculiar, axial, plate-like chloroplast containing two or more pyrenoids (Fig. 38*A*, *B*). The chloroplast can change its position in the cell, presenting its flat surface to dull light and

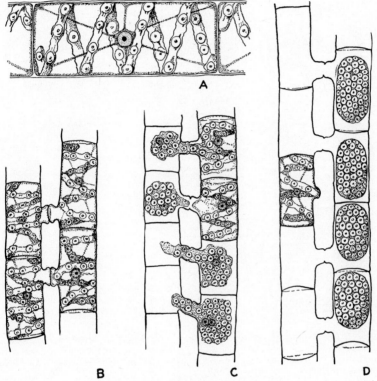

A

B   **C**   **D**

Fig. 39. *Spirogyra.* *A*, a vegetative cell, showing the central nucleus and the peripheral, band-like, spiral chloroplast with many pyrenoids, ×500; *B*, *C*, *D*, stages in conjugation, ×250.

its edge to bright light. Reproduction occurs by fragmentation, aplanospores, and by the conjugation of isogametes. The cells of two filaments lying parallel to each other put out short bud-like outgrowths that come into contact and form tubes. The protoplasts of two conjugating cells pass into one of these tubes and there fuse, producing a heavy-walled zygote (Fig. 38*C*). Upon germination, four cells are formed. Three of these die, the fourth producing a new filament. It is probable that the chromosome reduction takes place when the zygote germinates.

Spirogyra. *Spirogyra* is a well-known green alga very common in ponds, lakes, and streams, where it forms slimy bright green masses on or beneath the surface of the water. It is a large genus of over 100 species. The vegetative body is an unbranched filament with cylindrical cells that are usually elongated. Each cell has a single nucleus suspended in the center by strands of cytoplasm (Fig. 39*A*). It also has one or more peripheral, ribbon-like chloroplasts with many pyrenoids. The chloroplasts have the form of spiral bands, the number in each cell depending

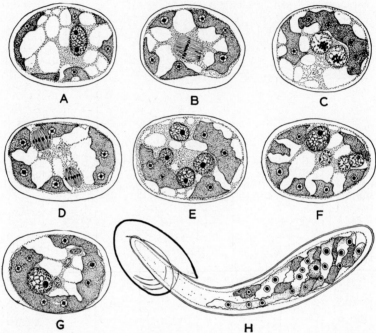

Fig. 40.   Nuclear changes in the zygote of *Spirogyra longata* (*A* to *G*) and germination of the zygote of *Spirogyra neglecta* (*H*).   *A, B, C,* first meiotic division of fusion nucleus in the zygote; *D* and *E,* second division; *F* and *G,* degeneration of three of the haploid nuclei. (*After Tröndle.*)

on the species. Any cell may divide by the formation of a cross wall, thus resulting in growth of the filament. In some species the cross walls possess characteristic infoldings.

In sexual reproduction the cells of the two filaments lying side by side put out lateral projections that come in contact (Fig. 39*B–D*). The contiguous portions of the cell walls at the ends of these projections then break down and form tubes leading from one filament to the other. Through these conjugating tubes the protoplasts of one filament pass to fuse with those of the other filament, forming zygotes. An entire vegetative protoplast thus becomes a large gamete. The zygote develops a heavy wall and goes into a resting stage. Upon germination, which usually occurs in the following spring, it directly produces a new filament

(Fig. 40*H*). The zygote becomes diploid by the fusion of the two nuclei derived from the conjugating protoplasts. When germination takes place, the fusion nucleus undergoes two successive divisions that result in a reduction of chromosomes (Fig. 40*A–G*). Of the four haploid nuclei thus formed, three degenerate, leaving one to function. In this way the zygote gives rise to a haploid filament.

Zoospores are never produced in *Spirogyra*. If conjugation fails to occur, a protoplast may round up and become a heavy-walled cell that, after a period of rest, gives rise to a new filament. Such a cell is often

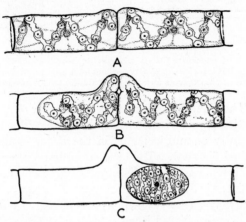

Fig. 41. A species of *Spirogyra* with lateral conjugation, gametic union occurring between adjacent cells of the same filament. *A, B, C,* development of conjugating tubes and formation of zygote, ×300.

called an aplanospore but would be more appropriately designated as a gamete that develops without undergoing conjugation.

Spirogyra, like the other Conjugales, is peculiar because an entire vegetative protoplast becomes a single large gamete that is not ciliated and does not escape into the water. Although the gametes show no differentiation in size, the active ones are regarded as male and the passive ones as female. The ordinary type of conjugation is known as *scalariform* (ladder-like) conjugation. In a few species *lateral* conjugation occurs (Fig. 41). In this type conjugating tubes are developed between adjacent cells of the same filament. At its completion a zygote is formed in one of the conjugating cells.

Zygnema. This is a genus closely related to *Spirogyra* and resembling it in many ways. Both forms grow in the same sort of places and look much alike to the naked eye. The filaments of *Zygnema* are unbranched and consist of cylindrical, more or less elongated cells (Fig. 42). Each has two spherical chloroplasts between which, at the center of the cell, lies the nucleus. Each chloroplast has a single pyrenoid surrounded by

radiating starch grains.   As in *Spirogyra,* sexual reproduction takes place
by the passage of isogametes, each representing an entire vegetative protoplast, through conjugating tubes and their fusion in the cells of one of
the filaments.   There is also the same degeneration of three of the haploid
nuclei derived from the nucleus of the zygote.

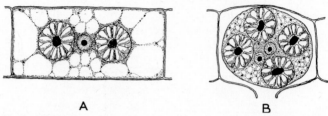

A   **B**

Fig. 42.   Single cells of *Zygnema,* ×750.   *A,* vegetative cell, showing central nucleus and
two spherical chloroplasts, each with a pyrenoid surrounded by radiating starch grains; *B,*
young zygote with four chloroplasts and the two gametic nuclei not yet fused.

Summary.   The Conjugales are an aberrant order of green algae showing no close relationship to any of the other orders.   The plant body may
be either unicellular or multicellular, in the latter case consisting of a
simple unbranched filament.   The cells are uninucleate and have one or
more peculiar chloroplasts.   The distinguishing feature of the order is the
absence of all ciliated cells in the life history.   No zoospores are produced,
but aplanospores may occur.   Sexual reproduction is accomplished by the
conjugation of two nonciliated isogametes, each derived from the entire
protoplast of a vegetative cell.   These either escape and fuse, unite in a
conjugating tube, or pass through a conjugating tube and fuse in one of
the cells.

6. Siphonocladiales

This is a group whose members are often distributed among other
orders, although its characters are rather well defined.   They are represented in both fresh and salt water, but most of them are marine, being
found principally in tropical and subtropical seas.   Many of the marine
forms are incrusted with lime.   Representatives of the group have been
found as fossils as far back as the Ordovician.   The Siphonocladiales
include about 37 genera and 450 species, the best-known genera being
Cladophora, Sphaeroplea, and *Acetabularia.*

Cladophora.   *Cladophora* is a genus of about 150 species, world-wide in
distribution.   It is found in great abundance in streams, ponds, and lakes,
usually attached to stones and piers.   Some of its species are marine.
The vegetative body is filamentous and much branched, its cells being
elongated and cylindrical (Fig. 43*A*).   A branch originates as an outgrowth from the upper end of a cell lying near the end of a filament.   Each
cell is a coenocyte, containing many nuclei.   The cytoplasm usually sur-

rounds a large central vacuole. When young, a cell has a large, peripheral, reticulate chloroplast with many pyrenoids. Later the chloroplast often appears to break up into numerous small chloroplasts, some of which have pyrenoids.

Many quadriciliate zoospores are formed, usually in cells at or near the ends of branches (Fig. 43B). The zoospores, which are uninucleate,

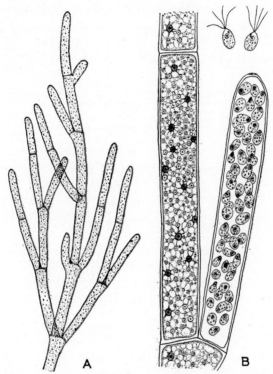

Fig. 43. *Cladophora.* *A*, portion of plant, a branching filament, ×65; *B*, a vegetative cell, a sporangium, and two escaped zoospores, ×300. Each vegetative cell has many nuclei and a large, peripheral, reticulate chloroplast with a large number of pyrenoids.

escape singly through a small pore in the cell wall. They develop into new filaments, but these, in turn, produce only isogametes. The gametes may arise in any vegetative cell. They escape into the water and swim by means of two cilia. The gametes pair and fuse, but fusion occurs, as a rule, only between gametes coming from different plants. The zygote, without undergoing a period of rest, gives rise to a new filament directly. This plant produces only zoospores. Although alike vegetatively, the gamete-producing plants are haploid and the spore-producing plants are diploid. The reduction of chromosomes occurs in connection with the formation of zoospores. Thus, as in *Ulva*, the life cycle of *Cladophora* involves a distinct alternation of generations of the isomorphic type.

Sphaeroplea. This is a fresh-water alga that grows in wet meadows and occasionally in pools. Although widely distributed, it is not common. The vegetative body consists of an unbranched filament with very long cylindrical cells, each containing numerous nuclei and chloroplasts (Fig. 44). The chloroplasts, some of which have pyrenoids, are parietally placed and grouped into wide annular bands of cytoplasm separated by

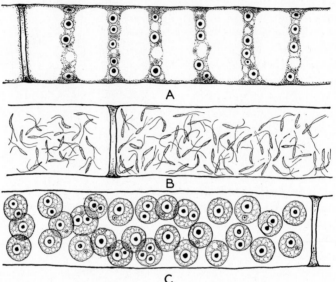

Fig. 44. *Sphaeroplea annulina*, ×400. *A*, portion of a vegetative cell with ring-like bands of cytoplasm containing many small nuclei, chloroplasts, and pyrenoids; *B*, antheridia producing sperms; *C*, portion of an oögonium with many eggs ready for fertilization.

wide vacuoles. The vegetative cells of *Sphaeroplea* do not produce any zoospores. Sexual reproduction is heterogamous, the two kinds of sex organs usually being borne in different filaments. Any vegetative cell, without undergoing a change in shape, may become an antheridium or an oögonium. The antheridium produces a large number of small biciliate sperms, while the oögonium gives rise to many large nonmotile eggs. The eggs are at first multinucleate, but later all the nuclei degenerate except one. The sperms escape through small pores in the cell wall, enter the oögonium through similar pores, and there fertilization takes place. Each zygote becomes thick-walled and, after undergoing a long resting period, gives rise usually to four biciliate zoospores. Each of these forms a new filament. The reduction of chromosomes occurs when the zygote germinates, and so the spores and vegetative filaments are haploid.

Acetabularia. This is a marine genus occurring in tropical and subtropical regions. It is called the mermaid's-wineglass. *Acetabularia crenulata* is a common species off the coast of Florida and throughout the West Indies. Its vegetative body, reaching a height of 6 to 9 cm., consists of a stalk bearing rhizoid-like holdfasts below and expanded above into a cup-like disk about 1 cm. in diameter (Fig. 45). The disk is composed of a whorl of elongated branches that are laterally coherent, each branch being a coenocyte. The plants are more or less incrusted with lime. At first the plant has a single nucleus that soon gives rise to many small nuclei. These pass up the stalk and enter the disk, which has now become divided into cells.

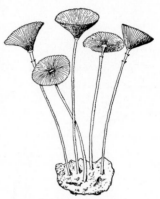

Reproduction begins by the formation of a large number of aplanospores (cysts) within the fertile branches composing the disk. The aplanospores are at first uninucleate but later become multinucleate. They are liberated into the water and, after a resting period, each gives rise to a large number of biciliate isogametes that escape and fuse in pairs. The zygote germinates immediately to form a new plant. The vegetative plant is diploid, the reduction of chromosomes occurring when the nucleus of the aplanospore divides.

FIG. 45. *Acetabularia crenulata,* natural size.

Acetabularia has been widely used by students of genetics and development, especially in experiments on regeneration and polarity.

Summary. The Siphonocladiales are multicellular algae with large multinucleate cells, these usually containing many small chloroplasts. The plant body is thus partially coenocytic. Vegetative growth takes place by cell division. Asexual reproduction usually occurs by zoospores, aplanospores, or akinetes. Sexual reproduction may be either isogamous or heterogamous. This order is related both to the Chlorococcales and to the Siphonales.

7. Siphonales

The Siphonales are a distinct group of mostly marine algae, only a few being found in fresh water. They are especially abundant in tropical seas. As in the Siphonocladiales, many marine forms secrete lime. Fossil members are known as far back as the Ordovician. The order includes 50 genera and about 350 species. Representative genera are *Vaucheria, Codium, Bryopsis,* and *Caulerpa.*

Vaucheria. This well-known alga grows in felt-like masses in fresh water and on damp soil. Some of its species live in brackish water and some live in the ocean.   The plant body consists of a sparsely branched coenocytic filament without any cross walls in the vegetative portion.   It is attached by means of colorless rhizoid-like holdfasts.   Numerous small nuclei and chloroplasts are scattered throughout the cytoplasm, which surrounds a large central vacuole.   There are no pyrenoids or starch grains, but oil droplets are usually present in abundance.   In this respect *Vaucheria* differs from the other Siphonales.

Vaucheria displays three methods of vegetative reproduction, as follows: (1) A branch may be constricted at the base, thus producing a

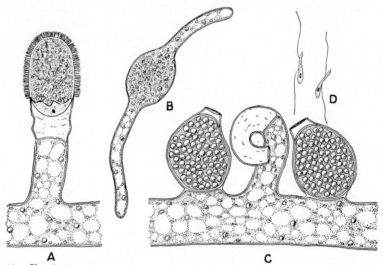

Fig. 46.   *Vaucheria*, a coenocytic green alga, ×250.   *A*, an escaping zoospore covered with many cilia; *B*, a zoospore giving rise to a new vegetative filament; *C*, two oögonia of *Vaucheria sessilis*, each with a zygote; also an antheridium that has discharged its sperms; *D*, two sperms, more highly magnified.

new plant body directly.   (2) The tip of a branch may swell slightly and become cut off by a cross wall to form a club-shaped sporangium (Fig. 46*A*).   The multinucleate protoplast in the branch rounds up and becomes a large zoospore entirely covered by cilia.   The cilia are in pairs and beneath each pair is a nucleus.   For this reason the zoospore is regarded as compound.   It escapes into the water through a terminal pore and, upon germination, gives rise to a new filament (Fig. 46*B*).   (3) The contents of an entire filament may break up into aplanospores, each developing a thick wall.

Vaucheria is heterogamous.   The antheridia and oögonia are not transformed vegetative cells but are developed on special branches of the filament (Fig. 46*C*).   In most species a short branch, sooner or later cut off by a wall, becomes a globular oögonium.   Its protoplast is organized as an egg, which becomes uninucleate.   It is uncertain whether this is accomplished by the degeneration of all its nuclei except one, as some observers have claimed, or, as others contend, by the passage back into the filament of all but one nucleus before the wall is formed at the base of the oögonium. Arising close to the oögonium is a longer and more slender branch, its curved tip being cut off by a wall to form an antheridium. In some species both kinds of sex organs are borne on the same branch, the antheridium being terminal and surrounded by two or more oögonia (Fig. 47). The antheridium produces many small biciliate sperms that are liberated into the water through a terminal pore. A sperm

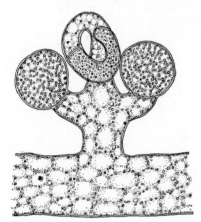

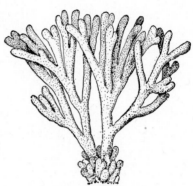

Fig. 47. Sex organs of *Vaucheria geminata*, two oögonia and an antheridium borne on the same branch, ×250.

Fig. 48. Thallus of *Codium fragile*, one-half natural size.

enters an oögonium through a terminal pore in its wall and fuses with the egg to produce a heavy-walled zygote. After remaining dormant, it gives rise to a new filament directly. The reduction of chromosomes probably occurs during germination of the zygote.

Codium. *Codium* is a widely distributed marine alga that grows on rocks between tide lines. The thallus is dark green and spongy, consisting of thick cylindrical branches composed of a dense mass of interwoven filaments (Fig. 48). It is anchored by means of a basal disk-like holdfast. Like other members of the order, the vegetative body is without cross walls. The cytoplasm is peripheral and has numerous small nuclei and chloroplasts. There is no asexual reproduction by means of spores. Two kinds of gametangia are produced, generally on different plants. They arise on the sides of large club-shaped branches that form a sort of cortex, and are cut off by a basal wall. The male gametangium, which is smaller than the female one, liberates many thousands of biciliate male gametes. In the female gametangium some of the nuclei degenerate, while others enlarge. Several hundred biciliate female gametes are

organized.   These escape through a terminal pore and are fertilized in
the water.   The zygote gives rise at once to a vegetative plant.   The
vegetative plants of *Codium* are diploid and the reduction of chromosomes
takes place in connection with the formation of the gametes.

Bryopsis.   Some of the marine Siphonales are highly branched, one of
these being *Bryopsis*.   The thallus is composed of a prostrate rhizome-
like portion, anchored by rhizoids, and an upright feathery portion, the

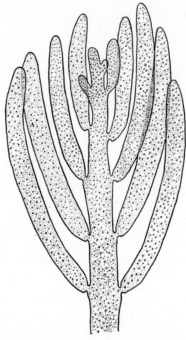

Fig. 49.   A small portion of the vegetative body of *Bryopsis*, showing branches of limited
growth, ×75.

latter consisting of an axis with branches of limited growth (Fig. 49).
In the formation of a gametangium, a branch is cut off by a cross wall and
gives rise to numerous bicilate gametes.   A gametangium produces
either male or female gametes and these are usually borne on different
plants.   The female gametes are about three times as large as the male
ones.   Both escape into the water, where they pair and fuse.   The
zygote secretes a cell wall and germinates immediately to form a new
vegetative plant.   There are no spores of any kind in the life cycle.   The
reduction of chromosomes occurs when the gametes are formed, and thus
the vegetative plant is diploid.

Caulerpa.   This is a marine form of interest because of the high degree
of differentiation of its coenocytic plant body (Fig. 50).   It consists of a

creeping axis with root-like holdfasts and erect leaf-like shoots of various form. In some species the shoots reach a height of 30 cm. Cross walls are absent in the vegetative part of the plant, but the central cavity is traversed by numerous slender strands. Asexual reproduction occurs only by fragmentation, sexual reproduction by biciliate isogametes.

Summary. The Siphonales are characterized by a completely coenocytic plant body that is usually much branched and often differentiated in form. Cross walls appear only in connection with the formation of

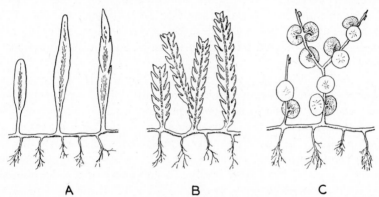

FIG. 50. Three species of *Caulerpa*, a coenocyte with a high degree of structural differentiation, one-half natural size. *A, Caulerpa prolifera; B, Caulerpa crassifolia; C, Caulerpa macrodisca.*

reproductive organs. The vegetative body contains innumerable nuclei and small chloroplasts. It is really a single multinucleate cell. Asexual reproduction may be accomplished by fragmentation of the thallus, by zoospores, aplanospores, or akinetes. Sexual reproduction ranges from isogamy to heterogamy. This is a highly specialized order related both to the Chlorococcales and the Siphonocladiales.

Summary of Chlorophyceae

The Chlorophyceae are algae with only chlorophyll and its associated carotinoids in their plastids, these being present in the same proportions as in the higher plants. In vegetative organization they are highly diversified. Some are unicellular but most of them are multicellular, the thallus being most commonly filamentous, sometimes plate-like, and rarely massive. Some are partially or completely coenocytic. There is relatively little cellular differentiation. A definite cell wall composed of cellulose is nearly always present, this seldom becoming mucilaginous. The cells contain a well-organized nucleus (often more than one) and one or more distinct plastids. Pyrenoids are usually present. Reserve food is stored generally as starch, sometimes as oil. Asexual reproduction occurs by fission (in some unicellular forms), fragmentation, or by zoo-spores, aplanospores, and akinetes. Sexual reproduction is either isoga-mous or heterogamous. In the heterogamous forms the sperms are ciliated, the eggs nearly always nonciliated. Motile reproductive cells generally have two or four cilia, equal in length and apically attached. The zygote nearly always becomes a resting cell.

Within the Chlorophyceae, three main evolutionary trends can be recognized. The occurrence of ciliated reproductive cells in practically all members, except the Conjugales, indicates that the common ancestor of the group must have been a form like *Chlamydomonas*. The Volvo-cales, retaining motility in vegetative cells, represent one line of evolution. It emphasizes the ciliated colonial type of organization that culminates in *Volvox*.

A second line of development, represented by the Chlorococcales, also emphasizes the colony but shows a loss of motility by the vegetative cells. A tendency toward the formation of multinucleate cells appears in this order. This leads to the development of coenocytic bodies, which reaches a climax in the Siphonales. *Protosiphon* is a connecting link between the Chlorococcales and Siphonales. Some regard the Siphono-cladiales as a transitional stage leading to the evolution of the Siphonales; others consider them an offshoot of that order, the incomplete formation of walls being a recent development. Still others think that at least some of the Siphonocladiales have arisen from the Ulotrichales.

A third line of development within the Chlorophyceae is represented by the Ulotrichales, an order in which several different types of multi-cellular bodies have appeared. All of these grow by division of uni-nucleate vegetative cells. The Oedogoniales may represent an offshoot from this order, but a connection between the Conjugales and the Ulotrichales seems rather remote, the lack of ciliated cells and peculiar type of sexual reproduction in the Conjugales being the chief obstacles. The Ulotrichales are of great interest in being the order of green algae most closely resembling the probable ancestors of the higher green plants. The occurrence of plate-like forms is particularly significant, inasmuch as the vegetative body of the simpler bryophytes is a plate-like thallus.

CHAPTER III

THALLOPHYTA: ALGAE (CONTINUED)

8. CHAROPHYCEAE

The Charophyceae, or stoneworts, constitute a very isolated group of highly organized green thallophytes with uncertain affinities. Although often included in the Chlorophyceae, they are so distinct that they belong in a separate and coordinate class. The Charophyceae are multicellular plants in which the only pigments present are chlorophyll and its associated carotinoids, these occurring in essentially the same proportions as in the green algae. They include 6 genera and about 200 species, nearly all of which belong to *Chara* and *Nitella*. The stoneworts grow in streams, ponds, and lakes attached to the bottom. They also live in brackish water but not in the ocean. Most species of *Chara* extract calcium carbonate from the water and deposit it in their walls, thereby becoming rough and brittle. Fossils belonging to the Charophyceae have been identified in deposits of the Cretaceous and later geologic periods. There is some evidence of their existence even as far back as the Devonian.

Vegetative Body. The vegetative body of the stoneworts consists of a slender cylindrical stem bearing many short branches in whorls (Fig. 51*A*). It grows erect and often reaches a height of 20 to 30 cm. The stem is attached to the substratum by means of colorless branched rhizoids. It is made up of short nodes and long unicellular internodes, the branches arising from the nodes. There are two kinds of branches: branches of unlimited growth, comprising the main axes, and branches of limited growth, the so-called leaves, in whose axils the main axes arise. All the cells contain numerous small spherical chloroplasts without pyrenoids. Reserve food is stored as starch.

Both kinds of branches grow by means of an apical cell, hemispherical in shape, that cuts off a longitudinal series of segments by successive transverse walls (Fig. 51*B*). Each segment again divides transversely into two cells, the lower one becoming the long internodal cell and the upper one the nodal cell. The latter, by vertical divisions, gives rise to a plate of cells that produce the branches. The internodal cell, often attaining a length of 10 cm., may become coenocytic by fragmentation of its nucleus. Its cytoplasm gives a striking demonstration of protoplasmic streaming. In *Chara* the internodal cells become ensheathed by cells that

63

arise from the nodes and form a one-layered cortex. Half of the cortical cells are derived from the node below and half from the node above, the two halves meeting in a zigzag line midway between the nodes. In *Nitella* the internodes remain uncovered.

Reproduction. No spores are produced in the Charophyceae. The nodes of the branches of limited growth bear unicellular branches and the sex organs, which are the most complex of all the algae. Most species are

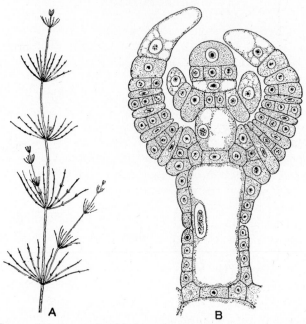

FIG. 51. *Chara.* *A*, upper portion of plant, showing branches of limited and unlimited growth, natural size; *B*, median longitudinal section through the stem tip, showing prominent apical cell and alternating nodes and internodes derived from it, ×200. The large internodal cell below is being ensheathed by a layer of cortical cells arising from adjacent nodes.

monoecious, an antheridium lying below an oögonium at the same node (Fig. 52). The antheridium is a stalked globular body that is brilliant red or yellow. It develops from a single initial cell that at first divides in three planes to produce octants. Each octant then undergoes two periclinal divisions to form an outer, a middle, and an inner cell. A jacket of eight triangular plate-like cells, called *shields*, is derived from the outer cells. The rapid enlargement of the shields results in the formation of a cavity within the antheridium. Projecting inward from the center of each shield is an elongated cell, the *manubrium*, that bears a rounded terminal cell, called a *primary capitulum*, which often divides in two. The manubria and primary capitula are derived from the middle and inner cells, respectively, of the young antheridium (Fig. 53*A*). The primary capitulum forms about six *secondary capitula*. Each of these gives rise to a pair of long filaments consisting of 100 to 200 small cells, from every one of which a sperm is liberated (Fig. 53*B*). At maturity, the entire antheridium falls apart. A single antheridium of *Chara* produces 20,000 to 50,000 sperms. These are coiled and biciliate, resembling the sperms of bryophytes.

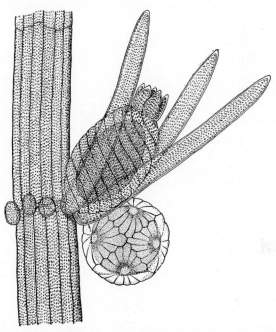

Fig. 52. Branch of *Chara* bearing an oögonium, with sterile jacket and crown, and an antheridium, with interlocking, shield-like wall cells, ×50.

An oögonium is an enlarged apical cell. It produces a single large egg. A unique feature of the oögonium is the presence of five elongated, spirally wound cells that arise below and completely surround it (Figs. 52 and 53*A*). At the top of the oögonium each jacket cell cuts off a small cell, these five cells forming a crown. In *Nitella* each spiral cell cuts off two crown cells, making ten in all. When the egg is ready for fertilization, the spirally twisted cells separate slightly just below the crown, forming five slits through which the sperms enter the oögonium. After a sperm nucleus has united with the egg nucleus, the walls of the surrounding cells harden, the whole structure becoming nut-like. In this condition the zygote rests. Before germination, the fusion nucleus gives rise to four nuclei. Each probably has the haploid number of chromosomes, although this has not been definitely established. Three of these nuclei degenerate. Upon germination, the zygote sends out a simple green filament and a colorless rhizoid. The adult shoot arises from this filament as a lateral branch.

Summary. The Charophyceae are an aberrant group, standing apart from the other algae. They resemble the Chlorophyceae in containing an excess of chlorophyll over the carotinoids and in storing starch as reserve food. The vegetative body is distinctive, being an erect thallus differentiated into nodes and internodes and with two kinds of branches

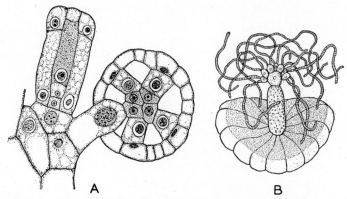

A   B

Fig. 53. *Chara.* *A*, longitudinal section of a young oögonium, invested by a sterile jacket, and a young antheridium, the latter consisting of a stalk cell, an outer layer of shield cells, four middle cells (manubria), and four inner cells (primary capitula), ×200; *B*, a shield cell from a mature antheridium with manubrium projecting from it. At the tip of the manubrium is a primary capitulum to which are attached smaller secondary capitula, each bearing a pair of spermatogenous filaments.

arising at the nodes. There is no reproduction by spores. The sex organs are multicellular and complex, both being enclosed by a jacket of sterile cells. In this respect the Charophyceae resemble the bryophytes, although the development of the sex organs in the two groups is very different. The sperms are also like those of bryophytes.

9. PHAEOPHYCEAE

The Phaeophyceae, or brown algae, are nearly all marine in distribution, occurring along most seacoasts but reaching their greatest display in cool waters. They range in color from olive green to dark brown as a result of the presence in their cells of chlorophyll and an excess of carotin and a unique xanthophyll, *fucoxanthin*, which is brown. There are no unicellular brown algae. Their multicellular bodies may be filamentous, plate-like, or may reach massive proportions and be highly differentiated in form. They are always attached. The Phaeophyceae are a specialized group, probably derived independently from flagellate ancestors and apparently not related to any of the higher plants. There is no satisfactory fossil evidence of their existence before the Jurassic. The Phaeophyceae number almost 1,000 species, nearly all of which are contained in six main orders: Ectocarpales, Sphacelariales, Cutleriales, Dictyotales, Laminariales, and Fucales.

1. Ectocarpales

The Ectocarpales include the simplest of the brown algae. They occur along all rocky seacoasts, growing attached to rocks, piers, and other plants. They include over 60 genera and 300 species, forming a diverse assemblage that is often broken up into several smaller orders. Of the many genera, perhaps the two that are best known are *Ectocarpus* and *Pylaiella*.

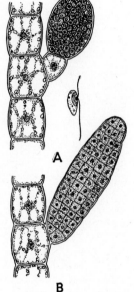

Ectocarpus. *Ectocarpus* is a simple brown alga, widely distributed along seacoasts, where it grows attached to rocks or to other algae. It is filamentous and usually much branched, the older portions sometimes being surrounded by rhizoid-like branches. Otherwise the body is strictly *monosiphonous*, each branch consisting of a single filament. An alga composed of parallel bundles of filaments is said to be *polysiphonous*. Growth of the filaments occurs mainly by intercalary cell divisions. Each cell contains a single nucleus and a number of small brown plastids.

Zoospores and isogametes are borne in sporangia and gametangia, respectively. These develop from the terminal cell of a short lateral branch, but may be either stalked or sessile. The sporangium is globular or somewhat elongated (Fig. 54A). It is unicellular and contains many (32 or 64) zoospores. It is at first uninucleate, becoming multinucleate and forming zoospores by cleavage of the cytoplasm. The gametangium

Fig. 54. A sporangium (*A*) and a gametangium (*B*) of *Ectocarpus*, ×400; also a single escaped zoospore, more highly magnified.

is longer than the sporangium and often ovate or cylindrical (Fig. 54B). It is divided by cell walls into many small cubical cells, in each of which an isogamete is formed. Both the zoospores and gametes are laterally biciliate, the cilia being of unequal length. The pairing gametes are generally of the same size but, in some species, one is slightly larger than the other and swims less vigorously. Where this slight tendency toward heterogamy exists, all the gametes in a gametangium are either smaller (male) or larger (female). As in all the brown algae, the zygote germinates without going into a resting stage.

Ectocarpus displays a primitive type of alternation of generations and one that is not well established. Although all the plants of a species are alike vegetatively, some are gametophytes and some are sporophytes. The gametophytes, producing gametangia, are haploid. The zygotes give rise to sporophytes, which are diploid. These produce two kinds of sporangia. One is multicellular and looks like a gametangium but gives

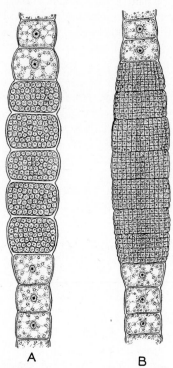

A   **B**

Fig. 55. A row of sporangia (*A*) and gametangia (*B*) of *Pylaiella*, ×500.

rise to diploid zoospores that develop into other sporophytes. The other is the unicellular sporangium already described. The division of the nucleus in the young unicellular sporangium is reductional, and so the zoospores that it produces are haploid. These haploid zoospores always give rise to gametophytes. Sometimes gametes, without pairing and fusing, develop directly into other haploid plants. It is apparent that much variation occurs in the behavior of the spores and gametes.

Pylaiella. This alga resembles *Ectocarpus* in its habitat and general structure. It differs chiefly in that the filaments are usually only slightly branched and any cell may become a sporangium or gametangium (Fig. 55). Consequently the reproductive organs are intercalary in position and usually appear in a linear series. They have the same structure as those of *Ectocarpus*, the sporangia being unicellular and the gametangia multicellular. Sometimes multicellular sporangia are produced on the plants bearing unicellular ones. Although *Pylaiella* is essentially isogamous, one of the pairing gametes is slightly larger than the other. An alternation of generations is seen also in this genus, the gamete-producing plants being haploid and the spore-producing plants diploid. The reduction of chromosomes occurs in the young unicellular sporangium.

Summary. The thallus of the Ectocarpales is usually composed either of freely branching filaments or wholly or in part of a plate-like or solid body composed of interlacing filaments. In some forms the thallus is parenchymatous. Vegetative growth is mainly intercalary, often being confined to basal portions of the branches. Reproduction occurs typically by zoospores borne in unicellular (and multicellular) sporangia and by motile isogametes borne in multicellular gametangia. There is an alternation of generations, the haploid plants being either similar to the diploid plants in size and vegetative structure, or much smaller and simpler.

A few heterogamous forms with unicellular sex organs borne on minute gametophytes, but otherwise resembling the Ectocarpales, are now segregated into two small orders: the Sporochnales and Desmarestiales. Some authors also segregate into the Chordariales, Punctariales, and Dictyosiphonales isogamous forms with multicellular gametangia but with dissimilar haploid and diploid plants.

2. Sphacelariales

The Sphacelariales are a small but distinct order related to the Ectocarpales. They are all littoral algae numbering 10 genera and 60 species, chiefly tropical but also occurring in temperate regions. The two chief genera are *Sphacelaria* and *Stypocaulon*.

Sphacelaria. This alga grows in small tufts attached to rocks and other algae. It occurs along both coasts of North America but is rather uncommon. The vegetative body is differentiated into a flat, plate-like, prostrate portion and a filamentous erect portion that is freely branched, the branches increasing in length by means of a large apical cell (Fig. 56). This cuts off a series of transverse segments that then divide both longitudinally and transversely to form a polysiphonous thallus. In most algae, growth is intercalary, which means that it occurs by division of all or many of its cells. Where there is an apical cell, all the cells of the body are descendants of it, even though some may later divide independently.

The sporangia and gametangia of *Sphacelaria* are similar to those of *Ectocarpus*, the sporangia being unicellular and the gametangia multicellular. Both are short-stalked and borne on the axes. The zoospores and gametes are laterally biciliate and, in some species, one of the pairing gametes is slightly larger than the other. As in *Ectocarpus*, there is an alternation of vegetatively similar generations and the number of chromosomes is reduced one-half in the young unicellular sporangium. A form of vegetative reproduction common in *Sphacelaria* involves the production of *propagules*. These are short, flattened, modified branches that become detached and give rise to new plants.

Summary. The thallus of the Sphacelariales is filamentous, being monosiphonous near the tips and polysiphonous below. Growth takes place by means of an apical cell. Reproduction occurs by zoospores borne in unicellular sporangia and motile isogametes borne in multicellular gametangia. The order displays an isomorphic alternation of generations.

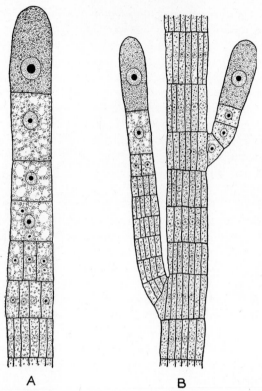

A   **B**

Fig. 56. *Sphacelaria*, ×200. *A*, tip of filament, showing large apical cell and segments derived from it; *B*, slightly older portion of thallus, showing development of branches.

3. Cutleriales

The Cutleriales are a very small order including only *Cutleria*, with 3 species, and *Zanardinia*, with 1. Both genera occur in the Mediterranean Sea, while *Cutleria* has been reported also from Florida, the West Indies, and the Gulf of California. The Cutleriales are more advanced than the two preceding orders, although apparently related to them.

Cutleria. The best-known species of *Cutleria* is found in the warmer parts of Europe. The plants grow just below the low-tide mark. *Cutleria* displays a *heteromorphic* alternation of generations, the gametophyte and sporophyte being unlike vegetatively. In fact, they are so different in general appearance that, before they were known to belong to the same life history, they were placed in separate genera. The gametophyte was called *Cutleria* and the sporophyte *Aglaozonia*. The sporophyte is a small, flat, lobed disk several layers of cells in thickness and about 2 to 5 cm. in diameter (Fig. 57*E*). The lower side bears numerous rhizoids. On the upper side are enormous numbers of elongated unicellular sporangia in crowded clusters. Each sporangium has a one-celled stalk and produces 8, 16, or 32 laterally biciliate zoospores (Fig. 57*F*). At first the sporangium has a single nucleus, the first two divisions of which result in a reduction of chromosomes. After three, four, or five simultaneous free-nuclear divisions have occurred, uninucleate protoplasts are

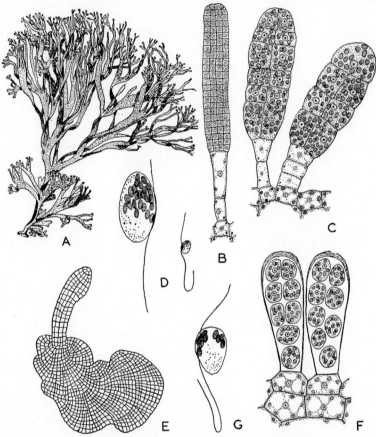

FIG. 57. *Cutleria multifida.* *A*, gametophyte, one-third natural size; *B*, male gametangium, ×600; *C*, two female gametangia, ×600; *D*, an egg and a sperm in the living condition; *E*, young sporophyte 30 days after fertilization; *F*, two nearly ripe sporangia, ×600; *G*, a zoospore in the living condition. (*A, after Thuret; D, E, G, after Yamanouchi.*)

formed by cleavage of the cytoplasm. Thus the zoospores are haploid (Fig. 57*G*).

The gametophytes, which are produced by the zoospores, are either male or female but are alike vegetatively (Fig. 57*A*). They are erect, ribbon-like, and dichotomously branched, reaching a length of about 20 cm. They are several layers of cells in thickness. The male and female gametangia, which are somewhat similar in appearance, are borne in clusters on both sides of the thallus, intermixed with sterile hairs called *paraphyses.* Each has a short stalk and a number of gamete-producing cells. The male gametangium (antheridium) is a club-shaped organ consisting of over 200 small cells arranged in many tiers (Fig. 57*B*). Each cell produces a single sperm. The female gametangium (oögonium) has fewer cells, about 20 to 60, each giving rise to an egg (Fig. 57*C*). The eggs are considerably larger than the sperms but both are laterally biciliate and free-swimming (Fig. 57*D*). The eggs are less active than the sperms, however, and usually come to rest first. The zygote germinates at once, giving rise to a sporophyte.

Zanardinia. This genus differs from *Cutleria* in several ways. The gametophyte and sporophyte are alike vegetatively, both being disklike, several layers of cells thick, and about 5 cm. or more in diameter. Each sporangium produces four large biciliate zoospores, the reduction of chromosomes occurring when they are formed. The gametophytes are monoecious, the two kinds of gametangia being intermixed. The male gametangium produces about 250 sperms, the female gametangium about 12 to 36 eggs. The gametes resemble those of *Cutleria,* both being laterally biciliate.

Summary. The Cutleriales have a flat plate-like thallus that may be either erect or prostrate. Its growth is entirely or partially intercalary. The zoospores are borne in unicellular sporangia, the gametes in multicellular gametangia. The group has well-marked heterogamy, but both the sperms and eggs are ciliated. A distinct alternation of generations is present, the gametophyte and sporophyte being either vegetatively similar (*Zanardinia*) or dissimilar (*Cutleria*).

4. Dictyotales

The Dictyotales are a distinct group of brown algae occupying a somewhat intermediate position with respect to the other groups. They are found in both tropical and temperate seas but always grow in warm waters. There are 18 genera and about 100 species. *Dictyota, Padina,* and *Zonaria* are well-known members.

Dictyota. Although found along both the Atlantic and Pacific coasts of North America, this genus does not occur north of about 35° latitude. The plants grow attached to rocks in tidepools and are always submersed. The vegetative body consists of a thin, flat, dichotomously branched thallus with a basal holdfast (Fig. 58). It is composed of three layers of cells: an upper and a lower layer of small photosynthetic cells with a layer of large colorless cells between them. The thallus grows by means of a large apical cell, one of which lies at the tip of each branch (Fig. 59). The sporophyte and gametophyte are alike vegetatively, and so alternation of generations is isomorphic.

Numerous unicellular sporangia are scattered over both surfaces of the sporophyte (Fig. 60). Each sporangium, borne on a one-celled stalk, produces four nonmotile spores (aplanospores). In connection with the formation of four free nuclei from the single nucleus of the young sporangium, the number of chromosomes is reduced one-half. Two of the

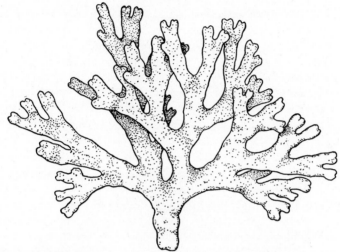

Fig. 58. *Dictyota binghamiae.* Portion of plant showing dichotomous branching, three-fourths natural size.

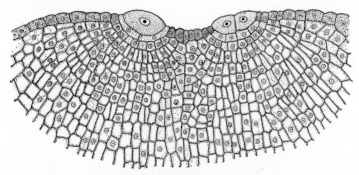

Fig. 59. Longitudinal section of a bifurcating thallus of *Dictyota dichotoma*, cut parallel to its flat surface. The branch tip on the left shows a large undivided apical cell, while the one on the right has just undergone a second dichotomy.

spores from each sporangium give rise to male plants and two to female plants.

Like other members of the order, *Dictyota* displays well-developed heterogamy. The antheridia are borne in clusters of about 100 to 300 on both surfaces of the male plants (Fig. 61A). The clusters are surrounded by several rings of sterile cells. Each antheridium is composed of a stalk

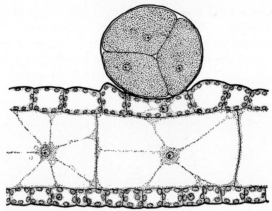

FIG. 60.   *Dictyota dichotoma.*   Cross section of thallus with a sporangium, showing three of the four spores.   (*After Mottier, Textbook of Botany, The Blakiston Company.*)

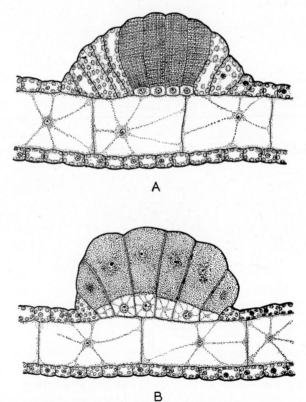

FIG. 61.   Sex organs of *Dictyota dichotoma.*   *A,* cross section of thallus with group of antheridia; *B,* cross section of thallus with group of oögonia.   (*After Mottier, Textbook of Botany, The Blakiston Company.*)

cell and about 1,500 small cells, each of which produces a sperm. Although the sperms are laterally biciliate, one cilium is very short. The oögonia are borne in groups of about 25 to 50 on both sides of the female plants (Fig. 61*B*). The groups are not surrounded by sterile cells. Each

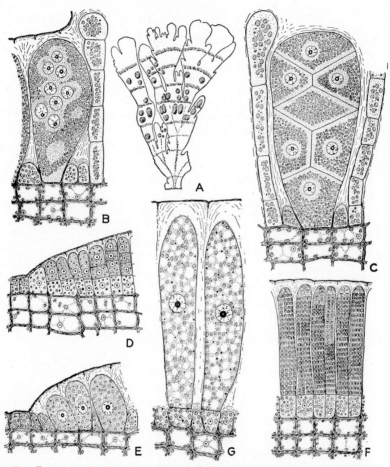

FIG. 62. *Zonaria farlowii.* *A*, portion of thallus with numerous groups of sporangia, ×1½; *B*, young sporangium with eight free nuclei; *C*, mature sporangium, the eight aplanospores cut off by walls; *D*, young antheridia; *E*, young oögonia; *F*, mature antheridia; *G*, two mature oögonia; *B* to *G*, ×300. (*After Haupt.*)

oögonium consists of a small stalk cell and a single large nonmotile egg. The eggs are discharged into the water and there fertilized. The zygote gives rise to the sporophyte without undergoing any resting period.

Zonaria. *Zonaria* has about the same distribution along both coasts of North America as *Dictyota.* The thallus consists of an erect fan-like cluster of thin flat branches arising from a stalk-like portion that is attached by a disk-shaped mass of rhizoids (Fig. 62*A*). It grows by means of a row of apical cells extending around the distal margin of each branch. The mature thallus is about eight layers of cells in thickness.

FIG. 63. *Laminaria,* a small kelp with a blade, stipe, and holdfast, about one-half natural size.

The diploid sporophytes bear groups of sporangia intermixed with paraphyses. Each sporangium, lacking a stalk cell, gives rise to eight large haploid aplanospores (Fig. 62*B, C*). These produce the gametophytes, which are either male or female and resemble the sporophytes vegetatively. The antheridia and oögonia are, in general, similar to those of *Dictyota* (Fig. 62*D–G*). The zygote produces a sporophyte.

Summary. The thallus of the Dictyotales is flat, plate-like, and erect. It grows by means of a single apical cell or a marginal row of apical cells. Reproduction occurs by aplanospores, four or sometimes eight being developed in a unicellular sporangium, and by heterogametes. Small biciliate sperms are borne in multicellular antheridia and large nonmotile eggs are borne singly in unicellular oögonia. A distinct alternation of generations is present, the gametophyte and sporophyte being similar vegetatively.

5. Laminariales

The Laminariales comprise the kelps, the largest of the brown algae. They are widely distributed throughout temperate and arctic regions, occurring mainly in cool waters and making their greatest display along shores bordering the North Pacific Ocean. Most of the Laminariales grow below the low-tide line. They include about 30 genera and 100 species. Some of the best-known members are *Laminaria, Macrocystis, Nereocystis, Postelsia,* and *Egregia. Laminaria,* with 30 species, is the largest genus.

Laminaria. Common along both coasts of North America, in cooler waters, are various species of *Laminaria.* Some are not more than 30 cm. long, while others reach a length of 9 to 12 m. They live attached to rocks just below the low-tide line. Alternation of generations is heteromorphic. The large vegetative plant is a sporophyte (Fig. 63). It consists of a long blade and a thick leathery stipe anchored by means of a branching basal holdfast. According to the species, the blade may be entire or divided lengthwise into segments. The cells of the stipe show a differentiation into an outer cortical region of photosynthetic tissue and a central pith that usually contains storage cells. Many of the central cells are elongated and have pores in their end walls, thus resembling the sieve tubes of vascular plants. Vegetative growth is not apical but results

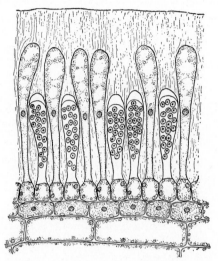

Fig. 64. Sporangia of *Laminaria*, intermixed with paraphyses, ×400.

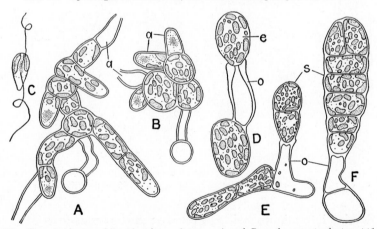

Fig. 65. Gametophytes of *Laminaria yendoana*. *A* and *B*, male gametophytes, ×1,200; *C*, a sperm, ×1,200; *D*, *E*, *F*, female gametophytes, ×800; *a*, antheridia, some empty; *e*, egg; *o*, oögonia; *s*, young sporophytes arising from the fertilized egg. (*After Kanda*.)

from the activity of a meristem situated at the junction of the blade and stipe. The meristem forms a new blade each year, replacing the old one, which dies off.

Numerous unicellular, club-shaped sporangia, intermingled with long sterile cells (paraphyses), arise in large patches on both sides of the thallus (Fig. 64). They produce 32 or 64 small, laterally biciliate zoospores. The reduction of chromosomes results from the division of the nucleus of the young sporangium. After four or five simultaneous free-nuclear divisions have taken place, the contents of the sporangium undergoes cleavage into uninucleate protoplasts, the zoospores. These are liberated

Fig. 66.   Apical portion of a plant of *Macrocystis pyrifera*, one-fifth natural size.

and develop into minute male and female gametophytes (Fig. 65). The sperms are laterally biciliate and are borne singly in antheridia that arise at the ends of short, branched filaments. The female plant usually consists of only a few cells, one of which becomes an oögonium. This produces a single nonmotile egg that is extruded through a terminal pore, to which it remains attached. The zygote germinates at once, giving rise to the large sporophyte.

Other Kelps. As in *Laminaria*, the bodies of nearly all the other kelps are differentiated into holdfast organs, stout stalks, and flat blades often much divided into narrow segments. Air bladders are frequently present. Reproduction is similar in all members of the order. The greatest variety and largest of the kelps occur along the Pacific coast of North America, where they live in water 10 to 30 m. deep, their stalks attached to rocky reefs and their blades often floating on the surface. *Macrocystis* may reach a length of 30 to 50 m. A single plant consists of a stalk with many blades, each blade having a float (Fig. 66). Another large kelp is *Nereocystis*, with a large hollow bulb at the end of a thick stalk and a number of blades arising from the bulb (Fig. 67). It reaches a length of 25 to 30 m. *Postelsia*, known as the "sea palm," has a stout stalk up to 60 cm. long bearing at its tip numerous branches terminating in narrow blades (Fig. 68). *Egregia*, the "feather-boa kelp," has a long stalk that bears two rows of lateral blades and floats, the blades producing sporangia being much narrower than the sterile ones.

Summary. The vegetative body of the Laminariales is highly differentiated both externally and internally. It consists of a massive thallus usually with a holdfast, stipe, and one or more blades. Growth is due to an intercalary meristem. The large plant body is a sporophyte bearing unicellular sporangia that contain many zoospores. The

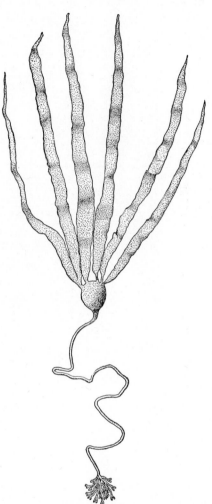

Fig. 67. Young plant of *Nereocystis luetkeana*, one-quarter natural size.

gametophytes are microscopic, dioecious, and heterogamous. The sperms are biciliate and produced singly in unicellular antheridia. The eggs are nonmotile and borne in unicellular oögonia. The Laminariales have a heteromorphic alternation of generations.

Fig. 68.   A sea palm (*Postelsia palmaeformis*) growing on a rock exposed at low tide, about one-quarter natural size.

6. Fucales

The Fucales, commonly known as rockweeds, are a highly specialized order of brown algae standing apart from the others.   They are widely distributed throughout tropical and temperate regions, most of them growing along rocky seacoasts in the intertidal zone.   They comprise 32 genera and 325 species, representative forms being *Fucus*, *Pelvetia*, *Ascophyllum*, and *Sargassum*.

Fucus.   *Fucus* is widely distributed in cool waters, being represented along both the eastern and western coasts of North America.   The thallus, rarely exceeding a meter in length, is coarsely ribbon-like and repeatedly forked, with a basal stalk arising from a disk-like holdfast (Fig. 69). It is rather tough and leathery. In some species air bladders, giving buoyancy to the plant, are conspicuous. Growth occurs by means of an apical cell that occupies a notch at the end of each branch. The

FIG. 69. *Fucus furcatus.* Portion of thallus, showing conceptacles, two-thirds natural size.

apical cell is complex, having the form of a truncated quadrangular pyramid and cutting off cells in three planes. When the thallus branches, the apical cell divides vertically into two nearly equal parts, each of which becomes the apical cell of a new branch. Internally the thallus is differentiated into a firm outer cortex of photosynthetic tissue and a central colorless pith that is rather spongy. The only method of asexual reproduction is by fragmentation of the thallus. There are no spores of any kind.

Within the swollen tips of some of the branches are numerous flask-shaped pits or chambers, called *conceptacles*, each with a pore-like opening (Fig. 70). Sperms and eggs are produced inside the conceptacles, the sperms in antheridia and the eggs in oögonia. The antheridia are oval

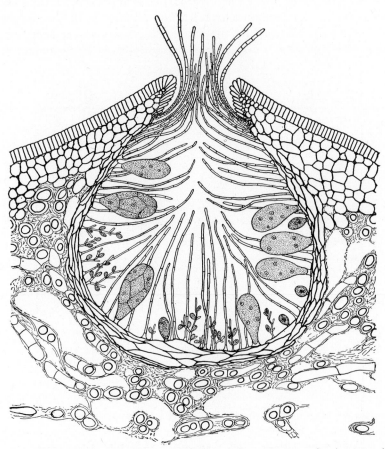

Fig. 70. Longitudinal section of a conceptacle of *Fucus furcatus*, showing oögonia in various stages of development, small branching filaments bearing antheridia, and numerous paraphyses, ×100.

and sac-like; they appear on special branching filaments that arise from the wall of the conceptacle (Fig. 71*A*). Each antheridium produces 64 small, laterally biciliate sperms. The antheridium is unicellular and, when young, is uninucleate. The number of chromosomes is reduced one-half when its nucleus divides. Free-nuclear divisions continue until there are 32 nuclei. Then the cytoplasm undergoes cleavage to form an equal number of uninucleate protoplasts, each of which divides again to produce two sperms. The sperms escape from the antheridium in a mass surrounded by a membrane that soon disappears.

The eggs of *Fucus* are borne in groups of eight inside the oögonia, which are large oval or globular cells, each of which has a one-celled stalk (Fig. 71*B–D*). The young oögonium has a single nucleus, the division of which is reductional. Three simultaneous divisions result in the formation of eight free nuclei. Cytoplasmic cleavage follows and an egg is organized around each nucleus. The eggs are extruded from the oögonium in a

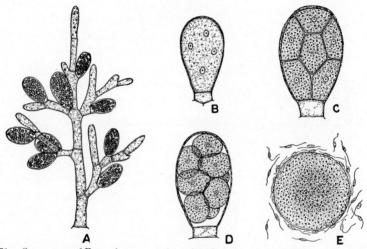

FIG. 71. Sex organs of *Fucus furcatus*. *A*, antheridial filament, ×320; *B*, young oögonium with four nuclei, ×160; *C*, longitudinal section of an older oögonium with eight nearly mature eggs, ×160; *D*, mature oögonium, ×160; *E*, escaped egg of *Fucus vesiculosus* surrounded by numerous sperms, ×240. (*E*, *after Thuret*.)

group surrounded by a membrane that soon ruptures. In *Ascophyllum* four eggs are organized in an oögonium, in *Pelvetia* two, and in *Sargassum* only one. In all the genera of Fucales, however, eight nuclei always arise in the oögonium, the nonfunctional nuclei either being extruded or degenerating. Thus *Fucus* represents the primitive condition from which the other genera, by progressive reduction, have been derived.

Depending on the species, the antheridia and oögonia of *Fucus* may occur in the same conceptacle, in different conceptacles on the same plant, or on different plants. In addition to the sex organs, the conceptacles contain numerous unbranched sterile filaments (paraphyses), some of which often project through the pore. Both the sperms and eggs escape from the conceptacles into the water but only the sperms are motile. The sperms surround the eggs in such vast numbers that they cause them to rotate (Fig. 71*E*). After fertilization has taken place, the zygote surrounds itself with a cell wall and divides at once to produce a new vegetative thallus. The reduction of chromosomes occurs when the nucleus of the young antheridium and that of the young oögonium divide. Thus from the four-nucleate stage to maturity the sex organs are haploid, the diploid condition arising at fertilization.

Although *Fucus* has no alternation of gametophyte and sporophyte plant bodies, there is a brief haploid phase and a prolonged diploid phase. Some botanists interpret the vegetative body of the Fucales as a sporophyte, the antheridia as microsporangia, and the sperms as microspores (small zoospores). They interpret the oögonia as megasporangia and the eggs as megaspores (large aplanospores). Then, to explain the sexual fusion, the microspores and megaspores are said to function directly as gametes. This interpretation implies that a gametophyte generation was once well developed and has become so reduced that it comprises only the haploid nuclei in the gametangia and the gametes themselves.

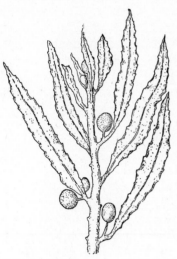

Fig. 72. Small portion of a plant of *Sargassum*, showing differentiation into stem, leaf-like blades, and berry-like air bladders, natural size.

Sargassum. This is a very large genus whose 250 species are widely distributed throughout tropical and subtropical seas, especially in the Southern Hemisphere. The vegetative body is more highly developed than that of *Fucus*, having distinct branches, leaf-like blades, and often small stalked air bladders as well (Fig. 72). *Sargassum* may live either in an attached or a floating condition. Like other rockweeds, it grows chiefly along seacoasts, but frequently plants are torn loose from the rocks and carried for hundreds of miles out to sea. The Sargasso Sea is a vast eddy lying west of the Canary Islands. Here great floating masses of "gulfweed," transported by the Gulf Stream from the West Indies and tropical America, accumulate and propagate themselves by fragmentation of the thallus.

Summary. The Fucales have a coarse, ribbon-like thallus that grows by means of an apical cell. Spores are not formed. The order displays well-developed heterogamy. The sex organs are unicellular, the antheridia producing numerous biciliate sperms, the oögonia producing one, two, four, or eight nonmotile eggs that escape before fertilization. The sex organs are borne in internal cavities (conceptacles). The Fucales are without a distinct alternation of generations.

Summary of Phaeophyceae

The Phaeophyceae are algae having in their plastids an excess of carotin and a brown xanthophyll pigment (fucoxanthin) over the chlorophyll. All of them are multicellular, the thallus being filamentous, plate-like, or massive, often with differentiated tissues. The cells contain a definite nucleus, generally several or many plastids, and a distinct cell wall. Reserve food is stored chiefly as laminarin (a dextrin-like carbohydrate) or oil. Except in the Fucales, zoospores are produced or, in the Dictyotales, aplanospores. Gametic reproduction may occur either by isogametes or heterogametes. In the heterogamous forms the eggs may be ciliated but are generally nonciliated. All motile reproductive cells are laterally biciliate, the cilia being unequal in length. No resting cells are formed. Most members exhibit an alternation of generations, the Fucales, with only a diploid plant body, being a notable exception. The gametophyte and sporophyte are either similar or dissimilar vegetatively.

10. RHODOPHYCEAE

Like the Phaeophyceae, the Rhodophyceae, or red algae, are almost all marine in distribution but, as a rule, live in deeper and warmer waters than the brown algae. They include the majority of the seaweeds. Most of the Rhodophyceae are rose red or violet, but some are dark purple, reddish brown, or olive green. In addition to chlorophyll and its associated carotinoids, a red pigment, *phycoerythrin,* is present in the cells. This more or less obscures the chlorophyll. Many of the Rhodophyceae also contain a small amount of phycocyanin, the blue pigment of the Cyanophyceae. Except for several unicellular forms, whose inclusion in the group is doubtful, all the red algae are multicellular. Their bodies are not large, most of them being less than 30 cm. in length, while only a few are as long as 1 m. They are rather varied in form, however, being filamentous, ribbon-like, or plate-like, but never massive. They are always attached. Some are heavily impregnated with lime. Lime-secreting forms are known as fossils as far back as the Ordovician. The Rhodophyceae are the most highly specialized of all the algae. They are probably not related to any of the higher plants except, perhaps, to some of the fungi. They include about 3,000 species.

There are seven orders of Rhodophyceae. These, together with one or more representative genera, are as follows: (1) Bangiales—*Bangia, Porphyra, Porphyridium;* (2) Nemalionales—*Nemalion, Batrachospermum;* (3) Gelidiales—*Gelidium;* (4) Cryptonemiales—*Corallina, Lithothamnion;* (5) Gigartinales—*Plocamium, Gracilaria, Chondrus, Gigartina;* (6) Rhodymeniales—*Rhodymenia;* (7) Ceramiales—*Callithamnion, Ceramium, Polysiphonia, Delessaria.*

Porphyra. *Porphyra* is a typical member of the Bangiales, the most primitive order of Rhodophyceae. It is widely distributed along rocky seashores, occurring on both coasts of North America. It grows in the intertidal zone on rocks and other algae. The thallus is plate-like and attached by means of a small basal holdfast (Fig. 73*A*). It is only one or

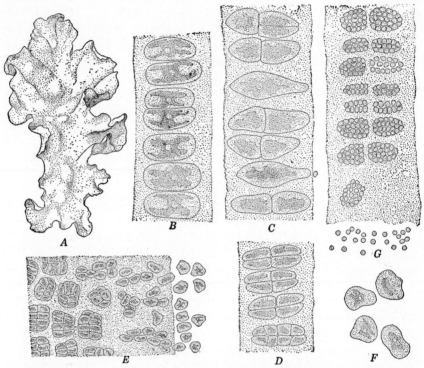

Fig. 73. *Porphyra perforata. A,* thallus, one-half natural size; *B,* vertical section of vegetative portion of thallus; *C* and *D,* vertical sections of thalli with carpogonia and developing carpospores; *E,* surface view, showing liberation of carpospores; *F,* amoeboid carpospores; *G,* vertical section through portion of a thallus liberating spermatia. (*From Gilbert M. Smith.*)

two layers of cells in thickness and, in most species, is less than 50 cm. long. The cells lie in a tough gelatinous matrix derived from their walls. They are without apparent cytoplasmic connections (Fig. 73*B*). Each cell has a nucleus that divides by a primitive type of mitosis. It also has a single large plastid with a central pyrenoid.

Some species of *Porphyra* are monoecious but most of them are dioecious. The antheridia develop directly from the vegetative cells. A cell undergoes repeated divisions in three planes until 64 or sometimes 128 small cells are formed. The walls gelatinize and free the protoplasts, which function as male gametes (Fig. 73*G*). Such naked, nonmotile male cells, a feature of all the red algae, are called *spermatia*. The female sex organs, or *carpogonia*, also arise from ordinary vegetative cells but without undergoing division, the protoplast functioning directly as an egg (Fig. 73*C*).

A spermatium, carried by water currents to the carpogonium, enters and fuses with the egg. The zygote divides at once to form a group of spores, usually 8 or 16, that are freed by the breaking down of the surrounding cell walls (Fig. 73*C–E*). These naked cells are *carpospores* and, like the gametes, are nonciliated. The freed carpospores exhibit an amoeboid movement (Fig. 73*F*). After coming to rest, each carpospore forms a cell wall and develops into a new thallus. The reduction of chromosomes occurs when the zygote germinates, and so the vegetative plant is haploid.

As compared with the higher orders of Rhodophyceae, the Bangiales have a simple type of nucleus and cells without evident protoplasmic continuity. They display intercalary rather than apical growth. The carpogonium either lacks a trichogyne or has a very short one. The zygote is transformed directly into carpospores. An alternation of generations is not present.

Porphyridium is a unicellular alga whose relationships are uncertain. It forms a reddish gelatinous layer on damp soil and moist walls. It was formerly placed in the Cyanophyceae but, because it has a true nucleus and a distinct plastid, is now included in the Rhodophyceae. The cells are spherical and surrounded by a mucilaginous matrix. Fission is the only known method of reproduction.

Nemalion. Although showing a considerable advance over *Porphyra*, this form is much simpler than members of the higher orders. *Nemalion* is widely distributed, growing on rocks between the high- and low-tide lines. The thallus, up to 60 cm. in length, consists of a slimy mass of branching filaments that are interwoven to form a worm-like cylinder. This is composed of a central core of slender colorless filaments from which tufts of larger chlorophyllose filaments radiate outward. The cells of the latter have a small nucleus and a large plastid with a conspicuous pyrenoid. As in all the algae except the Bangiales, growth is apical. Furthermore, the vegetative protoplasts are connected by a conspicuous strand of cytoplasm that passes through a pore in the cell wall.

Nemalion is monoecious, the sex organs occurring at the ends of short branches. The antheridium consists of a single small cell that is budded off laterally from an antheridial branch (Fig. 74*A*). Its protoplast, the *spermatium*, is discharged into the water. The female organ, called a *procarp*, consists of two parts, the *carpogonium* and the *trichogyne* (Fig. 74*B*). The protoplast of the carpogonium functions as an egg. The trichogyne is a long thread-like cell at the upper end of the carpogonium.

Its nucleus degenerates. The nonmotile male cell, or spermatium, is carried by water currents. After coming in contact with the trichogyne, it becomes binucleate. Both of the male nuclei may enter the trichogyne but only one passes into the carpogonium, where it fuses with the egg nucleus. The other male nucleus does not function.

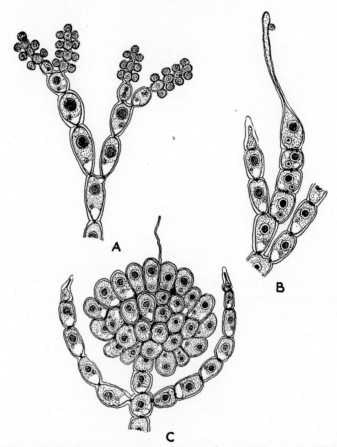

Fig. 74. *Nemalion lubricum*, ×700. *A*, portion of plant with four antheridial branches consisting of groups of small cells, each producing a single spermatium; *B*, a carpogonial branch, terminating in a carpogonium with its slender trichogyne to which a spermatium is attached; *C*, a cystocarp, composed of fertile filaments that cut off terminal carpospores.

Following fertilization, many short filaments, called *gonimoblasts*, arise from the carpogonium and at the tip of each a carpospore is organized. After a carpospore is shed, another may be cut off from the cell behind it. It is only in the Bangiales that carpospores are produced by direct division of the zygote. In *Nemalion* the carpogonium, fertile filaments, and carpospores collectively form the *cystocarp* (Fig. 74C). The carpospores, upon being set free as naked, nonmotile cells, develop into sexual plants.

The reduction of chromosomes occurs just after fertilization, when the fusion nucleus in the carpogonium divides. Thus the gonimoblasts, carpospores, and sexual plants are haploid. There is no true alternation of generations.

Batrachospermum. This is a widely distributed fresh-water alga, growing in streams attached to rocks along the bottom. The plants are blue-green, olive green, violet, or reddish. The variation in color is primarily a result of differences in light intensity, plants growing in shallow water being greener than those in deeper water. *Batrachospermum* is related to *Nemalion* but differs from it in several respects. The vegetative body consists of long branching filaments of unlimited growth bearing whorls of dwarf branching filaments of limited growth (Fig. 75). The long filaments consist of an axial row of cells which, in the older portions of the body, is covered by a layer of small-celled filaments that form a sheath around it. The cells of the sheath arise from the basal cells of the dwarf filaments. Growth occurs by means of an apical cell.

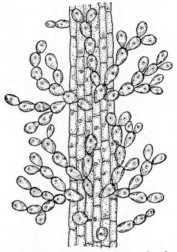

Fig. 75. Small portion of the vegetative body of *Batrachospermum*, showing dwarf filaments arising in whorls from the cylindrical main axis, ×400.

The sex organs are borne at the ends of some of the dwarf filaments and resemble those of *Nemalion* (Fig. 76). After coming in contact with the trichogyne, the spermatium remains uninucleate instead of becoming binucleate. Moreover, following fertilization, the cells at the base of the carpogonium send out loose filaments that grow up around and invest the cystocarp while the carpospores are being produced.

The germinating carpospore gives rise to a branching filamentous body that is much simpler than the gamete-producing plant. This plant, which represents a juvenile stage in the life cycle, may multiply by *monospores*, which are formed singly within sporangia at the ends of short lateral branches. Finally a special branch appears that becomes a gamete-producing plant. As in *Nemalion*, the chromosome number is reduced one-half when the fusion nucleus divides in the fertilized carpogonium. Consequently, the juvenile plant is not a sporophyte and there is no alternation of generations.

Polysiphonia. *Polysiphonia* is a widespread genus of about 150 species. It is abundant along the Atlantic coast of North America but is less common along the Pacific coast. It grows in tide pools on rocks and on other algae. It is a more highly developed but more typical red alga than any of the others that have been discussed. The plant body, reaching a length of 25 cm., is filamentous and polysiphonous, being made up of an

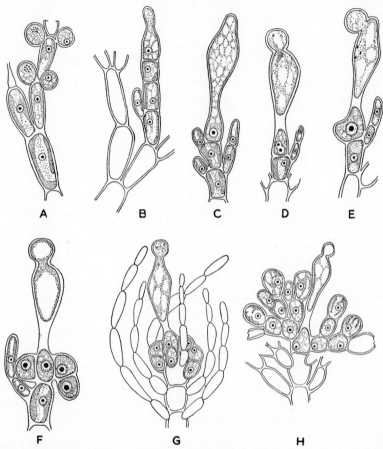

FIG. 76. *Batrachospermum.* *A*, antheridial branch with globular antheridia, one of which has liberated its protoplast; *B*, young carpogonial branch, the terminal cell forming the carpogonium and trichogyne; *C*, mature procarp with nucleated carpogonium and swollen trichogyne; *D*, later stage, showing spermatium united with trichogyne and male nucleus fusing with carpogonial nucleus; *E*, completed fusion of male and female nuclei; *F*, development of gonimoblasts from carpogonium, a sterile branch arising on the left; *G*, further development of gonimoblasts and sterile filaments; *H*, formation of carpospores; *A* to *F*, ×960; *G* and *H*, ×720. (*After Kylin.*)

axial row of elongated cells surrounded and completely covered by several rows of smaller peripheral cells that are cut off from the central cells by longitudinal divisions. Growth occurs by means of an apical cell.

The reproductive features of *Polysiphonia* are complex. Nonmotile

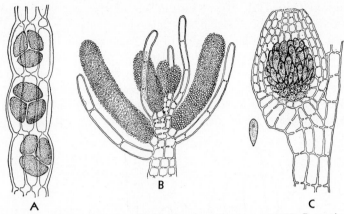

Fig. 77. *Polysiphonia.* *A*, portion of plant bearing tetraspores, ×160; *B*, portion of male plant bearing clusters of antheridia, ×200; *C*, portion of female plant with cystocarp containing carpospores; also a single carpospore, ×80.

spores are formed in groups of four in a one-celled sporangium (Fig. 77*A*). They are called *tetraspores*. Chromosome reduction occurs in connection with the formation of the tetraspores, and so each is haploid. Upon germination, two tetraspores from each sporangium produce male plants and two produce female plants. These sexual plants are like the tetrasporic ones in general appearance.

The antheridia occur in dense clusters on special lateral branches of the male plants (Fig. 77*B*). In their formation, a number of cells arise laterally from the cells of the axial filament, giving rise to a simple monosiphonous branch. Each cell of this branch develops two-celled lateral branches. An oblique division of the terminal cell of each branch produces a unicellular antheridium (Fig. 78). The antheridium discharges its protoplast, which functions as a nonmotile male cell, or spermatium. Other antheridia may then be budded off the same terminal cell.

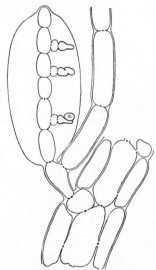

Fig. 78. Diagram of antheridial branch of *Polysiphonia*, showing three stages in the development of an antheridium (*a*), whose protoplast functions as a male cell. (*After Yamanouchi.*)

Besides the carpogonium and trichogyne, the procarp includes several other cells as well. It arises from a large *pericentral cell* that first produces a row of four cells, the terminal one becoming the carpogonium (Fig. 79*A*, *B*). The nucleus of the carpogonium divides into two nuclei, one of which passes into the trichogyne and finally disintegrates, while the other remains in the carpogonium and functions as an egg nucleus. The pericentral cell also gives rise to a group of *auxiliary cells*, one of which crowds in between the pericentral cell and the carpogonium (Fig. 79*C*). The entire structure comprises the procarp.

The free-floating spermatium, coming in contact with the trichogyne, remains uninucleate. The male nucleus enters the trichogyne, passes

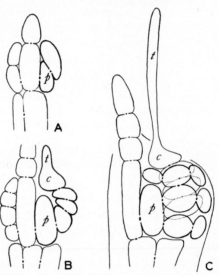

Fig. 79. Diagrams showing development of procarp of *Polysiphonia*. *A*, early stage; *B*, later stage, the pericentral cell (*p*) having produced four cells, the terminal one forming the carpogonium (*c*) and trichogyne (*t*); *C*, mature stage, a group of auxiliary cells having developed from the pericentral cell. (*After Yamanouchi*.)

into the carpogonium, and fuses with the female nucleus. A passageway to the pericentral cell now is opened through the intervening auxiliary cell and the fusion nucleus passes through. Then all the cells of the procarp unite and the fusion nucleus divides to form many nuclei. Lobes into which these nuclei pass are put out from the procarp and then the carpospores are cut off. The whole structure comprises the cystocarp (Fig. 77*C*). The usual envelope of sterile cells is formed around it.

After escaping from the cystocarp, a carpospore gives rise to a tetrasporic plant. A stalked sporangium is produced laterally from an axial cell, pushing through the cortical cells. The tetraspores give rise to sexual plants. *Polysiphonia* displays an isomorphic alternation of generations. The sexual plants, with haploid cells, are gametophytes. The tetrasporic plant, with diploid cells, is a sporophyte. The sporophyte generation, however, beginning with the zygote, includes also the cystocarp and carpospores. The gametophyte generation begins with the tetraspore.

Summary. In the Rhodophyceae both chlorophyll, with its associated carotinoids, and a red pigment (phycoerythrin) are present in the plastids. With only a few possible exceptions, all members are multicellular, the thallus being most commonly filamentous but often plate-like. The cells contain a definite nucleus (sometimes more than one), one or more plastids, and a cell wall that is often gelatinous. Reserve food is stored chiefly as "floridean starch." Reproduction occurs by means of aplano-spores and heterogametes. The female organ is a carpogonium. Carpo-spores arise from the zygote, either directly (in the Bangiales) or indi-rectly (in the other Rhodophyceae). Except in the Bangiales and Nemalionales, both carpospores and tetraspores are produced, the latter by a sporophyte. All reproductive cells are nonciliated. No resting cells are formed. A distinct alternation of generations is a feature of all red algae except the Bangiales and Nemalionales. The gametophyte and sporophyte are similar vegetatively.

COMPARISON OF THE CLASSES OF ALGAE

The most important distinguishing characters of the ten classes of algae are as follows:

Cyanophyceae. Cells containing, in addition to chlorophyll and carotinoids, a blue pigment (phycocyanin) and frequently a red pigment (phycoerythrin) also. Pigments not confined to definite plastids. Reserve food stored as glycogen. Plant body unicellular, generally colonial. Cells without a well-organized nucleus. Cell walls usually forming abundant mucilage. Reproduction by fission, never by zoo-spores or gametes No ciliated cells.

Euglenophyceae. Cells with green plastids containing an excess of chlorophyll over the carotinoids; frequently colorless. Reserve food stored as paramylon. Unicellular and usually solitary; sometimes colonial. Cell walls almost always absent. Free-swimming or, when colonial, attached. Reproduction by fission, rarely by isogametes (?). Motile cells with one or two cilia attached anteriorly, equal or unequal.

Chrysophyceae. Cells with golden brown plastids containing chloro-phyll and an excess of carotinoids; sometimes colorless. Food stored as oil or leucosin. Unicellular and often colonial, rarely multicellular. Cell walls almost always absent. Free-swimming or sometimes attached. Reproduction by fission, and sometimes by zoospores, rarely by isoga-metes (?). Motile cells with one or two cilia attached anteriorly, equal or unequal.

Dinophyceae. Cells with yellow-brown plastids containing chloro-phyll and an excess of carotinoids, or colorless, storing food as starch or oil. Unicellular and mostly solitary, rarely multicellular. Sometimes naked but usually with sculptured cell walls. Nearly all free-swimming. Reproduction by fission, and sometimes by zoospores, rarely by isogametes (?). Motile cells generally with two laterally attached cilia, one lying in a transverse groove.

Xanthophyceae. Cells with yellow-green plastids containing a larger proportion of carotinoids than chlorophyll. Reserve food stored as oil or leucosin. Unicellular (and uninucleate), coenocytic, or multicellular. Cell walls often absent, when present usually consisting of two overlapping halves. Reproduction by fission or by spores and isogametes. Motile cells with two unequal cilia attached anteriorly.

Bacillariophyceae. Cells with golden-brown plastids containing an excess of carotinoids over chlorophyll and storing food mainly as oil. Unicellular and either solitary or colonial. Cell wall consisting of two overlapping valves, highly silicified. Reproduction by fission, auxospores, and isogametes. Motile cells rare.

Chlorophyceae. Cells with plastids containing a greater proportion of chlorophyll than carotinoids. Reserve food usually stored as starch. Unicellular (and uninucleate), coenocytic, or multicellular. Unicellular forms solitary or colonial. Reproduction by fission or by spores and either isogametes or heterogametes. Motile cells generally with two or four cilia attached anteriorly.

Charophyceae. Cells with plastids containing a greater proportion of chlorophyll than carotinoids; usually storing food as starch. Multicellular. Reproduction by heterogametes formed in complex multicellular sex organs of a distinctive type. Sperms with two equal cilia attached anteriorly.

Phaeophyceae. Cells with plastids containing chlorophyll and an excess of carotin and a brown pigment (fucoxanthin). Reserve food occurring chiefly as laminarin or oil. Multicellular. Reproduction by spores and either isogametes or heterogametes. Motile cells laterally biciliate, the cilia of unequal length.

Rhodophyceae. Cells with plastids containing chlorophyll, carotinoids, and a red pigment (phycoerythrin). Reserve food stored chiefly as "floridean starch." With rare exceptions multicellular. Reproduction by spores and heterogametes, these never ciliated.

GENERAL CONCLUSIONS

The algae constitute the simplest and oldest group of green plants. Their bodies are adapted, both in structure and function, to live in water. Although knowledge is lacking concerning the nature of the first plants to have lived on the earth, they must have been aquatic and may have been similar to some of the existing blue-green algae. These plants are unicellular, have a very primitive cell structure, and reproduce by fission. Because they live in a variety of habitats, including hot springs, they may have lived on the earth before conditions were favorable for the existence of other green plants.

The algae are not a homogeneous assemblage but embrace a number of groups representing divergent lines of descent, all of which probably have had a common origin. Advanced students of the algae try to trace these lines of evolution, but we shall be concerned mainly with certain general tendencies and with the progress that the group as a whole has made.

Development of Multicellular Bodies. The unicellular plant body obviously represents the simplest condition of structural organization and, necessarily, also the oldest. It is characteristic of all the blue-green algae, flagellates, dinoflagellates, diatoms, and many of the green algae. Unicellular plants may be either solitary or colonial, the latter condition having arisen from the tendency of cells, following division, to remain together for a while before separating. In the evolution of the algae, close association of cells in a colony may have led to a dependence of the cells on one another, with the resultant establishment of a multicellular body. It is significant that, among the algae, no sharp distinction exists between highly organized colonies and simple multicellular plants. This intergradation strongly indicates that multicellular plants have been derived from unicellular ones through the formation of colonies.

Although the multicellular bodies of algae are very diverse in form, they may be referred to three main types: filamentous, plate-like, and massive. The filamentous type is most common, probably because it seems best adapted to aquatic life. In such a body all the cells are in direct contact with water and the absorbing surface is very large. Thus the absorption of gases is greatly facilitated. The massive type of body, as exemplified by many brown algae, is adapted to withstand the buffeting action of waves and water currents along rocky seacoasts. In the simple multicellular algae growth is intercalary, every cell having the power of division. In branching forms growth is often limited to definite regions, such as the terminal cell of each branch. In many brown and most red algae growth occurs by means of an apical cell that cuts off a series of posterior segments.

An important evolutionary tendency exhibited by the algae is for certain cells to become structurally differentiated in response to special functions. It occurs in both colonial and multicellular forms. A simple expression of this tendency is seen in those filamentous algae having the basal cell modified as a holdfast. In many branching filaments the cells of the branches are smaller than those of the main filament. The formation of sporangia and gametangia represents a specialization of certain cells for reproduction. Differentiation becomes marked among the brown algae, especially in the Laminariales and Fucales, where the body consists of distinct vegetative organs within which simple tissues may be formed. A highly differentiated vegetative body is also characteristic of the Charophyceae and many marine Siphonocladiales and Siphonales.

Asexual Reproduction. In reproduction, as in vegetative structure, the algae show a progressive advance. Most unicellular forms increase in number by fission, which is merely reproduction by cell division and is obviously the most primitive method in the plant kingdom. Among multicellular forms cell division results in growth and, to make reproduction possible by other means than fragmentation, cells must be liberated from the parent. The spores of algae are merely detached cells with the capacity of directly producing a new plant. They result not only in a multiplication of individuals but in their widespread distribution. Spores may be formed from a cell with or without previous division of its protoplast. The commonest kind of spores in the algae are zoospores—naked cells with cilia. Nonmotile spores with a cell wall (aplanospores and akinetes) are generally formed in response to adverse environmental conditions, to which they are very resistant. Obviously they have been derived from zoospores that have lost the power of locomotion. The same may be true of the nonmotile spores of the red algae. Fission and spores produced by a haploid plant body are a means of accomplishing vegetative or asexual reproduction because no reduction of chromosomes is involved. This is the only kind present in the blue-green algae, flagellates, dinoflagellates, many diatoms, and a few green algae.

Like vegetative spores, the spores produced by two successive divisions of a diploid cell, involving a reduction of chromosomes, are usually regarded as asexual. In reality, however, they belong to the sexual life cycle, since meiosis is always a necessary consequence of a previous gametic union. Although such spores are functionally equivalent to the zoospores and aplanospores produced by a haploid plant body, they are not homologous with them, and should be designated as *meiospores.* Meiospores are produced by the zygote in such green algae as *Ulothrix* and *Oedogonium,* and by the sporophyte in all algae with an alternation of generations.

In most green algae any ordinary vegetative cell is capable of producing spores. In nearly all the brown and red algae, however, spores are not borne in transformed vegetative cells but in sporangia, which are cells specialized for reproduction. Sporangia differ from ordinary vegetative cells in size or shape and sometimes are restricted to definite parts of the body.

Sexual Reproduction. Sexual reproduction is accomplished by gametes and represents a distinct advance over reproduction by vegetative spores. Its essential feature is the fusion of two cells to form a zygote. It seems certain that originally gametes were derived from vegetative zoospores that had become too small to form a new plant directly. This is shown by the fact that in *Ulothrix* and many other isogamous algae zoospores and gametes intergrade, the smaller spores often germinating but producing dwarf filaments. The derivation of gametes from zoospores is shown also by the striking similarity between them in form and in the number and arrangement of their cilia. Any peculiarity in the spores is duplicated in one or both of the gametes, as in *Oedogonium*, the brown algae, etc. With few exceptions (notably the Conjugales, Charophyceae, and Fucales), gametic reproduction has not replaced reproduction by vegetative spores but is supplementary to it. In nearly all the green algae the zygote is a resting cell, acquiring a heavy wall and carrying the plant through a period of severe conditions into the next growing season. In fact, the formation of gametes is often induced by the advent of such conditions. In the brown and red algae the zygote germinates at once.

Originally, in the evolution of the algae, both of the fusing gametes were ciliated and of the same size. This condition of isogamy is retained by the yellow-green algae, diatoms, and many of the simpler green and brown algae. In such forms as *Pandorina*, one of the pairing gametes is slightly larger and less active than the other. In *Cutleria* both gametes are ciliated, but the female gamete is considerably larger than the male. In *Dictyota* and *Fucus* the female gamete (egg) is increased in size still more and, although extruded into the water, is nonciliated, only the male gamete (sperm) being motile. Finally, in *Oedogonium* and many other algae, the large nonmotile egg is not liberated but is fertilized within the oögonium by the small motile sperm. Thus the evolution of heterogamy from isogamy has been gradual.

After sexual reproduction had become established, one gamete retained its motility and small size, while the other sacrificed its motility for an increased nutritive capacity. The advantage of heterogamy lies in the greater amount of reserve food that comes to be stored in the zygote. This advantage is reflected by the occurrence of heterogamy in many green algae, most brown algae, all stoneworts, and all red algae, as well as in all plants above the thallophyte level. It should be emphasized that heterogamy has arisen independently in the various groups of algae where it occurs.

The production of gametes in ordinary vegetative cells is characteristic of *Ulothrix*, *Oedogonium*, and most other green algae. A more advanced condition is seen in *Vaucheria*, the Charophyceae, and nearly all the brown and red algae, where the gametes are borne in gametangia or sex organs, which are specialized for reproduction, a function lost by the other cells of the body. This tendency parallels the production of spores in sporangia. The sporangia remain unicellular but the gametangia of some algae have become multicellular by the formation of cross walls, as in *Ectocarpus* and *Cutleria*. In *Dictyota* the antheridia are multicellular and the oögonia are unicellular.

Alternation of Generations. In nearly all the green algae the vegetative plant, of which there is but one kind, gives rise to gametes and is haploid. Here the diploid condition, which always results from fertilization, is restricted to the zygote itself, since the reduction of chromosomes takes place when it germinates. This reduction always involves the formation of four haploid nuclei. In *Oedogonium* each of the four zoospores (meiospores) coming from the zygote contains one of these nuclei. In *Spirogyra* three of the nuclei degenerate and the zygote gives rise directly to a haploid vegetative body. In *Coleochaete* four haploid cells are formed by the zygote, but each divides one, two, or three more times before zoospores are organized. In the two lower orders of red algae (Bangiales and Nemalionales) an analogous condition exists in the formation of carpospores.

In some of the algae, notably in the diatoms, *Acetabularia, Codium, Bryopsis,* and the Fucales, there is only one kind of vegetative body and it is diploid, the reduction of chromosomes occurring in connection with the formation of gametes, or in several nuclear divisions immediately preceding their formation. This is also the condition in animals.

Some botanists recognize an alternation of generations wherever there is a diploid and a haploid phase in the life history, even though one or the other is represented by only one cell—in other words, wherever there is sexual reproduction. Such a broad use of the term makes it almost meaningless. In algae displaying a true alternation of generations, a more or less prolonged growth phase intervenes between fertilization and meiosis, as well as between meiosis and fertilization. Here the life history involves two distinct and independent vegetative bodies, a haploid body (gametophyte) producing gametes and a diploid body (sporophyte) producing spores. The gametophyte arises from a spore, the sporophyte from a zygote. The reduction of chromosomes occurs when the spores are formed. A true alternation of generations is found in only a very few green algae, such as *Ulva* and *Cladophora*, in all brown algae except the Fucales, and in all red algae except the Bangiales and Nemalionales. The alternation may be isomorphic, with both generations alike vegetatively, as in *Ulva, Cladophora, Ectocarpus, Dictyota,* and *Polysiphonia*, or it may be heteromorphic, with both generations unlike vegetatively, as in *Cutleria* and *Laminaria*. In all algae possessing a true alternation of generations both gametophyte and sporophyte are free-living; one is never dependent upon the other.

Interrelationships. It is not possible to arrange the classes of algae in such a way as to indicate their true relationship. The sequence in which these groups have been presented is merely one denoting an ever-increasing complexity in vegetative and reproductive structures. It does not denote descent of one group from the one preceding it in the series, although in some cases this may be true. Each group merely stands for a different degree of progress from what was originally a primitive condition.

The most important evidence concerning the interrelationships of plant groups is derived from paleobotany. The dearth of fossils belonging to groups below the pteridophyte level is so great, however, that practically all conclusions regarding phylogeny must be based on the comparative structure and development of existing plants. This means that such conclusions, even though well substantiated, are largely speculative.

The Cyanophyceae are the most primitive group of autotrophic plants. Except for the presence of chlorophyll, they are strikingly like the bacteria. Which of these groups appeared first on the earth is very uncertain, but is unimportant in connection with the present discussion. Both groups are at a very low level of structural organization. The classes consisting mainly of flagellates show a considerable advance over the Cyanophyceae by their well-organized nuclei, definite plastids, and ciliated cells. In the absence of transitional forms, any direct connection between the Cyanophyceae and flagellates is difficult to visualize. It is easier to think of the flagellates as having arisen directly from the bacteria. A direct relationship between the Cyanophyceae and any of the higher algal classes is also unlikely, although there is some evidence of this in the case of the Rhodophyceae. Ciliated cells are not present in either group; some members of each have both phycocyanin and phycoerythrin; and a few primitive Rhodophyceae have a nuclear structure but little advanced over that of the Cyanophyceae. It is primarily the absence of ciliated cells that would seem to preclude the possibility of a relationship between either group and the flagellates.

That the Xanthophyceae and Chlorophyceae have arisen independently from a flagellate ancestry is strongly indicated by the presence of naked, free-swimming reproductive cells in the life history and by the occurrence of intermediate forms. The derivation of the Bacillariophyceae and Phaeophyceae directly from flagellate ancestors is less evident. The only connection between the diatoms and flagellates is the presence of ciliated reproductive cells in a few diatoms. The origin of the Phaeophyceae is obscure because the group is without unicellular members. Yet their motile reproductive cells suggest that they may have arisen from brown, laterally biciliate flagellates. There is also the possibility of a direct connection between the Phaeophyceae and Chlorophyceae. The Charophyceae are an isolated group, yet seem to represent a specialized offshoot from the Chlorophyceae.

CHAPTER IV

THALLOPHYTA: FUNGI

Fungi are dependent (heterotrophic) thallophytes. Lacking chlorophyll, they are unable to carry on photosynthesis and hence must obtain their food from an external source. Many are *saprophytes*, living on dead organic matter; others are *parasites*, obtaining nourishment from the bodies of living plants or animals, the organism attacked being the *host*. At least some of the fungi may have evolved directly from the algae through loss of power to carry on photosynthesis. Because of their relation to the decomposition of organic matter and to disease, fungi are of tremendous economic importance. The fungi comprise the five classes Schizomycetes, Myxomycetes, Phycomycetes, Ascomycetes, and Basidiomycetes. To these might be added the class Lichenes.

1. SCHIZOMYCETES

The Schizomycetes, or bacteria, are similar in many respects to the Cyanophyceae, differing from them chiefly in their smaller size and lack of chlorophyll. In fact the two groups are often combined into a single group, the Schizophyta. The bacteria are at once the smallest and simplest of all known organisms, unless the viruses are to be considered as living. They are also the most widely distributed, occurring under all conditions where life may exist—in fresh and salt water, in soil, in the air, and in the living and dead bodies of other organisms. Like the Cyanophyceae, they are a very ancient group and must have been among the first forms of life to have existed on the earth. The bacteria comprise about 1,500 species. Some common genera are *Streptococcus*, *Micrococcus*, *Sarcina*, *Bacterium*, *Bacillus*, *Pseudomonas*, *Microspira*, *Spirillum*, *Cladothrix*, and *Beggiatoa*.

Structure and Reproduction. Like the blue-green algae, bacteria are unicellular plants that reproduce by fission. Their cells are of three general types: spherical (*coccus*) forms, rod-shaped (*bacillus*) forms, and curved or spiral (*spirillum*) forms (Fig. 80). Some are nonmotile, while others bear cilia, by means of which they move rapidly. The cilia may cover the entire cell or may be restricted to one or both ends, where they occur either singly or in tufts. The rod-shaped types average about 2.5μ in length,[1] while many of the spherical forms are only about 0.5μ in diameter.

---

[1] The unit of microscopic measurement is the *micron*, abbreviated μ. It is one-thousandth of a millimeter (0.001 mm.), approximately equivalent to 1/25,000 inch.

The cells of bacteria are so simple that they might almost be said to be structureless. A mass of homogeneous protoplasm is surrounded by a thin cell wall, generally composed chiefly of chitin, a nitrogenous substance, whereas the cell walls of green plants are composed mainly of cellulose, a carbohydrate. Commonly the cell wall becomes mucilaginous, forming a slimy sheath or capsule. There is no organized nucleus but merely some scattered granules of a chromatin-like material that can be revealed by staining. In some bacteria these granules are aggregated to form a distinct central group. Other granules may also be present; these generally represent reserve food.

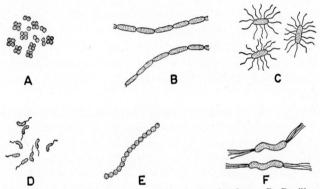

Fig. 80. Group of common bacteria, ×1,500. *A, Sarcina lutea; B, Bacillus subtilis; C, Bacillus typhosus; D, Spirillum cholerae; E, Streptococcus pyrogenes; F, Spirillum undulatum.*

In some bacteria the two cells separate following division, while in others they remain together in colonies. Spirillum forms are nearly always solitary. In the coccus forms the colonies may be cubical, plate-like, chain-like, filamentous, or irregular. In the bacillus forms the divisions occur only in one plane, and so the colonies are always filamentous. In *Beggiatoa*, a sulphur bacterium, the filaments are as highly organized as those of *Oscillatoria*. In *Cladothrix*, an iron bacterium, the filaments exhibit false branching.

As in the Cyanophyceae, cell division takes place by the formation of an inward-growing cell wall. Under favorable circumstances, cell division in many bacteria may occur as frequently as every 20 minutes, so that, in the course of 24 hours, a single cell may give rise to billions. Such a rate of multiplication is soon checked, however, by the exhaustion of the food supply or by the accumulation of poisonous waste products of metabolism. Although all bacteria are active only in the presence of moisture and other favorable conditions, if these fail, many bacteria can pass into a resting stage and remain inactive for a long time. Bacteria on dust particles in the air are in a dormant state and can resist desiccation and great extremes of temperature. In some bacilli the resting cell becomes an *endospore*. Here the protoplast rounds up inside the cell cavity and invests itself with a new cell wall, the old wall eventually disappearing. Endospores are extremely resistant. With the return of favorable conditions, they again become active vegetative cells. Thus "spore formation" in bacteria does not result in reproduction but merely in survival during a period of stress.

Although the bacteria are said to be without sexual reproduction, there is some evidence that it may occur at least in certain bacteria, since there seems to be Mendelian segregation resulting from mixtures of different types.

Activities. Most bacteria are either saprophytic or parasitic and in both cases food is absorbed through the cell wall. Some can live either as saprophytes or as parasites, while a few can make their own food without the aid of chlorophyll or light. *Aerobic* bacteria require free oxygen in respiration, while *anaerobic* bacteria obtain oxygen from organic compounds.

Most diseases of animals and many diseases of plants are caused by parasitic (pathogenic) bacteria, the disease itself being merely a response on the part of the host to the presence of the parasite. A disease manifests itself by symptoms, which are abnormalities in structure or function. Well-known human diseases of bacterial origin are typhoid fever, tuberculosis, diphtheria, pneumonia, cholera, and tetanus. Some bacterial diseases of plants are pear blight, cabbage rot, cucurbit wilt, and crown gall. The disease may be caused by direct attack of the bacteria on the host tissues, by the liberation of toxins, or by both.

The decomposition of dead organic matter is accomplished chiefly by saprophytic bacteria. They break up organic compounds into simpler substances through a series of intermediate steps, a succession of different bacteria being involved. The ultimate products of decomposition are such simple substances as water, carbon dioxide, ammonia, hydrogen sulphide, etc. Bacteria of decay cause fermentation and putrefaction. They play an important part in the economy of nature by returning to the air and soil substances that may again be used by other organisms.

All plants require nitrogen in order to synthesize proteins, but only the nitrogen-fixing bacteria and a few other forms are able to use the nitrogen of the air directly. Practically all green plants are dependent for nitrogen upon its compounds, particularly nitrates. Some of the nitrogen-fixing bacteria, such as *Clostridium* and *Azotobacter*, live free in the soil and are saprophytic on organic matter, while *Rhizobium* is parasitic in the roots of various Leguminosae, such as clover, alfalfa, peas, beans, etc. These bacteria combine atmospheric nitrogen with oxygen and other elements, particularly potassium, sodium, or calcium, and form nitrates, which may later be utilized by green plants. The root of the legume responds to the presence of these parasitic bacteria by forming local enlargements called *tubercles* or *nodules*.

Nitrifying bacteria also live in the soil but form nitrates in a different way. The decomposition of organic matter by bacteria of decay yields ammonia (NH_3). This is oxidized, first to nitrites (NO_2 compounds) by *Nitrosomonas*, and then to nitrates (NO_3 compounds) by *Nitrobacter*. An interesting fact about these bacteria is that, although lacking chlorophyll, they are able to synthesize carbohydrate food from water and carbon dioxide (or carbonates). They derive their energy, not from sunlight, but from the oxidations that they carry on. With respect to their nutrition, these bacteria, like green plants, are autotrophic, even though they do not carry on photosynthesis. The process by which they make their own food is sometimes called *chemosynthesis*. Such autotrophic bacteria may have preceded all other forms of life on the earth. In addition to the nitrifying bacteria there are other kinds that are autotrophic. They oxidize sulphur, hydrogen sulphide, free hydrogen, methane, or iron compounds. *Beggiatoa* is a colorless filamentous form that oxidizes hydrogen sulphide (H_2S) to form water and sulphur, storing the sulphur as yellow granules inside its cells. It is found in sulphur springs. Certain iron bacteria oxidize ferrous iron compounds to ferric hydroxide ($FeOH_3$), which accumulates to form a kind of iron ore. These bacteria are common in bogs.

Denitrifying bacteria live in the soil, especially where poorly drained. They convert nitrogen salts into gaseous nitrogen. This escapes into the air and so causes a loss of soil fertility.

Myxobacteria. The myxobacteria are a group of peculiar organisms that live as saprophytes on animal refuse. Their cells resemble those of true bacteria but form remarkable complex colonies held together by mucilage. Some of the myxobacteria form stalked sporangia that are often brightly colored. Some exhibit slow creeping movements. In these respects the group resembles the myxomycetes.

Summary. The Schizomycetes are the simplest of all plants. All of them are unicellular, the cells being either solitary or in colonies. A definite cell wall is present, generally composed of chitin rather than of cellulose, and usually breaks down to form mucilage. The protoplast shows little organization, a nucleus being represented only by scattered granules of chromatin. Reproduction occurs by fission. Some bacteria move by means of cilia, while others are nonmotile. In some species a resting cell (endospore) may form inside a vegetative cell, becoming invested with a new cell wall. The Schizomycetes are closely related to the Cyanophyceae, differing from them chiefly in the lack of chlorophyll, presence of cilia in some members, and character of the resting cell.

2. MYXOMYCETES

The Myxomycetes, or slime molds, are peculiar organisms that, like the flagellates, are claimed by both botanists and zoologists, the latter calling them Mycetozoa (fungus-animals). They are a widely distributed group, living in damp, shady places as saprophytes on humus, decaying wood, bark, fallen leaves, etc. All lack chlorophyll. The

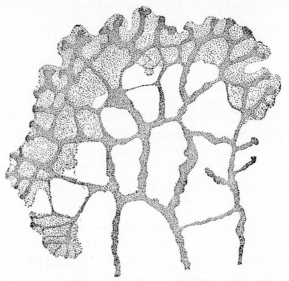

Fig. 81.   Plasmodium of *Didymium*, a slime mold, ×30.   (*From Gilbert M. Smith.*)

Myxomycetes number over 400 species.   Some of the common genera are *Lycogala*, *Stemonitis*, *Fuligo*, *Arcyria*, and *Trichia*.

Plant Body.   The vegetative body of a myxomycete is a *plasmodium*, which is a naked mass of multinucleate protoplasm (Fig. 81).   The nuclei, like those of the higher plants, are well organized.   The plasmodium is without definite form and may attain a diameter of several centimeters, or even a meter in some myxomycetes.   The plasmodium moves by the formation of pseudopodia and engulfs solid particles of food as it passes over them, digesting them within food vacuoles.   In these respects it resembles an amoeba.   It also absorbs food material in solution through the plasma membrane.   Depending on the species, the plasmodium may be white or some shade of yellow, orange, red, brown, or violet.   The plasmodium tends to move toward moisture but shows an avoiding reaction to light, appearing at the surface of its substratum only at night.   In times of drought it retracts itself into a waxy mass and hardens, forming a *sclerotium*. In this condition the organism may remain dormant for months, or sometimes even for years, becoming active again in the presence of water.

Reproduction. Although the myxomycetes are animal-like in their vegetative state, their reproductive features are distinctly plant-like. When reproduction is to occur, the entire plasmodium comes to the

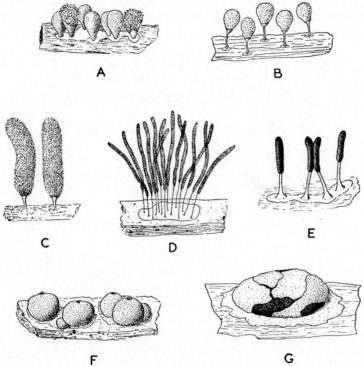

Fig. 82. Group of common slime molds, showing sporangia arising from the plasmodium. *A, Hemitrichia ovata, ×10; B, Craterum leucocephalum, ×10; C, Arcyria incarnata, ×5; D, Stemonitis herbatica, ×2; E, Diachea leucopoda, ×10; F, Lycogala epidendrum, ×1; G, Fuligo septica, ×½.*

surface of its substratum and contracts into a cushion-like mass. As this hardens, it forms one or more sporangia that are usually brown or yellow (Fig. 82). In some myxomycetes the entire plasmodium may be converted into a single giant sporangium, called an *aethalium,* but, more commonly, a number of small separate sporangia are formed. These may be either sessile or stalked. Throughout the various genera the sporangia exhibit much diversity in form, but are commonly spherical, oval, or cylindrical. The sporangium contains many nuclei and the remains of the plasmodium, the latter usually forming a network of tough strands known as the *capillitium* (Fig. 83). In the meshes of this network innumerable spores are formed, each one being uninucleate. The spores have cellulose walls and are scattered by the wind. In their dispersal the wall of the sporangium ruptures irregularly at the apex and the capillitium performs hygroscopic movements.

The myxomycetes display considerable variation with respect to the development of the plasmodium from a spore. Commonly the protoplast escapes from the spore wall and becomes a zoospore, developing one long cilium and one very short one, both anteriorly attached. Sometimes two to eight zoospores are produced. The zoospore may ingest food and undergo multiplication by fission.

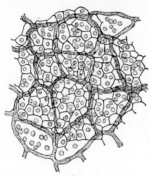

After a period of free swimming, the cilia are retracted and the protoplast becomes amoeboid. These amoeboid cells, called *myxamoebae*, may also take in food and divide repeatedly, or they may pass into a resting stage. Finally, however, they fuse in pairs. Then, instead of forming resting zygotes, a number come together to form a multinucleate plasmodium. In the fusion of the small amoeboid cells in pairs, the two nuclei unite, but there are no subsequent nuclear fusions. Consequently the nuclei of the plasmodium are diploid. They undergo repeated divisions as the plasmodium increases in size. Reduction of chromosomes to the haploid number occurs just prior to the formation of spores in the sporangium.

Fig. 83. Portion of capillitium of *Stemonitis* with spores in its meshes, ×250.

Summary. The Myxomycetes combine features found in both plants and animals. The body is a naked mass of multinucleate protoplasm (a plasmodium) that displays amoeboid movements and engulfs solid food particles. In a quiescent state it gives rise to sporangia containing numerous walled spores from which eventually, although not directly, a new plasmodium is formed. Sexual reproduction occurs by a fusion of similar amoeboid gametes. Certain aspects of the life history suggest a relationship to the flagellates. Any possible connection with the true fungi is very uncertain.

Other Slime Fungi. In addition to the Myxomycetes, or slime molds, there are two other groups of slime fungi that deserve some attention. These are the Acrasieae and the Labyrinthuleae. Many mycologists include all three groups in a separate assemblage, the Myxothallophyta, and place them outside and below the fungi. They have certain important characters in common: simple, naked, nucleated, amoeboid cells resembling protozoans but plant-like in their reproduction by the formation of spores. The interrelationships of the three groups of slime fungi are not well understood, but are not assumed to be close. They have probably been derived from protozoan ancestors and have evolved along independent lines.

Acrasieae. These simple forms are saprophytes on soil, decaying wood, and animal refuse. The vegetative body is a myxamoeba, a naked cell with a nucleus and a contractile vacuole. It reproduces by fission and in the presence of unfavorable conditions may encyst. Eventually, a number of myxamoebae come together without fusing to form a pseudo-plasmodium in which each myxamoeba retains its individuality. Not

Fig. 84. Three-dimensional graph showing the development of the fruiting body of *Dictyostelium discoideum* in height, time, and position. *A*, aggregation of a mass of individual myxamoebae; *B* to *D*, formation of the pseudoplasmodium; *E* to *G*, migration of pseudoplasmodium; *H* to *N*, formation of fruiting body with disk, stalk, and spherical spore mass. (*From J. T. Bonner.*)

only is a multinucleate plasmodium lacking, but no zoospores are produced. The pseudoplasmodium assumes a definite form, usually elongating and varying in length from several tenths of a millimeter to a millimeter or more.

The subsequent behavior of the pseudoplasmodium is remarkable in that it migrates over the substratum, apparently by a gliding of the amoebae over one another. After coming to rest, the pseudoplasmodium is transformed into a fruiting body consisting of a basal disk, a vertical stalk, and a terminal spherical region that is converted into a mass of spores (Fig. 84). In some species the fertile region consists of a series of spherical spore masses arranged at the ends of whorled branches. All these complex changes are accomplished by movements of individual myxamoebae to their proper place in the fruiting body, where each becomes the type of cell appropriate for its position, such as a disk cell, stalk cell, or spore. The spores have a cell wall. Upon germination, each spore gives rise to a myxamoeba.

Labyrinthuleae. In this little-known group the vegetative cell is spindle-shaped with tufts of pseudopodia at the ends. When the cells come in contact, their pseudopodia generally fuse, the union of numerous cells producing a net-like structure called a net-plasmodium. The individual cells, retaining their identity, appear to glide along the threads of the net in limited movements. During this stage they feed, increase in size, and undergo repeated division. In dividing, the cells become constricted at the middle and then separate, but are held together by a protoplasmic strand. At the close of the vegetative stage, the cells collect into sessile or stalked masses and become encysted. In some species the spores have cell walls, in others not. Later the spores germinate, freeing one to four spindle-shaped cells with polar pseudopodia.

3. PHYCOMYCETES

The Phycomycetes, or alga-like fungi, comprise the first group of "true fungi" (Eumycetes), as the higher fungi are often called in contrast to the bacteria and myxomycetes. All the true fungi have a definite nucleus and nearly all have a characteristic plant body called a *mycelium*. This is composed of branching filaments, each branch being a *hypha*. The hyphae may be either loosely or compactly interwoven. With few exceptions, the Phycomycetes are characterized by an absence of cross walls in the mycelium, and so, as in *Vaucheria*, the plant body is a coenocyte. Their spores are borne in indefinite numbers within a sporangium. The origin of the Phycomycetes is not clear. They may have evolved either from colorless flagellates or, through loss of chlorophyll, from the Chlorophyceae, a group which they resemble in both vegetative and reproductive features. A number of Phycomycetes cause diseases of economic plants, such as cranberry gall, brown rot of lemon, downy mildew of grape, and late blight of potato. The group is a relatively small one, numbering about 1,000 species. These are included in seven main orders: Chytridiales, Monoblepharidales, Plasmodiophorales, Saprolegniales, Peronosporales, Mucorales, and Entomophthorales.

1. Chytridiales

The Chytridiales are the simplest of the Phycomycetes. Nearly all of them are parasitic, many living on fresh-water algae and others attacking seed plants growing in moist situations. The order includes about 65 genera and 300 species, the best-known forms being *Chytridium*, *Olpidium*, and *Synchytrium*.

Chytridium. A common species of *Chytridium* attacks the green alga, *Oedogonium*. A uniciliate zoospore comes in contact with an oögonium of the host, loses its cilium, and sends into the host cell a tube through which food is absorbed. This tube represents a weakly developed mycelium. The external part of the fungus then becomes transformed into a sporangium, its protoplast undergoing cleavage into many zoospores (Fig. 85*A*). A zoospore may penetrate a zygote of the host and, by the secretion of a thick wall, become a resting spore. When the zygote germinates, the resting spore of the fungus sends out tubes that give rise to terminal sporangia.

Olpidium. This fungus grows on many different hosts, some of which are fresh-water algae. One species, *Olpidium brassicae*, attacks young

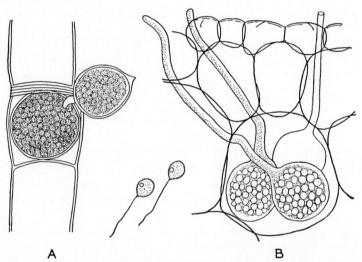

A   B

Fig. 85. Chytridiales. *A*, sporangium of *Chytridium olla* attached to zygote of *Oedogonium; B*, sporangia of *Olpidium brassicae* in root of cabbage seedling; also two zoospores of same to the left. (*A, after Campbell; B, after Woronin.*)

cabbage plants. A uniciliate zoospore comes to rest on the host, withdraws its cilium, and secretes a cell wall. It sends a short tube into the host and the protoplast enters one of the cells. At first the protoplast is naked and amoeboid. It enlarges and becomes multinucleate, finally occupying the whole cell cavity. Then it forms a cell wall and becomes a sporangium. A tube is sent to the surface of the host and numerous uniciliate zoospores escape through it (Fig. 85*B*). Sexual reproduction occurs by means of isogametes that are formed like the zoospores but escape and fuse in pairs. The zygote sends a short tube into a host cell, after which its protoplast enters, enlarges, and secretes a thick wall. After resting over the winter, it gives rise to a number of uniciliate zoospores.

Synchytrium. This form attacks the epidermal cells of various seed plants, such as cranberry, primrose, hog peanut, filaree, and many others. A disease called cranberry gall is caused by *Synchytrium vaccinii*, while the destructive black wart of the potato is caused by *Synchytrium endobioticum.* A uniciliate zoospore comes in contact with a young epidermal cell of the host and enters it. Without forming a cell wall, the protoplast of the fungus enlarges and lives symbiotically with the protoplast of the epidermal cell, not killing it but causing it and the adjacent cells of the

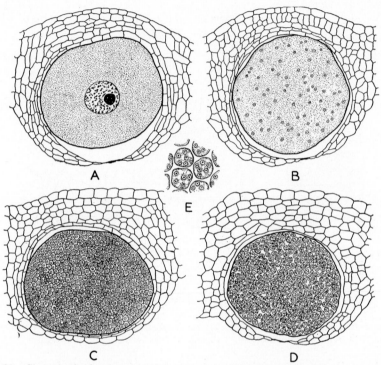

FIG. 86. Stages in the development of the sporangia of *Synchytrium decipiens.* *A*, greatly enlarged fungous protoplast in leaf of host after having destroyed one of its epidermal cells; *B*, division of large nucleus of fungus to form many small free nuclei; *C*, cleavage of protoplast into many small uninucleate cells; *D*, separation of small cells to form sporangia, each of which has become multinucleate; *E*, enlarged portion of same; *A* to *D*, ×125; *E*, ×500.

host to enlarge. A small gall or blister forms on the surface of the host, this serving as a means by which an infected plant can be recognized. Blisters usually appear both on the leaves and stems.

Finally, the infected epidermal cell dies. Then the fungus secretes a wall about itself and goes into a resting stage (Fig. 86*A*). Later its nucleus undergoes repeated divisions and progressive cleavage of the cytoplasm from the surface inward results in the formation of many protoplasts, each of which secretes a wall (Fig. 86*B*, *C*). These cells may be multinucleate when formed but, if uninucleate, they soon become multinucleate by additional free-nuclear divisions (Fig. 86*D*, *E*). Each of these cells becomes a sporangium and, when conditions are favorable, gives rise to a number of naked zoospores (usually 8 to 12) that escape. Frequently, however, the resting cell arising from a vegetative protoplast divides to form a number of gametangia rather than sporangia. Each of these produces many isogametes that, after escaping, fuse in pairs. The zygote invades a host cell and then goes into a resting stage, forming a thick wall. Later it gives rise to many zoospores. Both the zoospores and gametes of *Synchytrium* are uniciliate.

Summary. Most of the Chytridiales are unicellular fungi with either no mycelium or a very poorly developed one. Generally all or most of the vegetative body develops into a sporangium or gametangium. Reproduction occurs by uniciliate zoospores or isogametes. Because they possess the simplest type of sexual reproduction known among the fungi, the Chytridiales are regarded by some mycologists as primitive forms, while others consider them to be degenerate Phycomycetes.

2. Monoblepharidales

The Monoblepharidales are a very small order containing 2 genera: *Monoblepharis*, with 6 species, and *Monoblepharella*, with 2 species.

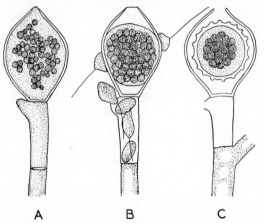

A   B   C

Fig. 87. *Monoblepharis sphaerica.* *A*, end of hypha with young oögonium and a young antheridium just below it; *B*, sperms escaping and approaching the mature oögonium with its single egg; *C*, zygote with empty antheridium below it. (*After Cornu.*)

Monoblepharis is a saprophyte on decaying aquatic vegetation. It has a well-developed mycelium that produces sporangia and sex organs. The sporangia are terminal club-shaped cells containing many uniciliate zoospores. Sexual reproduction is heterogamous. The oögonium is a globular cell, cut off by a wall commonly at the end of a hypha (Fig. 87). Its protoplast rounds up and becomes a large uninucleate egg. The antheridium usually arises immediately below the oögonium as a short slender branch that is cut off by a basal wall.   It gives rise to a number of uniciliate sperms that escape and swim in the water.   A sperm enters the oögonium through a terminal pore and unites with the egg.   The Monoblepharidales are remarkable in being the only fungi with swimming sperms.   According to the species, the zygote may mature either inside or outside the oögonium.   It becomes a thick-walled resting cell, later producing a new mycelium.

3. Plasmodiophorales

This order comprises 8 genera and 23 species, of which the best known is *Plasmodiophora brassicae*, a parasite attacking cabbages and other crucifers and causing a disease known as clubroot.   Another member of the group, *Spongospora subterranea*, is responsible for a disease of potatoes

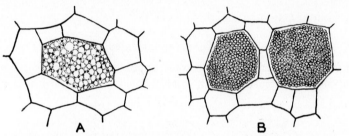

Fig. 88.   Section of a portion of a cabbage root, showing two stages in the development of *Plasmodiophora brassicae* within the cells, ×250.   *A*, plasmodium completely filling a cell; *B*, spore formation.

called powdery scab.   The Plasmodiophorales, once regarded as parasitic myxomycetes, are now generally considered to belong to the lower phycomycetes.

When cabbages are attacked by *Plasmodiophora*, the root undergoes a marked enlargement.   The cells of the root are invaded by biciliate zoospores.   The cilia, attached anteriorly, are of unequal length.[1]   The zoospores lose their cilia and become amoeboid, migrating directly through the cell walls of the host.   An amoeboid cell (myxamoeba) gives rise to a multinucleate plasmodium (Fig. 88*A*).   This soon undergoes cleavage into many uninucleate, walled cells, each of which is said to form four or eight biciliate isogametes that pair and fuse.   The amoeboid zygote enlarges, becomes multinucleate, and migrates into another cell of the root, which it finally fills.   The diploid nuclei of the young plasmodium continue to divide until the two reduction divisions have occurred.   Then a number of small spores are formed, each with a cell

[1] Until recently it was thought that the zoospores were uniciliate and, chiefly on this basis, *Plasmodiophora* and related forms were classified as a family under the Chytridiales.

wall (Fig. 88*B*). These are liberated by decay of the host. Upon germination, each gives rise to a zoospore.

4. Saprolegniales

The Saprolegniales, or water molds, are an order of aquatic fungi, usually occurring in ponds and streams. Most of them are saprophytic on plant or animal remains lying in the water, while a few are parasitic. Many also occur on damp soil. The order includes 20 genera and about 120 species, representative members being *Saprolegnia* and *Achlya*.

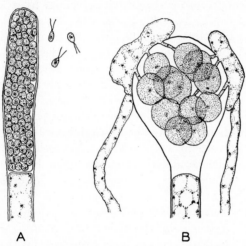

A   B

FIG. 89. *Saprolegnia.* *A*, a sporangium and three escaped zoospores, ×350; *B*, an oögonium with many eggs and with two antheridia in contact with it, ×350.

Saprolegnia. This common water mold usually lives on dead insects, fishes, tadpoles, and other aquatic animals. Sometimes it attacks living fishes and fish eggs. The vegetative body consists of a delicate, branching, coenocytic mycelium that penetrates the food supply. Some of the hyphae form terminal sporangia, each of which is a slender elongated cell, cut off by a basal wall, and giving rise to many uninucleate zoospores (Fig. 89*A*). These are developed by progressive cleavage of the cytoplasm within the sporangium. The zoospores escape singly into the water through a terminal pore in the sporangial wall. In *Achlya* they escape as a mass.

The zoospores of *Saprolegnia* are oval and have two equal cilia attached apically. After swimming for a while, they become quiescent, form a cell wall, and go into a dormant stage. After about 24 hours, the protoplasts escape and again become motile, but this time the spores are kidney-shaped and laterally biciliate. Finally they settle down and, on a suitable substratum, each produces a new mycelium. The occurrence of two types of zoospores is very puzzling and its significance has never been satisfactorily explained.

Saprolegnia is heterogamous, forming sex organs on special branches of the mycelium (Fig. 89*B*). The oögonium is a spherical cell that produces several eggs, sometimes many, rarely only one. At first they are multinucleate but, by degeneration of the extra nuclei, become uninucleate. The antheridium is a slender curved tube that arises just below the oögonium or, in most species, from an adjacent hypha. Each oögonium may be surrounded by several antheridia. Both kinds of sex organs are cut off from the vegetative mycelium by a basal wall. No sperms are organized. Instead, the tip of the antheridium comes in contact with the oögonium and sends into one or more of the eggs a fertilization tube through which some of the cytoplasm and a male nucleus pass. This nucleus unites with the egg nucleus, resulting in fertilization. The zygote secretes a heavy wall and usually remains dormant for several months, finally producing a new mycelium. In *Achlya* it has been shown that the reduction of chromosomes occurs when the zygote germinates. In some species of *Saprolegnia* the antheridia are nonfunctional, while in others antheridia are not even formed. Nevertheless the eggs become thick-walled and later germinate, thus developing by parthenogenesis.

In *Achlya*, which is dioecious, the appearance of sex organs is caused by hormone-like substances. These are secreted into the water by the male and female plants and stimulate production of sex organs of the opposite sex. A hormone produced by the male plants causes oögonia to appear on the female plants, while a hormone produced by the female plants results in the appearance of antheridia on the male plants.

Summary. The Saprolegniales are chiefly saprophytes. They are aquatic fungi with a well-developed mycelium. They produce biciliate zoospores in persistent sporangia. All of them are heterogamous. The oögonium contains one or more eggs that are fertilized by a male nucleus coming from the antheridium through a fertilization tube. In most members the entire oögonial protoplast enters into the formation of eggs. The absence of swimming sperms in an exclusively aquatic order is a noteworthy feature.

5. Peronosporales

The Peronosporales, or downy mildews, are mostly parasites that attack various seed plants, the mycelium living within the intercellular spaces of the host. The order includes about 12 genera and 150 species, representative members being *Pythium*, *Albugo*, *Phytophthora*, *Plasmopara*, and *Peronospora*.

Albugo. This fungus lives as a parasite on a number of different seed plants. A common species, *Albugo candida*, attacks various members of the Cruciferae, such as radish, turnip, mustard, and shepherd's-purse, causing a disease known as white rust of crucifers. The mycelium, which may live in almost any part of the host, ramifies throughout the intercellular spaces and sends short button-like haustoria into the living cells. Here and there beneath the epidermis the mycelium gives rise to compact clusters of erect sporangiophores from the ends of which thin-walled,

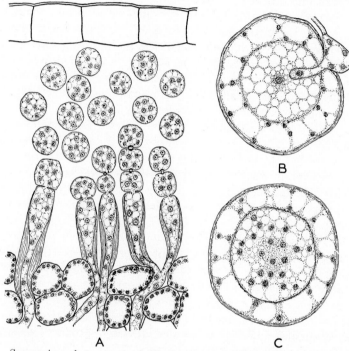

FIG. 90. Sporangia and sex organs of *Albugo*. *A*, cross section of a small portion of the stem of shepherd's-purse, showing sporangiophores of *Albugo candida* arising beneath the epidermis and giving rise to multinucleate sporangia, ×600; *B*, sex organs of *Albugo candida*, a fertilizing tube from an antheridium penetrating an oögonium with a single nucleus in the oöplasm, ×750; *C*, oögonium of *Albugo portulacae* with multinucleate oöplasm, ×500.

globular, multinucleate sporangia are cut off in chains (Fig. 90*A*). These push up the epidermis and form a white blister on the surface of the host. These blisters may appear on the leaves, stems, floral parts, or fruits. Finally, the epidermis is ruptured and the sporangia are carried by the wind to uninfected hosts. Here they give rise to 12 or more laterally biciliate zoospores that escape, swim about for a while, encyst, and finally produce new mycelia. When a spore germinates, it produces a hypha that enters the host through a stoma.

The sex organs of *Albugo candida*, appearing later in the season than the sporangia, are formed on the mycelium deep within the host tissues.

The oögonium is a globular multinucleate cell, cut off by a cross wall from the swollen end of a hypha (Fig. 90*B*). The cytoplasm becomes differentiated into a peripheral zone, the *periplasm*, and a central denser region, the *oöplasm*, which becomes the egg. At first both regions are multinucleate, but later all nuclei degenerate except a single nucleus in the oöplasm. The antheridium, appearing on a separate hypha, is a slender multinucleate cell. After coming in contact with the oögonium, it sends into it a fertilizing tube that extends into the egg, where a male nucleus and a small amount of cytoplasm are discharged. Following fusion of the male and female nuclei, the periplasm is used up in the formation of a heavy wall around the zygote. The zygote is finally freed by decay of the host tissues and, after undergoing a period of rest, gives rise to more than one hundred biciliate zoospores, each of which may, under appropriate conditions, produce a new mycelium.

Albugo bliti, a species common on the pigweed (*Amaranthus*), differs from *Albugo candida* in several respects. Periplasm and oöplasm are differentiated but the latter remains multinucleate. The entire contents of the antheridium are discharged into the egg and each male nucleus fuses with a female nucleus. In *Albugo portulacae*, which lives on the common purslane (*Portulaca*), multinucleate pairing and fusing also occur (Fig. 90*C*).

Other Downy Mildews. The Peronosporales include genera that bear sex organs like those of *Albugo*, but differ in the way their sporangia and spores are formed. Some of these are of considerable economic importance. A species of *Pythium* is frequently the cause of a disease of seedlings known as damping-off. It is particularly common in greenhouses and other warm, moist places. *Pythium* is intermediate between the Saprolegniales and Peronosporales in that it produces zoospores in both permanent and detachable sporangia.

Phytophthora infestans causes a serious potato disease called late blight, while another species, *Phytophthora citrophthora*, is responsible for the brown rot of lemon. *Plasmopara viticola* causes downy mildew of the grape, a very destructive disease. In both *Phytophthora* and *Plasmopara* the internal mycelium sends erect sporangiophores to the surface of the host (Fig. 91). Instead of forming blisters, as in *Albugo*, the sporangiophores push out through the stomata and bear solitary terminal sporangia on branches. The sporangia, which are shed without opening, are carried by the wind to uninfected hosts, where each produces several biciliate zoospores. These form a new mycelium within the leaf.

Peronospora is a large genus of about 60 species, some of which are parasitic on various garden vegetables, such as cabbage, spinach, onion, pea, etc. It is of interest in that, in many species, no zoospores are produced, the detachable sporangia giving rise to new mycelia directly.

Summary. The Peronosporales are almost all internal parasites on seed plants. They have a well-developed mycelium and small multinucleate sporangia that, with few exceptions, are borne on erect sporangiophores. The sporangia are almost always detachable and, after dispersal by the wind, give rise to biciliate zoospores or, in some cases, to a new mycelium directly. All members are heterogamous. The oögonium produces only one egg, in the formation of which the outer portion of the oögonial protoplast is not included. The male nucleus reaches the egg through a fertilization tube developed by the antheridium.

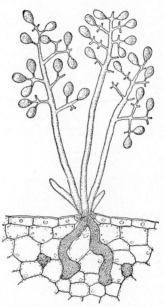

6. Mucorales

The Mucorales are the black molds, most of which are terrestrial saprophytes living on decaying vegetable and animal matter. There are about 30 genera and 400 species, common representatives of the group being *Rhizopus*, *Mucor*, and *Pilobolus*. The largest genus is *Mucor*, with about 50 species.

Rhizopus. The common black mold that grows on moist stale bread is *Rhizopus nigricans*. It also occurs on fruits, vegetables, jelly, and other decaying organic matter. The mycelium consists of a white fluffy mass of profusely branched coenocytic hyphae. These grow horizontally over the substratum, sending into it tufts of short

FIG. 91. *Plasmopara viticola* on the stem of grape. Sporangiophores bearing numerous sporangia are emerging through a stoma, ×200.

root-like haustoria through which food is absorbed (Fig. 92A). Erect unbranched sporangiophores arise in clusters from the mycelium at places where the haustoria are formed. Each sporangiophore produces a large, globular, terminal sporangium. In its development, the tip of the sporangiophore enlarges as additional cytoplasm and nuclei pass into it (Fig. 93A). Soon the peripheral part of the enlarging sporangium becomes denser than the central portion and a line of vacuoles appears between them (Fig. 93B). These two regions are then separated by a cleavage furrow, arising from below, and finally by a dome-shaped wall. This projects into the sporangium to form a *columella* (Fig. 92B).

The portion of the sporangium lying between the columella and the outer wall now undergoes a process of progressive cleavage, whereby it becomes divided into numerous small, multinucleate protoplasts by

furrows that start at the surface and grow inward (Fig. 93*C–E*).   Finally,
each protoplast secretes a cell wall and becomes a minute, black, multinucleate spore (Fig. 93*F*).   The spores, produced in enormous numbers,
are liberated into the air by rupture of the sporangial wall.   Upon reaching a suitable supply of food, they give rise to new mycelia.   The replace-
ment of zoospores by aerial spores is a notable feature of the Mucorales.

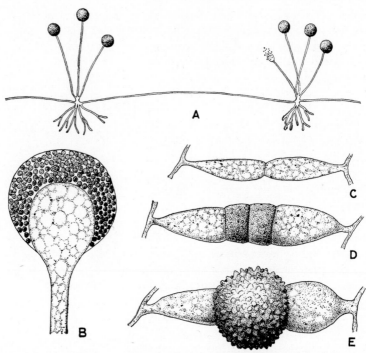

Fig. 92.   *Rhizopus nigricans.*   *A*, horizontal branch of mycelium producing haustoria and
sporangia, ×15; *B*, a mature sporangium, showing central columella, ×150; *C, D, E*, stages
in sexual reproduction, resulting in the formation of a heavy-walled zygote, ×150.

Sexual reproduction occurs in *Rhizopus* only under special conditions
(Fig. 92*C–E*).   A short lateral branch is put out by each of two hyphae
lying parallel to each other.   Their tips come in contact, enlarge, and
from each a multinucleate cell is cut off by a cell wall.   Although ordinarily of the same size, often one cell is slightly larger than the other.
Finally, the wall between the cells is dissolved and their contents fuse to
form a zygote.   Many of the nuclei become associated in pairs and fuse,
the others disintegrating.   The zygote enlarges and becomes a thick-
walled resting cell.   The two conjugating cells are usually interpreted as
gametangia and their contents as large compound isogametes.   It has
been observed in other Mucorales, but not in *Rhizopus*, that the zygote,

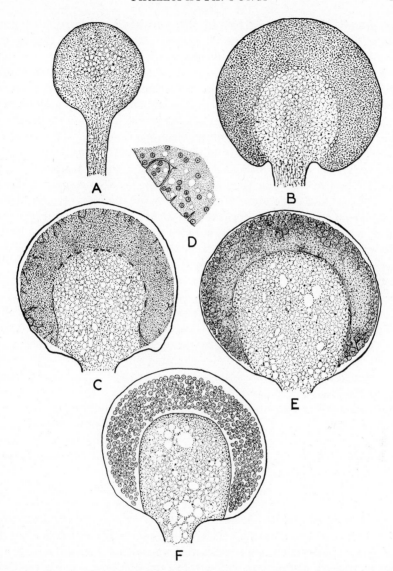

Fig. 93. Development of the sporangium of *Rhizopus nigricans*. *A*, young sporangium; *B*, appearance of small vacuoles between outer and inner parts of sporangium; *C*, enlargement and fusion of vacuoles to form columella cleft; appearance of cleavage furrows at outer surface; *D*, enlarged view, showing early cleavage furrows and scattered nuclei and vacuoles; *E*, sporangium completely cut off from columella; cleavage further advanced; *F*, mature sporangium. (*After Swingle.*)

upon germination, gives rise to a short hypha bearing a terminal sporangium. This contains many aerial spores. Meiosis occurs during the first two divisions of the fusion nucleus in the zygote.

Although all the mycelia of *Rhizopus* appear to be alike, gametic reproduction does not take place unless two sexually differentiated mycelia, designated as plus and minus strains, come together. This may happen very infrequently for, when a mycelium produces spores, all the resulting mycelia belong to the same strain and conjugation does not take place between them. Molds with sexually differentiated strains are said to be *heterothallic*, while those without such differentiation are *homothallic*. In homothallic species conjugation may take place between any two hyphae, even those of the same mycelium. In some of the heterothallic Mucorales, when a sporangium is formed at the end of a hypha arising from the zygote, a segregation of strains occurs, so that some of the spores in the sporangium produce plus mycelia and others minus mycelia. In other heterothallic species this sporangium contains spores of one kind or the other, but not both kinds. In *Rhizopus nigricans* it is not known where the segregation of strains takes place.

Pilobolus, which lives on barnyard refuse, is an interesting mold with a peculiar method of spore dispersal. As the sporangium ripens, the portion of the sporangiophore just below it enlarges and becomes very turgid. Finally it bursts suddenly, shooting out the entire sporangium with considerable force, sometimes to a distance of 2 m., and always toward the brightest source of light.

Summary. The Mucorales are largely saprophytic fungi with a well-developed mycelium. They produce no zoospores, asexual reproduction occurring by aerial spores borne in sporangia. Sexual reproduction is isogamous, conjugation occurring between the entire contents of two multinucleate gametangia.

7. Entomophthorales

The Entomophthorales constitute a small group of fungi, most of which are parasitic on insects. The order includes 6 genera and about 50 species, the best-known genera being *Empusa* and *Entomophthora*. A common species, *Empusa muscae*, attacks the housefly. The mycelium, which is feebly developed, penetrates the body of the host and eventually kills it. Then it sends out numerous sporangiophores, from each of which a single multinucleate sporangium is cut off (Fig. 94). This is forcibly discharged into the air and, upon coming in contact with an uninfected fly, produces a new mycelium. Although it becomes detached and functions directly as a spore, the sporangium of *Empusa* corresponds to the sporangium of the Mucorales. In *Entomophthora* the sporangiophores are branched and the sporangia uninucleate. Sexual reproduction seems to be absent in *Empusa muscae* but, in several other species, as in the Mucorales, it occurs by the conjugation of multinucleate protoplasts, each representing the whole contents of a gametangium.

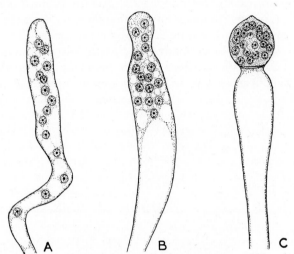

Fig. 94. Development of the sporangium of *Empusa muscae*, ×600. *A*, hyphal body elongating to form a sporangiophore; *B*, migration of nuclei to apex; *C*, formation of multinucleate sporangium at tip of sporangiophore.

4. ASCOMYCETES

The Ascomycetes, or sac fungi, constitute the largest group of fungi. They differ from the Phycomycetes in having a septate mycelium, that is, one divided by cross walls into cells. They are also characterized by the production of spores in a sac-like structure called an *ascus*. This is a cell that at first contains two nuclei. These fuse and the fusion nucleus typically gives rise to eight nuclei by three successive divisions, the first two of which are reductional. From these haploid nuclei, eight walled *ascospores* are then organized. In all except the lowest orders, the asci are enclosed by a definite fruiting body, the *ascocarp*, composed of interwoven hyphae. The relationships of the Ascomycetes are obscure. They may have been derived either from the Phycomycetes or from the Rhodophyceae. The group is of immense economic interest, many members causing serious plant diseases, such as peach leaf curl, brown rot of stone fruits, black knot of plum, apple scab, and bitter rot of apple. There are about 25,000 species of Ascomycetes. These are included in nine main orders: Protoascales, Protodiscales, Plectascales, Perisporiales, Pezizales, Helvellales, Tuberales, Pyrenomycetales, and Laboulbeniales.

1. Protoascales

The Protoascales include the yeasts and other simple forms, most of which are regarded as degenerate Ascomycetes. They number about 500 species. These are mainly saprophytes but some are parasites on animals. A few of the saprophytic forms have a mycelium. In the yeasts, which are unicellular fungi, a mycelium ordinarily is not developed. Yeasts are of economic value in breadmaking and in the preparation of alcoholic beverages. The best-known genus is *Saccharomyces*. Some yeasts reproduce by fission but most of them reproduce by budding (Fig. 95). A bud

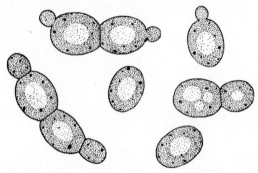

Fig. 95. *Saccharomyces cerevisiae.* Cells in the living condition, showing reproduction by budding, ×1,500.

arises as a small outgrowth, usually at one end of the cell. The nucleus divides to form two nuclei, one of which goes into the bud. The bud enlarges and becomes abstricted from the parent cell. It may either separate at once or remain attached and produce another bud. In this way short chains may be formed.

In many yeasts, under conditions unfavorable for vegetative activity, the contents of any cell may divide to form four or, in some species, eight thick-walled spores, thus becoming a simple ascus. In some yeasts a conjugation of two cells precedes the formation of ascospores. The development of an ascus directly from the zygote is a feature occurring only in the Protoascales.

There is considerable variation in the life history of different yeasts, and even in the same yeast under different environmental conditions. Thus the ascospores may enlarge to form vegetative cells that undergo a long period of multiplication, or they may conjugate at once. The zygote may become an ascus directly, or may give rise to vegetative cells that later become asci. Under unfavorable conditions, vegetative multiplication may be omitted. If no conjugation occurs, the ascospores are formed by parthenogenesis.

Yeasts present three different types of life cycles. The first may be illustrated by *Schizosaccharomyces octosporus*, a fission yeast. Here the vegetative cells are haploid, and eight spores arise in the cell formed by the conjugation of two cells (Fig. 96). The zygote is the only diploid cell in the life history, meiosis occurring when its nucleus divides. In the second type of life cycle, the vegetative cells are diploid. Two ascospores unite and the zygote, without undergoing meiosis, gives rise to vegetative cells that multiply and finally produce ascospores. Meiosis occurs when the spores are formed, and so they are the only haploid cells in the life history.

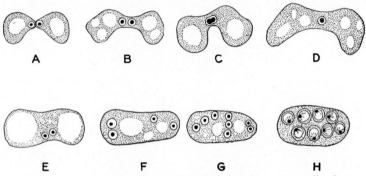

Fig. 96. *Schizosaccharomyces octosporus.* *A* to *D*, conjugation of two cells, the two nuclei uniting to form a single nucleus; *E* to *G*, three successive divisions of the fusion nucleus to form eight nuclei; *H*, formation of eight ascospores. (*After Guilliermond.*)

The third type of life cycle, represented by *Saccharomyces cerevisiae*, is more complicated. Here the vegetative cells are either haploid or diploid. When two haploid cells conjugate, the zygote gives rise to a large number of diploid vegetative cells by budding. Meiosis occurs when one of these cells forms four ascospores. The spores give rise to haploid vegetative cells that multiply by budding. These are smaller than the diploid vegetative cells.

Yeasts live in sugar solutions and are the principal agents in causing alcoholic fermentation. They use as food only a small part of the sugar that they absorb. The rest is broken down into carbon dioxide, ethyl alcohol, and small amounts of other substances. This process of fermentation is accomplished by the production of an enzyme called *zymase*. It is most active in the absence of free oxygen and serves as a means of releasing energy when the ordinary type of respiration cannot be carried on.

2. Protodiscales

The Protodiscales, numbering less than 100 species, are internal parasites attacking seed plants, especially trees. The only genus is *Taphrina*. A common species, *Taphrina deformans*, causes a disease of peaches known as peach leaf curl, while *Taphrina pruni* produces a disease of the domestic plum called plum pockets, in which the fruit becomes shriveled. *Taphrina cerasi* attacks branches of the cherry, causing brush-like deformities known as witches'-brooms.

The mycelium of *Taphrina* grows in the intercellular spaces of the host and sends to the surface groups of asci that arise just beneath the cuticle (Fig. 97). Each ascus contains eight ascospores. The asci are crowded to form a layer, called the *hymenium*, but are without accompanying sterile hyphae. Moreover, an ascocarp is not developed and

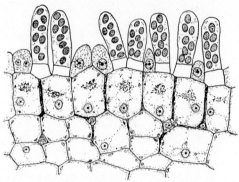

Fig. 97. *Taphrina deformans*. Cross section of portion of peach leaf, showing layer of asci and ascogenous cells on the surface, ×500.

there is no formation of sex organs. The cells of the mycelium are binucleate. The two nuclei in the young ascus fuse, three successive divisions result in the formation of eight free nuclei, and from these the eight ascospores are organized. Upon germination, the ascospores, which are haploid, may give rise to one or more uninucleate cells by a process that resembles budding in yeasts. In some species these cells, which are called *conidia*, are formed while the ascospores are still within the asci. The ascospores, or the conidia produced by them, infect new host plants, a hypha penetrating the cuticle and pushing its way between the epidermal cells. The germinating spore may become binucleate by division of its nucleus, or a pair of ascospores or conidia may conjugate, a nucleus passing from one to the other. The binucleate condition is then transmitted to the cells of the vegetative mycelium.

3. Plectascales

The Plectascales include the blue and green molds, saprophytes that are abundant everywhere, occurring on bread, cheese, jelly, fruits, vegetables, meat, leather, etc. The order includes over 30 genera and 800 species. The two commonest genera are *Aspergillus* and *Penicillium*, the latter numbering over 500 species. One species, *Penicillium notatum*, produces a substance, called *penicillin*, that has remarkable germicidal properties. It has recently come into prominence as a valuable agent in the treatment of many infections and diseases caused by certain bacteria, particularly cocci. Its great advantage over many other drugs lies

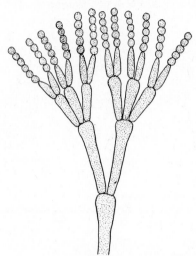

FIG. 98. Branching conidiophores of *Penicillium* producing chains of conidia, ×800.

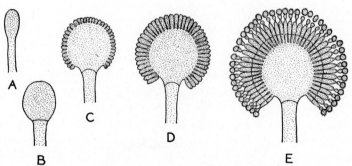

FIG. 99. *Aspergillus niger.* *A* to *E*, successive stages in the development of a conidiophore and its conidia, as seen in optical section, ×400.

in its almost complete nontoxicity to the human body. Substances like penicillin are called *antibiotics*.[1]

The mycelium of the Plectascales produces special branches, called *conidiophores*, that cut off chains of spores, or *conidia*, enormous numbers

[1] Most antibiotics, including streptomycin, aureomycin, and chloromycetin, are derived from actinomycetes, a group of organisms of which some are mold-like and others bacteria-like. They are variously classified with the Fungi Imperfecti, the bacteria, or as a distinct group of fungi. Some are parasites but most are saprophytes prevalent in the soil.

of which are liberated into the air. Upon coming in contact with a suitable food supply, the conidia produce new mycelia. In *Penicillium* the conidia arise from the ends of branched conidiophores (Fig. 98). In *Aspergillus* the conidia are abstricted from the ends of short hyphae that radiate from the enlarged tip of a conidiophore (Fig. 99).

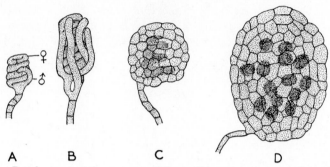

A   B   C   D

FIG. 100. Development of the ascocarp of *Aspergillus*. *A*, sex organs; *B*, sterile hyphae enclosing the sex organs; *C* and *D*, later stages, showing the development of asci. (*From a Turtox classroom chart.*)

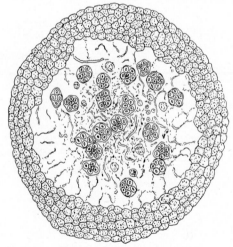

FIG. 101. Section through a mature ascocarp of *Aspergillus*, showing the completely enclosed asci, ×500.

The sex organs are represented by two short, spirally twisted filaments, the contents of which appear to fuse (Fig. 100). Then *ascogenous hyphae*, bearing numerous small asci, arise from one of the filaments. These are intermixed with and surrounded by sterile hyphae, those on the outside forming a minute, globular, closed ascocarp. A fruiting body of this type is known as a *cleistothecium*. There is no definite hymenium in the

Plectascales, the asci being irregularly scattered throughout the mass of sterile hyphae (Fig. 101).

4. Perisporiales

The Perisporiales, or powdery mildews, are superficial parasites attacking many kinds of seed plants, such as grape, lilac, willow, rose, squash, bean, pea, apple, grasses, and numerous others. They number about 500 species. Common genera are *Sphaerotheca, Erysiphe, Uncinula, Podosphaera, Microsphaera,* and *Phyllactinia.* The mycelium lives on

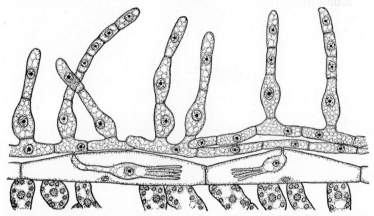

Fig. 102. *Erysiphe graminis* growing on surface of grass leaf, showing haustoria in epidermis of host and conidia in various stages of development, ×500.

the surface of the leaves, forming whitish patches. Short haustorial branches are sent into the epidermal cells and through them food is absorbed. During the summer the mycelium produces erect conidiophores, which give rise to chains of conidia (Fig. 102). These are very abundant and result in a rapid spread of the fungus to uninfected hosts. In the autumn closed ascocarps (cleistothecia) appear. They are minute, spherical, dark brown or black bodies with long appendages that, in some genera, are branched at the tip (Fig. 103). Inside the ascocarps are the asci, each usually with eight ascospores. The ascocarps, scattered by the wind, survive the winter. During the next season the ascospores produce new mycelia.

The character of the appendages produced by the ascocarps is important in distinguishing genera from one another. Thus in *Sphaerotheca* and *Erysiphe* the tips of the appendages are undivided, while in *Podosphaera* and *Microsphaera* they are dichotomously divided. In *Uncinula* the tips of the appendages are hooked or curved, while in *Phyllactinia* they are straight but the appendages are swollen at the base so as to form an enlarged plate.

The sex organs arise from uninucleate cells formed at the tips of special branches of the mycelium, all the cells of which are uninucleate (Fig. 104). The antheridium, slightly smaller than the oögonium (ascogonium), comes in contact with it. The intervening cell wall is dissolved and the male nucleus passes over to fuse with the female nucleus. Sterile hyphae, arising from the cell beneath the oögonium, form a closed ascocarp. Following fertilization, the fusion nucleus gives rise to three

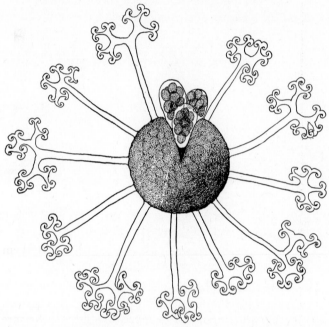

FIG. 103.   Ascocarp of *Microsphaera alni* with characteristic appendages, crushed slightly so that three asci, each with eight ascospores, have appeared, ×250.

to five (often more) free nuclei and then transverse walls come in, forming a short row of cells. All of these are uninucleate except the penultimate cell, which is binucleate. In *Sphaerotheca* and *Podosphaera* this cell directly forms a solitary ascus in which the two nuclei fuse, while in the other genera it gives rise either to a row of cells, each of which becomes an ascus, or to ascogenous hyphae that, in turn, produce the asci. Although in *Sphaerotheca* and *Podosphaera* the ascocarp has only one ascus, in the other genera it contains a basal layer of several parallel asci. The development of the ascus takes place in the regular way, except that it frequently contains less than eight ascospores. Eight nuclei are formed as usual, but some are not organized into spores. The asci are generally not intermixed with sterile hyphae.

If the male and female nuclei actually fuse in the oögonium, the fusion in the young ascus involves two diploid nuclei, necessitating a double reduction of chromosomes in the two meiotic divisions that immediately follow. This behavior has been disputed by some investigators, who assert that the only nuclear fusion occurs in the young ascus and involves haploid nuclei, some claiming that the male and female nuclei remain

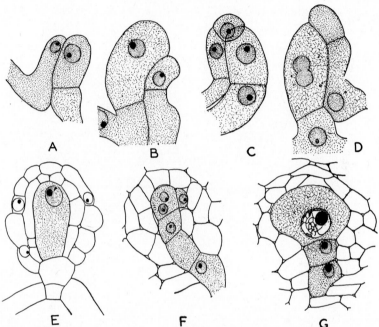

FIG. 104. *Sphaerotheca castagnei.* *A*, antheridial and oögonial branches in contact; *B*, antheridial branch cut off by a wall; *C*, antheridial cell separated from stalk cell; *D*, union of male and female nuclei in oögonium; *E*, oögonium with zygote nucleus and two layers of investing hyphae derived from cell just below; *F*, multicellular ascogonium, the penultimate cell, with two nuclei, becoming the ascus; *G*, young ascus with fusion nucleus and two ascogonial cells below it. (*After Harper.*)

distinct in the oögonium, others that the antheridium is nonfunctional and a male nucleus does not enter the oögonium. If these views are correct, the fusion nucleus in the young ascus is diploid and divides meiotically in the usual way.

5. Pezizales

The Pezizales, or cup fungi, grow mostly on decaying wood or humus, but some are parasitic on seed plants. They are a large order of approximately 5,000 species. The principal genera include *Pyronema*, *Peziza*, *Ascobolus*, *Lachnea*, and *Sclerotinia*.

Pyronema. This is a saprophyte on soil, especially where it has been burned over. The mycelium grows as a white fluffy layer on the surface.

It bears well-developed sex organs.   The female organ resembles the
procarp of *Nemalion*.   It consists of a globular, multinucleate basal portion, the *ascogonium*, and an elongated curved cell, the *trichogyne*, arising
from its upper end (Fig. 105*A*).   The antheridium, which is terminal,
club-shaped, and multinucleate, arises from an adjacent hypha.   It comes
in contact with the tip of the trichogyne, whose nuclei degenerate, and
discharges its contents into it.   The wall at the base of the trichogyne

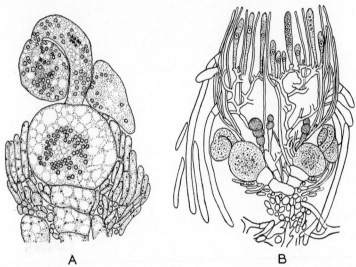

A   B

Fig. 105. *Pyronema confluens*.   *A*, ascogonium and trichogyne with antheridium in contact with its tip and discharging nuclei into it.   Antheridium is curved around trichogyne
and appears in section to be cut in two.   *B*, somewhat diagrammatic section of a young
ascocarp, involving two ascogonia from which ascogenous hyphae and paraphyses have
arisen.   Asci are shown in various stages of development.   (*After Harper*.)

disappears and the male nuclei migrate into the ascogonium, where multinucleate pairing of male and female nuclei occurs.   The nuclei do not
fuse, however, until an ascus is formed.

Following fertilization, the ascogonium is cut off from the trichogyne
by a new wall and branching ascogenous hyphae arise from it (Fig. 105*B*).
These give rise to asci.   Sterile hyphae (paraphyses) grow up from the
mycelium and intermingle with the asci, the entire group of fertile and
sterile hyphae becoming surrounded by a fleshy ascocarp.   Ordinarily
several sets of sex organs enter into the formation of a single ascocarp.
The ascocarp of *Pyronema* is disk-shaped, red or yellow, and only 2 or 3
mm. in diameter.   The asci and paraphyses form a definite layer, the
hymenium, that covers its upper surface.   A broadly open ascocarp is
called an *apothecium*, a type of fruiting body that is characteristic of the
Pezizales.

The origin of the asci is somewhat complex (Fig. 106).   The paired nuclei of the ascogonium pass into the ascogenous hyphae, where they multiply. The members of each pair remain together as walls are formed. The terminal cell of a branch that is to become an ascus bends back to form a hook and its two nuclei divide simultaneously. Three

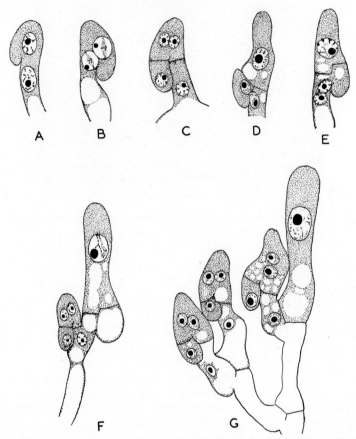

FIG. 106. Origin of the ascus in *Pyronema confluens*. *A*, hook formation at tip of ascogenous hypha; *B*, simultaneous division of nuclei; *C*, formation of uninucleate terminal and basal cells and of binucleate penultimate cell; *D*, fusion of nuclei in penultimate cell to form an ascus; also migration of nucleus of basal cell into terminal cell; *E*, same stage except that nucleus of terminal cell has migrated into basal cell; *F*, later stage showing development of hook from basal cell; *G*, development of three hooks and an ascus from binucleate tip of an ascogenous hypha. (*After Claussen.*)

cells are now cut off by walls. The terminal and basal cells are uninucleate but the middle one (the penultimate cell) has two nuclei of opposite sex, these being the descendants of a male and female nucleus that came from the fertilized ascogonium. The two nuclei may now fuse and the middle cell become an ascus, or the nucleus from the terminal cell may migrate into the basal cell and another hook may be formed. This behavior may be repeated a number of times. Each cell in which a nuclear fusion occurs may become an ascus, the fusion nucleus under-

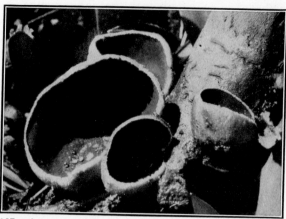

Fig. 107.   Ascocarps of *Peziza* growing on decaying wood, natural size.

going the usual three successive divisions to produce eight ascospore nuclei. The significance of hook formation, which occurs in many Ascomycetes, is a puzzle.

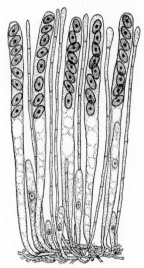

Fig. 108. Several mature asci of *Peziza*, each with eight ascospores, intermixed with paraphyses, ×250. So m e young asci are arising below.

Peziza. *Peziza* is one of the best-known cup fungi, including about 150 species. It is a common saprophyte on rich humus or on decaying wood. The mycelium, which is extensive and much branched, penetrates the substratum and gives rise on the surface to smooth, fleshy, cup-like ascocarps 1 to 5 cm. or more in diameter (Fig. 107). These are generally bright red, brown, or gray. As in *Pyronema*, the ascocarp is lined with a layer of parallel asci and paraphyses, these constituting the hymenium (Fig. 108). Each ascus contains eight ascospores. Upon germination, these produce new mycelia. In *Peziza* the ascocarp apparently arises directly from the mycelium without any formation of sex organs.

Sclerotinia. A parasitic cup fungus, *Sclerotinia fructicola*, attacks plums and peaches, causing a disease known as brown rot of stone fruits. The twigs, flowers, and fruits become infected with the mycelium. As the fruit turns brown and decays, great numbers of conidia are formed on the surface. These are cut off in chains from the ends of short conidiophores. The conidia carry the fungus to uninfected trees.   The fungus is usually carried over the winter on dried diseased fruits, called "mummies," that remain on the tree and furnish a fresh source of conidia the following spring.   Brown cup-like ascocarps, which are rare, resemble those of *Peziza* and may be formed early in the season on mummified fruits lying on the ground.

Summary.   The Pezizales are mostly saprophytes but some are parasites.   All have a well-developed mycelium.   The asci, accompanied by paraphyses, form a hymenial layer that lines an open, disk-like or cup-like ascocarp, the apothecium.   This may be fleshy or leathery and sessile or stalked.   Some members have well-developed sex organs, the asci arising from the fertilized ascogonium.   In other members the asci arise directly from the mycelium, sex organs being absent.

6. Helvellales

The Helvellales are related to the Pezizales, being distinguished from them mainly by the form of the ascocarp, which is also an apothecium but

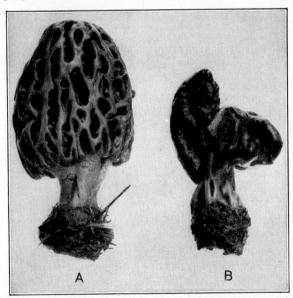

FIG. 109.   Ascocarps of *Morchella* (*A*) and *Helvella* (*B*), natural size.

is more highly differentiated.   The Helvellales are saprophytes that grow chiefly on humus.   They number about 300 species.   The best-known genera are *Morchella* and *Helvella*.

Morchella.   The common edible morel (*Morchella esculenta*) has a much-branched mycelium growing in rich humus soil.   On it are formed compact masses of hyphae that develop into fleshy ascocarps of characteristic form.   These come to the surface of the soil, where they often attain a height of 15 to 20 cm. A mature ascocarp of *Morchella* is differentiated into a thick hollow stalk and a conical cap (Fig. 109*A*). The surface of the cap contains numerous depressions lined with a hymenium consisting of parallel asci and paraphyses.

Helvella. The mycelium is subterranean and composed of hyphae with multinucleate cells. It gives rise to fleshy ascocarps that push upward to the surface of the ground, there reaching a height of about 5 cm. These are differentiated into a stout stalk and a saddle-shaped cap, the outer surface of which is covered with a hymenium consisting of parallel asci and paraphyses (Fig. 109*B*). The asci contain eight ascospores and discharge them into the air with considerable force.

7. Tuberales

The Tuberales are the well-known truffles, esteemed as a gastronomic delicacy. There are nearly 300 species, the representative genus being *Tuber*. The mycelium is subterranean, especially in woods, some forming the mycorrhiza of forest trees. Truffles occur in California and in various parts of southern and central Europe. Their life history is incompletely known. The ascocarp is fleshy and matures underground. It is more or less globular, its diameter rarely exceeding 8 cm. It is usually open when young but later nearly or completely encloses the asci. The ascocarp is thus a modified apothecium. The hymenium may surround a large central cavity or it may form irregular folds that divide the cavity into chambers.

8. Pyrenomycetales

The Pyrenomycetales, or black fungi, are a large order of about 450 genera and 14,000 species that are generally segregated into three smaller orders, the Hypocreales, Dothideales, and Sphaeriales. They include saprophytes that live on decaying wood, humus, etc., and parasites that attack various seed plants. Some representative genera are *Nectria*, *Claviceps*, *Plowrightia*, *Venturia*, *Xylaria* and *Neurospora*.

Nectria. This large genus of about 250 species grows on living or dead wood. It is responsible for several important fungous diseases. One of the most destructive of these, canker of woody plants, is caused by *Nectria cinnabarina* and *Nectria galligena*. They attack a great variety of shrubs and trees, but not conifers. The fungus gains entrance through wounds in the stem. The cortex becomes infected and its cells are immediately killed. This results in a wound that gradually enlarges. Sometimes enough cork tissue is developed around the infected area to close the wound, but usually this is not possible and the trunk is finally girdled. During the summer the mycelium produces large, pinkish, disk-like masses, or *stromata*, that break through the bark and give rise to large numbers of conidiophores, the conidia being carried by the wind to new hosts. Later in the season small, red, flask-shaped ascocarps, called *perithecia*, are developed on the stromata (Fig. 110).

Claviceps. The common ergot disease of rye and other grasses is caused by *Claviceps purpurea*. Its damage to the rye is usually slight, but the eating of diseased grain by animals results in a paralysis and other serious conditions. A drug derived from the fruiting bodies of this fungus, called *ergotine*, has important uses in medicine. The ovaries of the rye are infected by ascospores in the early summer and become hypertrophied, a

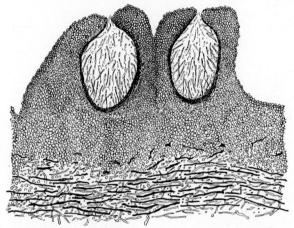

Fig. 110. Stroma of *Nectria cinnabarina* on bark of *Ribes*, showing two perithecia with young asci and paraphyses, ×75.

mycelium developing within. The formation of conidia soon follows. The conidia are minute cells abstricted from the tips of short conidiophores. As they are formed, a sweet liquid is exuded from the spikelet. This attracts insects, which carry the conidia to uninfected flowers. Later the mycelium hardens to form a compact *sclerotium*, which replaces the ovary of the flower. The sclerotia are elongated, slightly curved, purplish bodies that project from the ears of the rye. Many of them eventually fall to the ground, where they pass the winter. In the spring the sclerotium produces several or many globular, stalked *stromata*, which are compact mycelial masses containing numerous flask-shaped, deeply embedded perithecia (Fig. 111). The entire stroma is cream-colored at first, becoming grayish violet. Each perithecium is lined with a hymenium consisting of many asci and paraphyses. The ascospores, which are needle-shaped, are discharged forcibly and dispersed by the wind.

The sex organs of *Claviceps* are borne on hyphae lying below the surface of the stroma. The ascogonium is broader than the antheridium and both are multinucleate. The contents of the antheridium enters the ascogonium, which then gives rise to ascogenous hyphae. As in *Pyronema*, the asci arise as a result of hook formation at the tips of the ascogenous hyphae. Their development occurs in the typical manner.

Plowrightia. This is another parasitic genus, its best-known species, *Plowrightia morbosa*, causing a destructive disease of the plum and cherry known as black knot. The mycelium passes the winter under the bark of

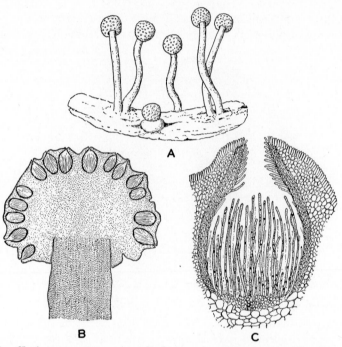

Fig. 111. *Claviceps purpurea.* *A*, stalked stromata arising from a sclerotium, ×4; *B*, longitudinal section through a stroma, showing the embedded perithecia, ×30; *C*, a perithecium with young asci and paraphyses, ×250.

a branch or twig. In the spring it breaks out on the surface to form an elongated gall or knot consisting of both mycelium and hypertrophied host tissue (Fig. 112). Leaves and fruits are not attacked. The elongated knots, often reaching a length of 12 cm. or more, are developed mostly on one side of the stem, which becomes more or less deformed. In early summer the mycelium within the knot gives rise to innumerable short conidiophores that form a velvety layer on the surface. The conidia, distributed by the wind, spread the fungus to other hosts. Later in the season conidium formation ceases and the knot becomes hard and black, forming a stroma in which hundreds of perithecia appear (Fig. 113). These are small flask-shaped organs, embedded in the stroma, and lined with a hymenium consisting of asci and paraphyses. The ascospores mature and are liberated during the following spring. Like the conidia, they directly infect new hosts.

Venturia. *Venturia inaequalis* is the cause of an apple disease known as apple scab. It affects chiefly the leaves and fruits, producing brown spots that become scaly as a result of cork formation. The mycelium grows between the cuticle and the epidermis. It forms large numbers of

Fig. 112. Galls produced on cherry twigs by the black-knot fungus, *Plowrightia morbosa*, natural size.

conidiophores that break through to the surface (Fig. 114*A*). Conidia, abstricted from their tips, spread the fungus during the summer to other apple trees. In the autumn, after the infected leaves fall to the ground, the mycelium becomes saprophytic and produces perithecia in the following spring (Fig. 114*B*). These appear on the lower side deeply embedded within the leaf tissues. Sex organs are produced, but the ascocarp begins to develop before fertilization has occurred. The ascogonium is long, coiled, and multinucleate. It has a trichogyne with which the antheridium comes in contact. Following fertilization, the ascogonium gives rise to ascogenous hyphae from which asci are developed as a result of hook formation at their tips. The ascocarps (perithecia) are dark brown and flask-shaped when mature, discharging the ascospores forcibly.

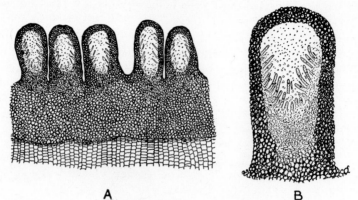

A   **B**

Fig. 113. *Plowrightia morbosa.* A, section of stroma bearing young perithecia, ×50; B, a single perithecium with young asci and paraphyses, ×150.

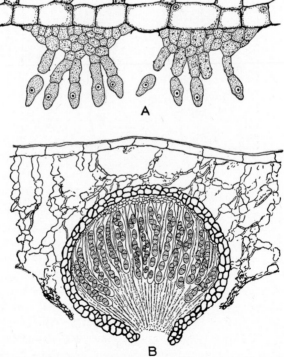

A

B

Fig. 114. *Venturia inaequalis.* A, conidiophores arising on lower side of apple leaf, ×600; B, section of mature perithecium on old apple leaf, ×250.

Xylaria. *Xylaria* is a large genus of about 200 species. It is a common saprophyte, the mycelium living in decaying wood. It produces sclerotia from which black, club-shaped, often branched stromata arise. At first these are covered with a mass of white conidiophores from which small oval conidia are abstricted. Later the stromata produce numerous embedded, flask-shaped perithecia lined with a hymenium (Fig. 115).

Neurospora. This is the pink bread mold, a form much used experimentally in genetics. The mycelium produces conidia in branched chains. Perithecia are rarely formed. They are dark-colored, pear-shaped, and without paraphyses. Like *Rhizopus*, *Neurospora* is heterothallic and sexual reproduction occurs only when a plus and a minus strain come together. The young perithecium contains a coiled ascogonium from which trichogynal hyphae grow out. If these come in contact with spermatia, conidia, or hyphae of the opposite strain, the perithecia mature and asci are produced. Two nuclei of opposite sex fuse in the young ascus, the fusion nucleus undergoes three divisions of which the first two are meiotic, and eight ascospores are formed in the usual way. Experiments have shown that sexual differentiation occurs in connection with ascospore formation, usually during the first meiotic division but sometimes during

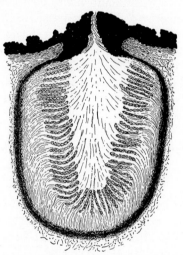

Fig. 115. Longitudinal section through a perithecium of *Xylaria*, showing asci arising from the hymenium, ×100.

the second. As a result, four ascospores in each ascus will produce plus mycelia and four minus mycelia. Other genetic characters behave similarly.

Summary. The Pyrenomycetales include both saprophytes and parasites. They are characterized by a flask-shaped ascocarp (a perithecium) with a small opening at the top. It is lined with a hymenium composed of parallel asci and paraphyses. The perithecia may arise singly on the mycelium, in small groups, or may be embedded in a compact mycelial mass, the stroma. Sex organs are present in some members.

Differences in the character of the perithecia and stromata provide a basis for splitting up this large order into three smaller orders.

1. *Hypocreales.* These forms have soft, bright-colored perithecia with a definite wall. The perithecia may occur singly or in a stroma, which is also bright-colored. They include *Nectria* and *Claviceps*.

2. *Dothideales.* Members of this group have black stromata in which

the perithecia, lacking independent walls, are developed as stromatal cavities. *Plowrightia* belongs here.

3. *Sphaeriales.* The Sphaeriales have dark-colored perithecia with a distinct wall. The perithecia may be free or embedded in the substratum or in stromata that are firm, leathery or brittle, and dark-colored. Here belong *Venturia*, *Xylaria*, and *Neurospora.*

9. Laboulbeniales

The Laboulbeniales comprise an order of about 50 genera and 1,200 species. They are parasitic on insects, especially aquatic ones. As a rule the mycelium grows on the surface of the host and is very small, usually less than 1 mm. in length. The Laboulbeniales are of particular interest because their sex organs are remarkably like those of the red algae. The antheridium is unicellular and produces a nonmotile male cell, the spermatium. The ascogonium has a trichogyne and auxiliary cells. Ascogynous hyphae arise from the fertilized ascogonium, small perithecia are formed, and the asci bud out from the auxiliary cells. The whole process resembles cystocarp formation in the red algae.

5. BASIDIOMYCETES

The Basidiomycetes, or club fungi, comprise the highest group of fungi. They resemble the Ascomycetes in having a mycelium with cross walls. They are characterized by the production of spores externally on a club-like structure known as a *basidium.* This arises from the swollen end of a hypha and may consist of either four cells or one. Four slender branches (sterigmata) arise from the basidium, each forming a *basidiospore* at its tip. The young basidium contains a nucleus derived from the fusion of two nuclei. Two successive divisions, which are reductional, result in the formation of four haploid nuclei, each passing into one of the basidiospores. In the higher members the basidia are borne on a distinct fruiting body, the *basidiocarp*, composed of interwoven hyphae. The Basidiomycetes are related to the Ascomycetes and are generally regarded as having been derived from them. Some are of great economic importance, particularly the smuts, rusts, and mushrooms. The Basidiomycetes number about 20,000 species. They embrace seven principal orders: Ustilaginales, Uredinales, Auriculariales, Tremellales, Exobasidiales, Hymenomycetales, and Gasteromycetales.

1. Ustilaginales

The Ustilaginales, or smuts, are parasites that live on various herbaceous seed plants. They attack chiefly floral organs, particularly those of grasses. They are most destructive to oats, less so to wheat and corn. The smuts number about 500 species. The principal genera are *Ustilago* and *Tilletia.*

Ustilago.   The life history of the corn smut (*Ustilago zeae*) will be described.   The mycelium ramifies throughout the stem and leaves of the corn plant and in its vegetative condition does not seem to do much damage.   It lives in the intercellular spaces, sending short haustoria into the host cells.   When flowers appear, some of the ovaries become packed with the mycelium and, as a consequence, become greatly swollen and distorted.   Swellings may also appear in other parts of the plant.   Later the mycelium divides up into countless numbers of black spores, called

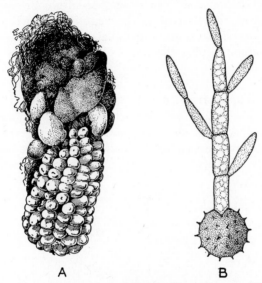

A   B

FIG. 116.   *Ustilago zeae.*   *A*, an ear of corn infected with smut, some of the grains of which are greatly enlarged and filled with chlamydospores, one-half natural size; *B*, a germinating chlamydospore, the four-celled basidium producing basidiospores, ×1,400.

chlamydospores, which form large powdery masses (Fig. 116*A*).   A chlamydospore is a heavy-walled cell representing merely a transformed cell of the vegetative mycelium.

A chlamydospore may germinate at once but, as a rule, falls to the ground and remains dormant until the following spring.   Then it sends out a short filament of three or four cells that lives saprophytically on organic matter in the soil (Fig. 116*B*).   Thin-walled basidiospores are budded off each cell of the filament, often in great numbers.   This filament is a basidium but, because of the large number of spores produced, is not a typical one.   In some smuts, however, only one spore is budded off each of the four cells of the basidium.   The basidiospores infect young corn plants in the spring.

The cells of the vegetative mycelium are binucleate, as are the young chlamydospores.   But before the chlamydospore is mature the two nuclei fuse, thus establishing the diploid condition. The fusion nucleus divides reductionally in the young basidium and four cells are formed by the appearance of transverse walls, thus separating the four haploid nuclei. When a basidiospore is budded off, two nuclei are formed, one of which passes into the spore while the other remains in the basidium. The latter may divide again, if another spore is budded off, and this may be repeated many times. These haploid basidiospores produce on the young corn plant mycelia of limited extent and with uninucleate cells. When two mycelia of opposite sex come together within the host, a union of cells takes place without a fusion of nuclei. The binucleate cells formed in this way give rise to a mycelium that spreads throughout the host, eventually producing chlamydospores.

2. Uredinales

The Uredinales, or rusts, are destructive parasites. They attack a great variety of vascular plants, including ferns, conifers, and angiosperms, being especially common on grasses. The mycelium lives in the intercellular spaces, particularly of the leaves. There are about 3,000 species of rusts, the most important genera being *Puccinia, Uromyces,*

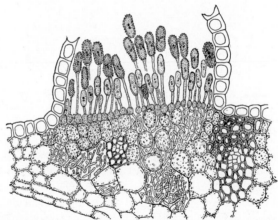

Fig. 117. *Puccinia graminis.* Section through a uredinium on a leaf sheath of wheat, showing uredospores in various stages of development, ×200.

Gymnosporangium, Phragmidium, Cronartium, Coleosporium, and *Melampsora.* The largest genus, *Puccinia,* has about 700 species.

Puccinia. The common wheat rust (*Puccinia graminis*) is the best-known member of the order. Its life history is very complicated, involving two different hosts and several kinds of mycelia and spores, all with a definite relation to one another.

The mycelium that lives on the wheat is an internal parasite, extending throughout the entire body of the host. It does not directly kill the host cells, but lives on their food materials, which it absorbs by means of haustoria. During the late spring and early summer numerous spores are produced. They break through the epidermis of the leaves, groups of them, known as *uredinia*, appearing on the surface as reddish brown streaks or lines (Fig. 117). These spores are called *uredospores*. Each consists of a stalked binucleate cell with a rather thick cell wall. They are scattered by the wind, directly infecting other wheat plants, and are chiefly responsible for the rapid spread of the disease, especially during a wet season. Successive crops of uredospores may be produced throughout the summer.

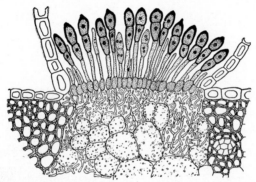

Fig. 118. *Puccinia graminis.* Section through a telium on a leaf sheath of wheat, showing teliospores in various stages of development, ×200.

Later in the season, at harvest time or thereabouts, the same mycelium that produced the uredospores earlier now gives rise to elongated groups of black spores called *teliospores*. These groups, known as *telia*, appear chiefly on the stems and leaf sheaths (Fig. 118). The teliospores are also stalked but are two-celled and heavy-walled. At first each cell has two nuclei, but the members of each pair fuse as the spore matures. The teliospores do not germinate until the next spring, thus carrying the fungus over the winter. Upon germination, one or both cells of the teliospore gives rise to a short filament. This filament is the basidium (Fig. 119*A*). It consists of four cells, each of which sends out a short branch, called a *sterigma*, bearing a small terminal basidiospore. The basidiospores cannot infect wheat plants. They are carried by the wind to leaves of the common barberry (*Berberis vulgaris*), where they germinate and produce an extensive internally parasitic mycelium. It is mainly this species that is susceptible to infection by the basidiospores of wheat rust. Most other barberries are immune.

The mycelium produced by the basidiospores on the barberry develops *spermogonia* (pycnidia), small flask-shaped organs appearing on the upper side of the leaves (Fig. 119*E*).   In these organs small cells, called *spermatia* (pycnospores), are formed by abstriction from the ends of slender hyphae.   The spermatia are exuded from the spermogonia in drops of a sweet liquid.   This attracts insects that aid in their dissemination.   Soon

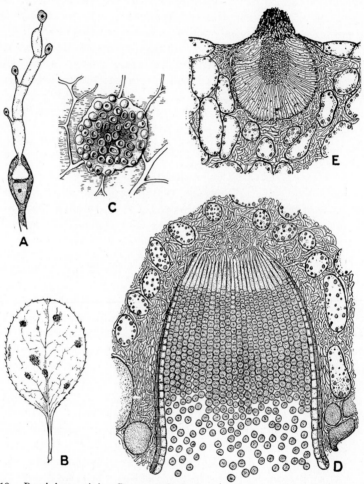

FIG. 119.   *Puccinia graminis.*   Stages on the barberry.   *A*, four basidiospores arising from a basidium produced by a teliospore, ×300; *B*, leaf of common barberry with groups of aecia, natural size; *C*, enlarged view of group of aecia, ×10; *D*, longitudinal section of aecium with numerous aeciospores arising in chains, ×200; *E*, longitudinal section of spermogonium producing numerous small spermatia, ×200.   (*A, after Chamberlain.*)

after the appearance of the spermogonia, the mycelium on the barberry produces larger, cup-like structures that appear in clusters on the lower side of the leaves (Fig. 119*B* and *C*).   These *aecia*, or cluster cups, contain large numbers of *aeciospores*, which arise in chains from the bottom of the cup (Fig. 119*D*). The chains consist of alternating spores and sterile cells, the latter disintegrating. The aeciospores cannot infect the barberry. Instead, carried by the wind, they infect wheat plants during the late spring and summer, thus completing the life cycle.

The cells of the mycelium produced by the basidiospores on the barberry, as well as the spermatia, are uninucleate, but the aeciospores are binucleate. The binucleate condition appears to arise by the spermatia coming in contact with special receptive hyphae of the opposite sex. These extend from the basal cells of the young aecium to the orifice of the spermogonium, through which they project. A spermatium enters a receptive hypha and passes down into the basal cell, which then becomes binucleate. Each binucleate basal cell gives rise by repeated division to a chain of aeciospores. The binucleate condition is carried over by the aeciospores to the mycelium on the wheat and to the uredospores and young teliospores produced by it.

The fusion of the two nuclei in each cell of the teliospore introduces the uninucleate condition. When the teliospore germinates, the diploid nucleus in each of its cells undergoes two successive meiotic divisions that result in the formation of four haploid nuclei. Each of the four cells in the basidium receives one of these nuclei, which then passes into a basidiospore. The uninucleate basidiospores, being haploid, produce a haploid mycelium on the barberry. Thus, although there is an alternating haploid and diploid phase in the life history of *Puccinia*, the latter is not initiated by a nuclear fusion, as in most plants, but by the coming together in the same cell of two nuclei that retain their identity throughout a large number of cell divisions. Eventually the nuclear fusion occurs, but is then followed by the reduction divisions, which mark the beginning of the haploid phase.

Other Rusts. The wheat plant is attacked not only by *Puccinia graminis*, its most destructive rust, but by several related species. One of these is *Puccinia coronata*, whose alternate host is the buckthorn (*Rhamnus*); another is *Puccinia rubigo-vera*, which produces the aecial stage on blueweed (*Echium*) and other Boraginaceae. All three species may attack other grasses than wheat, such as barley, oats, rye, and various meadow grasses, producing the same morphological type of mycelium and spores on each kind of grass but a different physiological strain.

Many rusts have a shorter life cycle than *Puccinia graminis*. All rusts produce teliospores and these always give rise to basidia and basidiospores, but one or more of the other spore forms may be missing. Thus the aecia may be omitted, the uredospores, the aecia and spermatia, or the aecia, spermatia, and uredospores. If a rust requires two different and unrelated hosts to complete its life cycle, it is said to be *heteroecious;*

if all stages are passed on the same host, or on closely related hosts, it is *autoecious*. *Gymnosporangium juniperi-virginianae*, a heteroecious rust, has no uredospores. It develops the telial stage on the red cedar (*Juniperus virginiana*), or related species, and the aecial-spermogonial stage on the apple, pear, and quince (*Pyrus*). A heteroecious rust of great economic importance is *Cronartium ribicola*, the white pine blister rust. Its uredospore-teliospore stage is passed on various species of currants and gooseberries (*Ribes*), its aecial-spermogonial stage on the white pine (*Pinus strobus*) and related species. The damage to white pines has been so great that it has resulted in their virtual extinction in many parts of the country. *Puccinia asparagi* is an autoecious rust, producing uredospores, teliospores, aeciospores, and spermatia on the asparagus. *Puccinia malvacearum*, another autoecious rust, has a very short life cycle, producing only teliospores on the hollyhock and other Malvaceae.

3. Auriculariales

The Auriculariales are the ear fungi, an order of about 15 genera and over 100 species. They are chiefly saprophytes growing on bark and decaying wood. The representative genus is *Auricularia*. The mycelium produces brightly colored, gelatinous, ear-shaped bodies, each being a *basidiocarp*. When dry, the basidiocarps become wrinkled and hairy. The inner surface is lined with a hymenium consisting of basidia intermixed with paraphyses. As in the Uredinales, the basidia are four-celled and have sterigmata. Each basidium produces four basidiospores. This order may be regarded as transitional between the lower and higher Basidiomycetes.

4. Tremellales

The Tremellales, or trembling fungi, are somewhat similar to the Auriculariales. They include 18 genera and nearly 100 species, the best-known genus being *Tremella*. The mycelium lives in decaying wood and bark, producing gelatinous basidiocarps. These are indefinite in form and more or less wavy or folded. The hymenium occurs on the upper surface. The basidia are characteristic, being longitudinally divided into four cells instead of transversely divided. Each basidium bears four basidiospores on long sterigmata.

5. Exobasidiales

The Exobasidiales are internal parasites attacking particularly members of the Ericaceae, such as blueberries, cranberries, huckleberries, azaleas, etc. There are about 30 species, nearly all belonging to the genus *Exobasidium*. Galls composed of mycelium and host tissue are produced on stem tips, leaves, and floral organs. The basidia are formed under the epidermis and, when they break through, cover the host with a whitish bloom. There is no formation of basidiocarps, the basidia arising directly from the mycelium. In this and succeeding orders the basidium is one-celled. The young basidium has two nuclei that fuse, two successive nuclear divisions follow, and four basidiospores are developed, each at the end of a sterigma.

6. Hymenomycetales

This large order of approximately 15,000 species is usually split up into several smaller orders, but here will be regarded as one homogeneous group. Most of the members are saprophytic on humus, bark, decaying wood, etc. Some are parasitic on trees, often causing considerable damage. The Hymenomycetales have complex basidiocarps with basidia in a definite hymenial layer that becomes freely exposed. The basidia are one-celled and bear four basidiospores, each at the end of a slender sterigma.

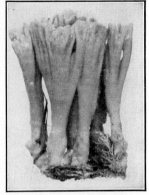

Fig. 120. A coral fungus (*Clavaria*), natural size.

Families. The families of Hymenomycetales are distinguished from one another on the basis of the form of the basidiocarp and the position of the hymenium. The principal families are as follows:

1. *Thelephoraceae.* These forms produce simple basidiocarps appearing on tree trunks. Some resemble leathery incrustations with the hymenium on the smooth upper surface, while some are bracket-like with the hymenium on the lower surface. Others have the hymenium on the outside of a funnel-like basidiocarp. The representative genus is *Thelephora*, with about 150 species.

2. *Clavariaceae.* The coral fungi produce erect, fleshy basidiocarps that are usually branched like coral, the hymenium covering the surface of the branches (Fig. 120). They are commonly white or yellowish, but sometimes are more brightly colored. In some forms the basidiocarps are club-shaped and unbranched, with a complete hymenial covering. The principal genus is *Clavaria*, with about 250 species.

3. *Hydnaceae.* These are the tooth fungi, the hymenium being borne on tooth-like or spine-like processes that generally point downward. The simpler forms occur as rounded masses or thin sheets of indefinite form. Some are more or less branched. Others have a stalk and an umbrella-like pileus that bears teeth on its lower side. The main genus is *Hydnum*, with about 150 species.

4. *Polyporaceae.* The pore fungi bear a number of tubes or grooves lined with a hymenium. The basidiocarp may be crustaceous, the tubes

FIG. 121. *Agaricus campestris*, four-fifths natural size. *A*, mature basidiocarp, showing pileus, stipe, and annulus; *B*, view of underside of pileus with stipe removed, showing the radiating gills; *C*, young basidiocarp before the pileus has expanded; *D*, young basidiocarp cut in half, showing velum attached to stipe.

opening on its upper side. Ordinarily, however, the basidiocarp is bracket-like or umbrella-like, the tubes opening on its lower side. The texture of the basidiocarp may be leathery, fleshy, or hard and woody. Some of the largest genera are *Merulius, Poria, Fomes, Polyporus, Polystichus,* and *Boletus*. *Polyporus*, the largest genus, has about 500 species.

Merulius lacrymans is the dry-rot fungus, a species attacking woodwork and structural timbers. It often causes great destruction to wooden buildings.

5. *Agaricaceae.* This is the large family of gill fungi, a group to which the common mushrooms and toadstools belong. The basidiocarp may be bracket-like but more commonly is umbrella-like. It is usually fleshy, rarely leathery in texture. In this family the hymenium covers blade-like radiating plates known as *gills.* Of the numerous genera, a few common ones are *Coprinus, Agaricus, Amanita, Lepiota, Hypholoma, Russula,* and *Marasmius.* The largest genus is *Marasmius,* with about 450 species.

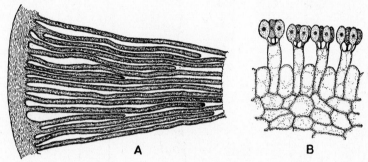

A   B

Fig. 122. *Coprinus micaceus.* *A*, cross section through a few of the gills, ×10; *B*, enlarged portion of same, showing four basidia arising from surface of gill, each with four stalked basidiospores, ×750.

Agaricus and Other Mushrooms. The common field mushroom (*Agaricus campestris*) grows in lawns, fields, and along roadsides. It is the principal species used for food and practically the only one that is cultivated. The mycelium lives on organic matter in the soil. The fleshy basidiocarp arises just below the surface as a "button" composed of interwoven hyphae. Soon a stalk or *stipe* and a cap-like *pileus* become differentiated. The gills, which develop on the lower side of the pileus, are covered by a membrane called the *velum.* This extends from the margin of the pileus to the stipe, becoming ruptured as the pileus expands. In *Agaricus* and many other mushrooms a portion of the velum remains attached to the stipe, forming an *annulus* around it (Fig. 121). In *Amanita*, a genus of poisonous mushrooms, the young basidiocarp is completely enclosed by an outer membrane that ruptures as the stipe elongates, forming a cup or sheath, called the *volva,* at the base of the stipe.

The hymenium of the Agaricaceae, covering the surface of the gills, consists of innumerable basidia, each of which typically bears four basidiospores on slender sterigmata (Fig. 122). The cells of the vegetative mycelium are typically binucleate and there are two nuclei in the young

basidium. These fuse, two successive divisions take place, and the four
resulting nuclei pass through the sterigmata into the basidiospores (Fig.
123*E-G*). The reduction of chromosomes occurs when the fusion nucleus
divides. The cultivated variety of *Agaricus campestris* is exceptional in
that only two basidiospores are borne on a basidium, each of which

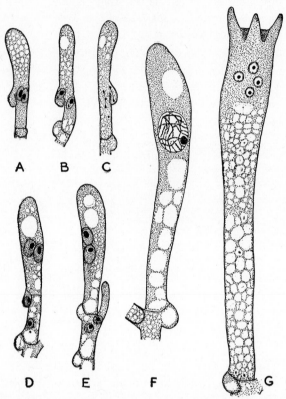

Fig. 123. Clamp formation and development of the basidium in *Armillaria mucida*.
A, beginning of clamp formation in binucleate terminal cell; *B*, one nucleus passing into the
clamp; *C*, conjugate division of the two nuclei; *D*, appearance of walls cutting off uninucleate clamp and basal cells from young binucleate basidium; *E*, fusion of clamp and
basal cells, the latter sending out another branch; *F*, basidium with diploid fusion nucleus;
G, basidium with four haploid nuclei and the developing sterigmata. (*After Kniep.*)

receives two of the four haploid nuclei. The mycelium of both the wild
and cultivated form is multinucleate and probably unisexual (homothallic).

In most mushrooms the basidiospores, upon germination, give rise to
mycelia of two different sexes. These have uninucleate cells. When two
mycelia of opposite sex come together, fusions take place between vegetative cells, resulting in the formation of a binucleate mycelium. Upon
this the basidiocarps are produced.

Following the formation of a binucleate cell by the fusion of two uninucleate cells, a short branch arises into which the two nuclei pass. A hook-like lateral outgrowth, pointing toward the base of the cell, then appears at a point directly opposite the two nuclei (Fig. 123*A*, *B*). After both of these divide, one of the daughter nuclei passes into the hook and a cross wall forms at its base, another wall continuing across the branch (Fig. 123*C*, *D*). Thus two nuclei of opposite sex are in the terminal cell, one nucleus being in the lower cell and one in the hook. The tip of the hook now fuses with the lower cell to form a "clamp connection." The nucleus in the hook passes into the lower cell, which thereby becomes binucleate (Fig. 123*E*). The terminal cell continues to grow and, at each cell division, a new clamp connection is formed.

A mycelium with clamp connections is characteristic of many Basidiomycetes, occurring in at least some members of all the orders except the Uredinales. Clamp formation in the Basidiomycetes is thought to correspond to hook formation in the Ascomycetes where, however, it is limited to the ascogenous hyphae. It must be remembered that in both groups there are many members without any such formations, the ascus or basidium developing directly from the terminal cell of a hypha. Clamp connections are not present on the mycelium of *Agaricus campestris* or its cultivated variety.

7. Gasteromycetales

Like the Hymenomycetales, the Gasteromycetales are often broken up into several smaller orders. Nearly all its members are saprophytic on humus, but a few grow on decaying wood. There are about 1,000 species. The very complex basidiocarp entirely encloses the hymenium, remaining closed or opening only after the spores are mature. The basidiocarp is composed of an outer *peridium* and a central *gleba*, the latter generally containing many chambers. In the lower forms the chambers are filled with hyphae bearing terminal basidia; in the higher forms the chambers are lined with a definite hymenium. The basidia are one-celled and bear four terminal basidiospores, each at the end of a sterigma.

Families. The principal families of Gasteromycetales, distinguished from one another by the character of the peridium and gleba, are as follows:

1. *Hymenogastraceae.* This family is intermediate between the Hymenomycetales and the Gasteromycetales. The peridium is simple, being one-layered and rupturing irregularly. The glebal chambers are lined with basidia borne at the ends of lateral branches of the glebal hyphae. Because the basidiocarps are subterranean, these forms are not commonly seen. The chief genera are *Hymenogaster* and *Rhizopogon.*

2. *Sclerodermaceae.* In this family the basidiocarp is nearly spherical, with a thick, leathery, one-layered peridium that ruptures at the apex. The gleba is indistinctly chambered. The basidia are borne on lateral branches of the glebal hyphae. There are no sterigmata, the basidiospores being sessile. The representative genus is *Scleroderma.*

3. *Lycoperdaceae.* These are the familiar puffballs. The globular basidiocarps are usually less than 8 cm. in diameter but sometimes reach 50 cm. or more. The peridium is two-layered and has no definite dehiscence. In *Lycoperdon* the outer layer flakes off, the inner one bursting at the apex to liberate the spores. In *Geaster* the outer layer splits into stellate segments that spread out on the ground, the inner one dehiscing by a terminal pore. In this family the gleba is distinctly chambered. It is lined with a hymenium and contains a capillitium consisting of fibrous interwoven hyphae that aid in spore dispersal.

4. *Nidulariaceae.* The bird's-nest fungi resemble the puffballs in their younger stages, but at maturity the peridium opens and becomes cup-shaped. The separate glebal chambers, with much-thickened walls, lie at the bottom of the cup like eggs in a nest. The two chief genera are *Nidularia* and *Cyathus.*

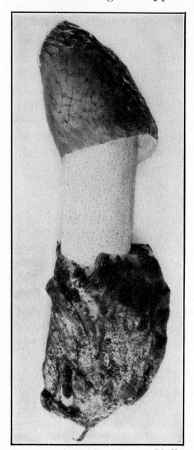

Fig. 124.   A stinkhorn fungus, *Phallus impudicus*, natural size.

5. *Phallaceae.* The stinkhorn fungi are the highest of the Basidiomycetes. Their basidiocarps are extremely complex (Fig. 124). At first they are white and egg-shaped. The peridium is two-layered but the tissue within is differentiated into a hollow sterile axis and an investing, dome-like, chambered gleba. When the basidiocarp is mature, these become the stipe and pileus, respectively. The gleba becomes mucilaginous and foul-smelling, attracting carrion flies that distribute the spores. The principal genera are *Phallus, Mutinus,* and *Dictyophora.* In *Dictyophora* there is a conspicuous net-like veil that hangs down beneath the pileus and spreads out around the stipe like a skirt.

FUNGI IMPERFECTI

The Fungi Imperfecti constitute a large assemblage of forms that, because of an incomplete knowledge of their life histories, cannot be assigned to any of the three natural classes of true fungi: the Phycomycetes, Ascomycetes, and Basidiomycetes. Generally the only known method of reproduction is by conidia. Zygotes, ascospores, or basidiospores are unknown. In many cases the unknown stage has apparently been lost from the life history. When a member of this artificial group is found to possess any reproductive stage previously not reported, it is transferred to its proper genus, family, order, and class. Meanwhile it is placed in a "form genus." Many of the imperfect fungi cause important plant diseases, such as potato scab, early blight of potato, flax wilt, and various anthracnose and leaf-spot diseases. Practically all the fungi that cause such human diseases as ringworm and athlete's foot are imperfect fungi.

LICHENES

A lichen is a plant consisting of a unicellular alga and a fungus living together in symbiotic relationship. This association, resulting in a body having a distinctive form and structure, suggests a single plant rather than a composite one. Lichens are commonly regarded as constituting an autonomous group of thallophytes, the Lichenes, which are either made coordinate with the Algae and Fungi, or included with the latter as a distinct class. By those who consider lichens to be merely fungi parasitic upon algae, they are sometimes broken up and distributed among the fungous groups that they most closely resemble.

Lichens are commonly seen growing on rocks, tree trunks, dead wood, and on the ground. They are a widely distributed group of which about 400 genera and 15,000 species are known. A few of the largest genera are *Lecidia*, *Buellia*, *Lecanora*, *Parmelia*, *Physcia*, *Collema*, *Sticta*, *Cladonia*, *Ramalina*, and *Usnea*. Lichens are mostly gray or grayish green, but some are more conspicuously colored. Based on their external form, three general types are recognized: (1) *crustose* lichens, which occur as incrustations on rocks and bark; (2) *foliose* lichens, which are flat, leaf-like, and only partially attached to the substratum; and (3) *fruticose* lichens, branching forms that hang from trees or grow either erect or prostrate on the ground (Fig. 125).

The greater part of a lichen is composed of a compact mass of tangled fungous hyphae, among which are numerous algal cells, either scattered irregularly or in a definite layer (Fig. 126). The body is usually differentiated into a compact cortical region and a lower region of looser texture, in either of which the algal cells may occur. In some lichens the algae live on the surface of the mycelium, closely covering it.   With only a few rare exceptions, lichen-forming fungi are ascomycetes belonging either to the Pezizales or to the Pyrenomycetales.   In three genera of lichens the fungus is a basidiomycete, the best-known species being *Cora pavonia*, which is widely distributed throughout Central and South America.   The lichen-forming algae are members either of the Cyanophyceae or Chlorophyceae, most of the latter belonging to the Chlorococcales.

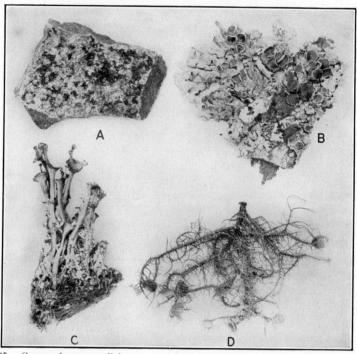

Fig. 125.   Group of common lichens, natural size.   *A*, a crustose form (*Placodium*) growing on rock; *B*, a foliose form (*Parmelia*) growing on bark; *C*, a fruticose lichen (*Cladonia*) which grows erect on the ground; *D*, a branching form (*Usnea*) that hangs from the limbs of trees.

Lichens were once regarded as single plants.   In 1868, their dual nature was demonstrated.   In 1889, lichens were first synthesized by sowing spores from the fungous element of a lichen among appropriate free-living algae.   The developing mycelium was seen to enclose the algae and develop into a lichen.   Although the algal symbionts are forms that may exist independently, the fungi are known only as constituents of lichens.

Vegetative reproduction takes place mainly by *soredia*, globular or scale-like bodies composed of a few hyphae closely investing one or more algal cells.   They arise as buds on the upper surface of the thallus, become detached, and are scattered by the wind.   The algal components multiply by fission within the lichen body. The fungous components produce ascocarps, generally in abundance (Fig. 127). These are either apothecia or perithecia. Sex organs have been observed in many lichens. The ascogonium is a spirally coiled multicellular filament commonly terminating in a trichogyne. The male cells, or spermatia, are borne on branching hyphae arising within a flask-like chamber, or spermogonium. After

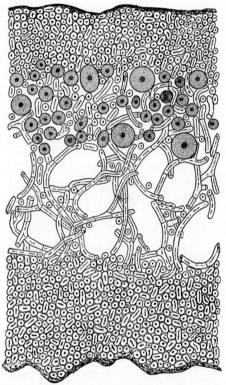

Fig. 126. Cross section through the body of a lichen (*Physcia*), showing cells of the alga (shaded) surrounded by a mass of interlacing fungous hyphae, ×500.

fertilization, which may not always take place, the ascogonium gives rise to many ascogenous hyphae and paraphyses (Fig. 127*B*). At the tips of the ascogenous hyphae typical asci with eight ascospores are formed. An ascospore, in germination, produces hyphae that die unless they come in contact with a suitable alga.

The relation of the two lichen components to each other is important to understand. The fungus lives on the alga as a parasite but does not kill it. In fact, the alga seems to be only slightly injured, merely sacrificing some of the food that it makes. At the same time, however, the alga is benefited in that the fungous body readily absorbs and retains moisture, without which the alga could not live.   The fungus derives food from the alga, while the alga obtains moisture from the fungus.   This reciprocal relation makes it possible for many lichens to live in dry exposed situations where neither the alga nor the fungus could live alone.   Thus the relation between the two lichen components is one of mutual advantage.

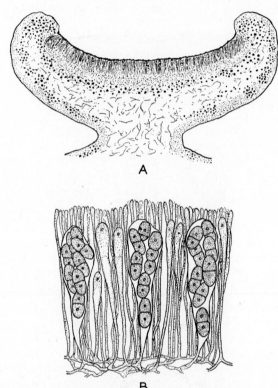

Fig. 127.   *A*, longitudinal section through an apothecium of *Physcia*, showing hymenium and embedded algal cells, ×60; *B*, enlarged view of hymenium, showing asci and paraphyses, ×500.

COMPARISON OF THE CLASSES OF FUNGI

The chief distinguishing characters of the five classes of fungi are as follows:

Schizomycetes.   Plant body unicellular, solitary or colonial, ciliated or nonciliated.   Cells without a definite nucleus.   Cell walls usually forming mucilage.   Reproduction by fission.

Myxomycetes.   Plant body a naked amoeboid mass of multinucleate protoplasm (a plasmodium).   Asexual reproduction by small uninucleate spores, each with a cell wall and usually borne within sporangia of definite form.   Sexual reproduction by amoeboid isogametes.

Phycomycetes. Plant body typically a nonseptate multinucleate mycelium. Asexual reproduction by spores formed by cleavage and borne in indefinite numbers in sporangia. Lower members with zoospores, higher members with aerial spores. Sexual reproduction isogamous or heterogamous. Heterogamous forms with well-developed sex organs.

Ascomycetes. Plant body typically a septate mycelium. Spores borne usually in groups of eight in a sac-like structure, the ascus, their nuclei arising by three successive divisions of a fusion nucleus. Zoospores wanting. Sex organs reduced, obscure, or entirely absent.

Basidiomycetes. Plant body a septate mycelium. Spores borne usually in groups of four on a club-like structure, the basidium, their nuclei arising by two successive divisions of a fusion nucleus. Zoospores wanting. Sex organs not present.

GENERAL CONCLUSIONS

The fungi are a heterogeneous assemblage of thallophytes of diverse origin held together by a physiological character—the absence of chlorophyll. Two classes, the Schizomycetes and Myxomycetes, stand apart from each other and from the three classes of "true fungi" (Eumycetes). In their unicellular organization, cell structure, and reproduction the Schizomycetes resemble the Cyanophyceae much more closely than they resemble any of the other fungi. The Myxomycetes, with their naked plasmodia, highly developed sporangia, and amoeboid isogametes, exhibit similarities to some of the Protozoa, on the one hand, and to some of the lower Phycomycetes (Plasmodiophorales) on the other.

Some botanists believe that the "true fungi" are a monophyletic group that have arisen from colorless flagellates and have subsequently differentiated into the three existing classes of Phycomycetes, Ascomycetes, and Basidiomycetes. According to this theory, no direct relationship exists between the algae and fungi, their resemblances being a result of parallel evolution along two independent lines. Other botanists believe that the "true fungi" have been derived from the algae through loss of chlorophyll, their origin having been either monophyletic or polyphyletic. According to this theory, the Phycomycetes have evolved from the Chlorophyceae, the Ascomycetes from either the Phycomycetes or the Rhodophyceae, and the Basidiomycetes from the Ascomycetes.

Vegetative Body. The characteristic plant body of the fungi[1] is a mycelium, made up of branching hyphae that may be either nonseptate and coenocytic (Phycomycetes) or septate (Ascomycetes and Basidiomycetes). Only a few forms are unicellular. The hyphae elongate by apical

---

[1] In the following discussion the term *fungi* will be limited to the three classes of "true fungi."

growth. They may be either loosely or compactly arranged. Sometimes they are aggregated to form root-like strands or a compact resting body (sclerotium). In the development of fruit bodies in the higher fungi —ascocarps and basidiocarps—masses of hyphae become interwoven to form a pseudoparenchymatous structure, but no tissue is formed by cells dividing in three planes. In the lower Phycomycetes the cell wall consists largely of cellulose, but in the other fungi its composition is altered by the presence of chitin and other substances, such as fatty acids. Within the cells of the mycelium are one, two, or many nuclei embedded in the cytoplasm. Sugars and glycogen represent the reserve carbohydrates, no starch being present. Varying amount of fats may also occur.

Spore Reproduction. The Phycomycetes produce spores in sporangia, either zoospores in the lower orders or aerial spores in the higher orders. The spores are formed in indefinite numbers by cleavage. After escaping, they germinate into a mycelium. The entire sporangium may be persistent, as in the Saprolegniales and Mucorales, or detachable, as in most of the Peronosporales. In many of the Ascomycetes and Basidiomycetes the detachable sporangia are replaced by conidia, which function as spores and produce a new mycelium directly. Many conidia, as well as certain other spores, multiply by budding, like the vegetative cells of the yeasts.

Many fungi produce resting spores that are thick-walled and resistant to adverse conditions. Often the same species has two or more different kinds of spores, as in the rusts. Ascospores, which are characteristic of the Ascomycetes, arise by free-cell formation. They are borne internally in an ascus, usually in groups of eight, while basidiospores, characteristic of the Basidiomycetes, are produced externally on a basidium, usually in fours. The formation of ascospores and basidiospores is related to the sexual process.

Gametic Reproduction. In the Phycomycetes sexual reproduction is alga-like. The Chytridiales and Plasmodiophorales produce free-swimming isogametes that fuse in pairs to produce a zygote. Among the heterogamous Phycomycetes (Monoblepharidales, Saprolegniales, and Peronosporales), all of which have well-developed antheridia and oögonia, only the Monoblepharidales have swimming sperms; in the two other orders a male nucleus reaches the egg by passing through a fertilization tube. The gametes are nearly always formed within special cells, the gametangia or sex organs. In the higher Phycomycetes (Mucorales and Entomophthorales) the gametangia are not differentiated as antheridia and oögonia, but the entire contents of two gametangia conjugate to form a zygote.

The Ascomycetes show various stages in the degeneration of the sex organs. Where these are well developed, the oögonium (ascogonium) often resembles that of the red algae. The zygote may develop directly into an ascus or, more commonly, may give rise to many ascogenous hyphae that, in turn, produce the asci. The Basidiomycetes have no sex organs (unless the spermogonia of the rusts are so regarded), but fusions between vegetative cells are common. In the Ascomycetes and Basidiomycetes the sexual nuclei come together without immediately fusing. The nuclear fusion, which takes place in the ascus or basidium, is followed at once by the production of ascospores or basidiospores, respectively.

CHAPTER V

BRYOPHYTA

The bryophytes, numbering about 20,000 species, form a well-defined division comprising the two classes Hepaticae (liverworts) and Musci (mosses). They are small, rather inconspicuous, green plants nearly all of which live on land in moist, shaded places. The bryophytes doubtless have been derived from aquatic ancestors, probably from some group of green algae, but it is uncertain whether they have given rise to any of the higher plant groups. Nevertheless, the bryophytes represent a general condition of structural organization through which the higher plants may have passed in the course of their evolution. Although abundant moisture is necessary for vigorous vegetative growth, some forms live in dry situations and endure considerable desiccation during long rainless periods. A few liverworts and mosses live in fresh water, but the aquatic habit in the bryophytes, as in the higher groups, has undoubtedly been secondarily acquired.

A well-defined alternation of generations is an established feature of all bryophytes, the gametophyte and sporophyte always being morphologically dissimilar. The gametophyte, arising from the spore, is the haploid generation, producing sperms and eggs. The sporophyte, arising from the zygote, is the diploid generation. It produces spores, the reduction in chromosome number taking place in connection with their formation, as in all the higher plants. Swimming spores are entirely eliminated. In the green algae the zygote is liberated into the water and is nearly always a resting cell, while in the bryophytes and all higher groups it germinates at once, without escaping, to produce an embryo sporophyte.

In the bryophytes the gametophyte, or haploid generation, is always an independent individual, while the sporophyte, or diploid generation, is entirely or largely dependent on it for its nutrition. Although the gametophyte is thalloid in some of the liverworts, in most bryophytes it is differentiated into stem and leaves. Growth takes place through the activity of an apical cell. The sex organs, antheridia and archegonia, are always multicellular and provided with an outer sterile jacket. Throughout the algae the gametangia are prevailingly unicellular but, where multicellular, all their cells produce gametes (except in the Charophyceae). The antheridium is a stalked, spherical or club-shaped organ consisting of a mass of spermatogenous tissue enclosed by a jacket of

160

sterile cells. It gives rise to numerous small biciliate sperms, two of which arise from each sperm mother cell. The presence of swimming sperms, universal among bryophytes and pteridophytes, represents the retention of a primitive algal character.

The archegonium is a very characteristic organ of bryophytes and pteridophytes. Although corresponding to the oögonium of the algae, it is much more highly developed. The archegonium is usually stalked and flask-shaped. It is composed of an axial row of cells surrounded by a sterile jacket. The axial row consists of an egg—the basal and largest cell of the series—and a variable number of canal cells, which disorganize and become mucilaginous prior to fertilization. The fertilized egg gives rise to an embryo that develops within the archegonium, the basal portion of which enlarges to form a protective covering, the *calyptra*.

In all bryophytes the sporophyte is without differentiation into stem and leaves and is without a direct connection with the soil. In nearly all bryophytes the sporophyte consists of a basal absorbing organ (*foot*), a stalk (*seta*), and a terminal spore-producing portion (*capsule*). The capsule is a sporangium. All bryophytes are *homosporous*, the spores of a given species being alike in size and form. On germination, the spore produces either the main gametophyte directly or, more commonly, a filamentous *protonema* from which the main gametophyte sooner or later arises.

1. HEPATICAE

The liverworts are primitive land plants, most of them growing in the presence of abundant moisture on soil, rocks, and tree trunks. With very few exceptions, the gametophyte is dorsiventral. It may be thalloid, but more commonly is leafy, the leaves being nearly always without a midrib. Unicellular unbranched rhizoids maintain a connection with the substratum. The Hepaticae are widely distributed but are more numerous in the tropics than elsewhere. A few fossil forms are known from the Upper Carboniferous of England. There are about 6,000 species of liverworts, nearly all being included in four principal orders, the Marchantiales, Sphaerocarpales, Jungermanniales, and Anthocerotales.

1. Marchantiales

The Marchantiales are a well-defined order of about 30 genera and 400 species. They range from arctic to tropical regions and are well represented in the Temperate Zones. In the tropics they occur chiefly between altitudes of 900 and 1,500 m. Nearly all of them are terrestrial, growing mainly on damp soil or rocks. Some common genera of Marchantiales, all of widespread distribution, are *Riccia*, *Reboulia*, *Asterella*, *Conocephalum*, and *Marchantia*. The largest genus is *Riccia*, with over 100 species.

Gametophyte. The Marchantiales are characterized by a flat, dorsi-ventral, thalloid gametophyte—with few exceptions ribbon-like and nearly always rather fleshy.   It branches either dichotomously from the apex or, less commonly, by means of adventitious outgrowths arising apically or ventrally.   In *Riccia* the thallus is small and, as a result of repeated dichotomy, often grows in the form of a fan or rosette (Fig. 128).   In all the Marchantiales growth takes place by means of an apical cell situated in an apical notch.   It is of the *cuneate* (wedge-shaped) type,

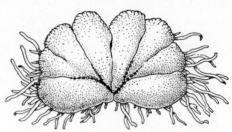

Fig. 128.   Dorsal view of the gametophyte of *Riccia natans*, showing sporophytes in the grooves and scales arising from the ventral surface, ×3.

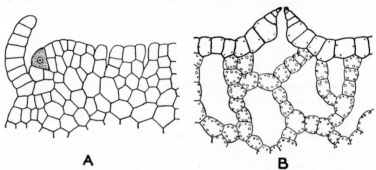

A   **B**

Fig. 129.   *Reboulia hemisphaerica. A*, longitudinal section of portion of growing region of thallus with apical cell and developing air chambers, ×160; *B*, portion of upper region of thallus, showing air pore and air chambers, ×85.

cutting off segments on four sides—above and below as well as left and right (Fig. 129*A*).

The gametophyte is of simple external form but exhibits a high degree of internal differentiation, nearly always consisting of (1) an upper epidermal layer; (2) a loose, green, dorsal region having one or more layers of air chambers; (3) a compact, colorless, ventral region.   The epidermis, usually colorless or pale green and often with slightly thickened walls, nearly always contains numerous air pores that communicate with the air chambers.   Air pores and air chambers are not developed in a few genera (*e.g., Dumortiera* and *Monoclea*), their absence being a result of reduction.

In most species of *Riccia* the dorsal region is composed of erect rows of cells separated by very narrow, vertical air chambers, but in some species it is spongy, consisting of a loose network of large irregular air chambers separated by one-layered partitions that extend in all directions (Fig. 137*A*). The uppermost cells form a rather ill-defined epidermis. In *Riccia natans* simple air pores are present, but in the other species air pores are either rudimentary or wanting. Simple air pores consist of a single tier of cells surrounding a small central opening, the cells being in

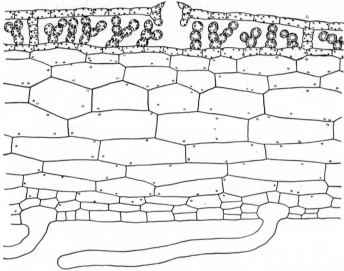

Fig. 130. Section through the thallus of *Marchantia polymorpha*, showing epidermis with an air pore that leads to an air chamber with green filaments, ×200. Rhizoids are shown below.

several concentric circles (only one circle in *Riccia natans*). Simple air pores occur on the thallus of most of the genera of Marchantiales (Fig. 129*B*). In *Marchantia* and a few related forms, however, the thallus bears compound air pores. These are barrel-shaped, consisting of four or five superimposed layers of cells and having both an upper and a lower opening (Fig. 130). *Conocephalum*, *Marchantia*, and many other genera have a single layer of air chambers from the floor of which special chlorophyllose filaments arise. *Reboulia* and *Asterella* have several layers of air chambers without green filaments (Fig. 129*B*). In many forms the limits of the air chambers are plainly visible on the dorsal surface of the thallus as polygonal areas, an air pore occurring in the center of each.

In practically all the Marchantiales the lower surface of the thallus bears numerous rhizoids and scales. The rhizoids are of two kinds, smooth and tuberculate. The former have smooth walls, the latter peg-like thickenings that project into the lumen. In *Riccia* rhizoids are usually abundant, but frequently ventral scales are rudimentary or absent.[1] In nearly all the Marchantiales the ventral scales are arranged in two longitudinal rows; in *Marchantia* they are in four or more rows.

Throughout the order decay of the older parts of the thallus results in the isolation of branches, each of which forms a new plant. In some species vegetative propagation occurs by the formation of adventitious branches that become detached. In two genera, *Lunularia* and *Marchantia*, multicellular *gemmae* are produced. These are flat, stalked, discoid bodies that arise in groups on the dorsal side of the thallus inside *cupules*.

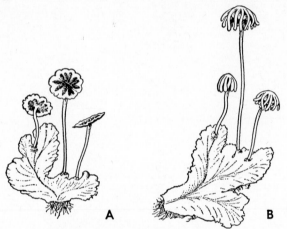

Fig. 131. Male (*A*) and female (*B*) plants of *Marchantia polymorpha*, natural size.

In *Lunularia* the cupules are crescentic, while in *Marchantia* they are cup-shaped. The gemmae arise from the floor of the cupule. Each gemma has two notches, one on either side, and in each notch is an apical cell. Upon separation from the cupule, a single gemma gives rise to two new thalli.

Sex Organs. The sex organs of the Marchantiales are invariably dorsal in origin, arising either directly on the thallus itself or on a more or less specialized receptacle. Both kinds of sex organs arise in acropetal succession from segments of an apical cell. According to the species, the antheridia and archegonia occur on the same plant or on separate plants. In *Riccia* each branch of the thallus has a median dorsal groove extending backward from the growing apex; in this groove the sex organs are borne. Although generally scattered irregularly, they sometimes tend to be segregated into separate groups. The sex organs arise singly just behind

---

[1] When *Riccia natans* floats on the surface of quiet water, it has numerous large scales and few or no rhizoids. When it grows on muddy banks and flats, it has many rhizoids and few scales.

the apical cell and soon become sunken in the thallus by upgrowth of the surrounding tissues, each coming to lie in an individual pit.

In the other Marchantiales the antheridia are similarly sunken in pits but the archegonia are not. The antheridia may be borne in irregular median groups on the dorsal side of the thallus, as in some species of *Asterella*, but more commonly they occur on a definite receptacle. This may be cushion-like and sessile, as in *Reboulia* and *Conocephalum*, or raised above the thallus on a stalk, as in *Marchantia*. The antheridial receptacle of *Marchantia* has a number of marginal growing points, from each

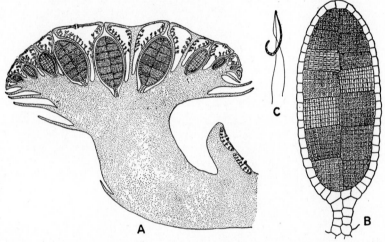

Fig. 132. Male structures of *Marchantia polymorpha*. *A*, longitudinal section through young male receptacle, showing embedded antheridia, ×40; *B*, nearly mature antheridium, ×200; *C*, a single sperm, more highly magnified.

of which an acropetal series of antheridia extends toward the center, the antheridia being sunken in the upper surface of the receptacle (Figs. 131*A* and 132*A*).

In *Reboulia, Asterella, Conocephalum*, and many other genera the archegonia are borne on a stalked receptacle that, with few exceptions, is terminal in position and represents a specialized upright branch of the thallus. Unlike the antheridia, the archegonia are not embedded in pits. The female receptacle is commonly hemispherical or conical and more or less lobed. Each lobe represents a separate growing point back of which either one or several archegonia arise. As the receptacle grows, the archegonia are carried to a position on its lower side close to the stalk. In *Marchantia* the archegonial receptacle reaches its greatest degree of specialization. It does not have lobes, but consists of a number of rays alternating with groups of archegonia (Figs. 131*B* and 133*A*). The archegonia hang with the necks downward.

Air chambers and air pores are developed on both the male and female receptacles. In *Reboulia* and *Asterella* the air pores on the female receptacle are compound, while those occurring elsewhere on the plant are simple. In *Conocephalum* the air pores are compound on both the male

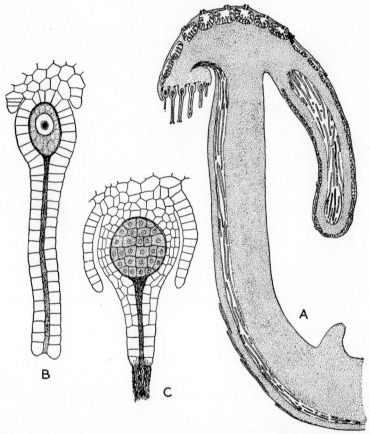

FIG. 133. Female structures of *Marchantia polymorpha*. *A*, longitudinal section through young female receptacle, showing a row of archegonia, ×40; *B*, mature archegonium with egg ready for fertilization, ×300; *C*, young embryo lying within the archegonium, ×300.

and female receptacles, but are simple on the thallus. In *Marchantia* the air pores are everywhere compound.

The mature antheridia of the Marchantiales are club-shaped structures with a short stalk (Fig. 132*B*). The chamber in which each lies communicates with the surface of the thallus or receptacle by a pore through which the sperms escape. The antheridium arises from a single superficial initial cell that becomes papillate and then divides transversely (Fig. 134*A*). The outer segment undergoes several additional transverse divisions, resulting in the formation of about four superimposed cells (Fig. 134*B–D*). In each of these vertical walls appear at right angles to each other and later, by the formation of periclinal walls in the upper part of the antheridium, an outer layer of sterile cells is cut off from a central group of spermatogenous cells (Fig. 134*E–H*). The lower portion of

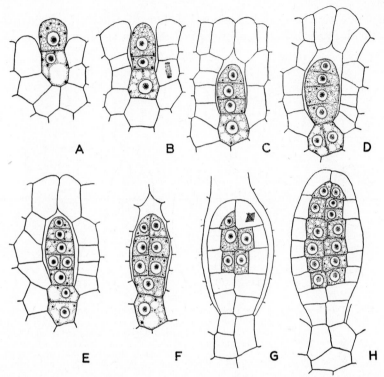

FIG. 134. Early stages in the development of the antheridium of *Marchantia polymorpha*, ×750. *A*, division of initial into an inner and outer cell; *B*, *C*, *D*, formation of a filament of four cells from the outer cell; *E* and *F*, appearance of vertical walls; *G*, appearance of periclinal walls; *H*, later stage, showing sterile jacket surrounding spermatogenous cells, with stalk below.

the antheridium forms the stalk. By continued division, the spermatogenous cells give rise to many small, cubical, sperm mother cells, each of which produces two biciliate sperms (Fig. 132*B*, *C*).

The archegonium also arises from a single superficial initial that becomes papillate and divides transversely (Fig. 135*A*). Three vertical walls now appear in the outer segment, these being arranged in such a way that a middle cell and three peripheral cells are formed (Fig. 135*B*, *H*). The middle cell is the *primary axial cell*, the peripheral ones the *primary wall cells*. The primary axial cell, by a transverse division, gives rise to a *cover cell* and a *central cell* (Fig. 135*C*). The archegonium now grows in length, the central cell dividing to form a *primary neck canal cell* and a *primary ventral cell* (Fig. 135*D*). As a result of additional transverse divisions, the primary neck canal cell gives rise to a vertical row of neck canal cells, most commonly either four or eight in number, while the primary ventral cell divides transversely to form the *ventral canal cell* and *egg* (Fig. 135*E–G*).

By this time the archegonium has become distinctly flask-shaped, the slender *neck* being sharply marked off from the bulbous *venter*. In

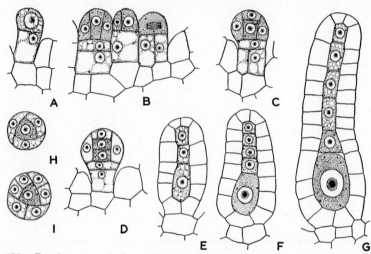

FIG. 135. Development of the archegonium of *Marchantia polymorpha*, ×600. *A*, division of initial into an inner and outer cell; *B*, appearance of three vertical walls in the outer cell; *C*, formation of cover cell and central cell from the primary axial cell; *D*, formation of primary neck canal cell and primary ventral cell from the central cell; *E* and *F*, later stages, with two and four neck canal cells; *G*, nearly mature archegonium, with egg and ventral canal cell derived from the primary ventral cell; *H*, cross section of very young archegonium, showing primary axial cell surrounded by primary wall cells; *I*, later stage, showing six neck cells surrounding a neck canal cell.

all the Marchantiales the neck consists of six vertical rows of jacket cells surrounding the canal (Fig. 135*I*). The canal cells disorganize, forming a mass of mucilage through which the sperms can swim (Fig. 133*B*). The egg is fertilized within the venter of the archegonium, which enlarges to form the *calyptra*, the embryo developing within (Fig. 133*C*). In all the Marchantiales except *Riccia*, an *involucre* arises around the archegonia. In *Asterella*, *Marchantia*, and several other genera an additional envelope, the *pseudoperianth*, arises after fertilization and generally becomes very conspicuous (Fig. 139).

Sporophyte. *Riccia* displays the simplest sporophyte among the Bryophyta. In its development, the fertilized egg divides by a transverse wall, resulting in two cells approximately equal in size (Fig. 136).

Each of these now divides by a vertical wall, followed by another at right angles to it. Additional divisions, without definite sequence, take place in all three planes. Then periclinal walls cut off an outer layer, the *amphithecium*, from a central group of cells, the *endothecium*. As the embryo continues to grow, the entire central group becomes sporogenous, while the outer layer remains sterile. After the sporogenous cells have divided for the last time, they separate and round off to become *spore mother cells* (Fig. 137). Each of these then enlarges and undergoes two

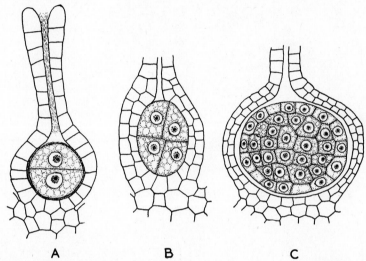

A   B   C

FIG. 136. Development of the embryo of *Riccia natans*, ×400. *A*, two-celled stage; *B*, four-celled stage; *C*, later stage, showing differentiation into amphithecium and endothecium.

consecutive divisions during which the number of chromosomes is reduced one-half, and a *tetrad* of cells is formed. The walls thicken and the four members of the tetrad separate as mature spores. During the early development of the sporophyte, the venter of the archegonium becomes two-layered and forms the calyptra (Fig. 136). The sterile jacket of the sporophyte and the inner layer of the calyptra break down before the spores have ripened, leaving them enclosed within the outer layer of the calyptra. *Riccia* has no spore-dispersing mechanism, the spores being liberated by progressive decay of the thallus.

In practically all the other Marchantiales the sporophyte consists of a *foot*, *seta*, and a *capsule* containing both spores and elaters. As in *Riccia*, the first division of the fertilized egg is transverse. In some genera, such as *Reboulia*, *Asterella*, *Conocephalum*, and others, the next two divisions are also transverse, resulting in a filament of four superimposed cells (Fig. 138). Then vertical walls come in and, with the formation of

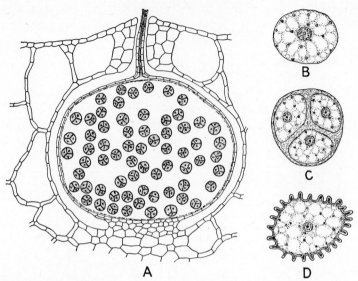

FIG. 137. Sporophyte of *Riccia natans*. *A*, longitudinal section of nearly mature sporophyte embedded in the gametophyte, showing spore tetrads enclosed within the calyptra;
B, spore mother cell; *C*, tetrad; *D*, mature spore; *A*, ×100; *B, C, D,* ×500.

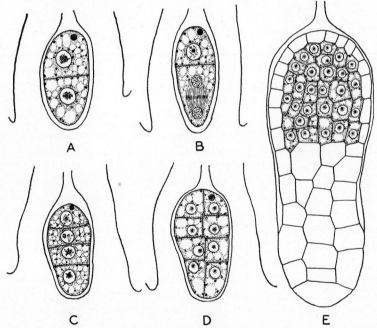

FIG. 138. Development of the embryo of *Cryptomitrium tenerum*, ×400. *A*, two-celled
stage; *B*, division of lower cell; *C*, four-celled stage, the two lower cells giving rise to the
foot and seta, the two upper cells to the capsule; *D*, eight-celled stage; *E*, older stage,
showing differentiation of sporogenous tissue in the capsule. (*After Haupt.*)

additional walls in the upper part of the embryo, the foot, seta, and capsule are differentiated. In other genera, such as *Marchantia*, the first
division of the fertilized egg is followed by the appearance of two vertical
walls at right angles to each other in both the upper and lower segments,
thus forming octants, as in *Riccia*. Additional walls in all three planes
produce a globular embryo rather than an elongated one (Fig. 139).

An early formation of periclinal walls in the capsular region cuts off the
amphithecium from the endothecium, the former forming the capsule

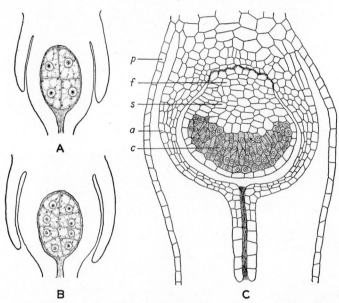

Fig. 139. Development of the embryo of *Marchantia polymorpha*. *A*, four-celled stage,
×320; *B*, slightly later stage, ×320; *C*, older embryo, showing the foot (*f*), seta (*s*), capsule
(*c*) with sporogenous tissue differentiated, pseudoperianth (*p*), and calyptra (*a*), ×200.

wall and the latter the sporogenous tissue (Fig. 138*E*). In *Riccia* the
sporogenous tissue is derived equally from both halves of the embryo. In
practically all the other genera, whether the embryo is of the filamentous
or of the octant type, apparently only the upper half contributes to the
sporogenous tissue, the lower half giving rise to the foot and seta. The
foot anchors the sporophyte and absorbs nourishment. The seta elongates, especially after the spores ripen, pushing the capsule through the
calyptra.

In most genera, except *Riccia*, some of the potentially sporogenous cells
of the young capsule give rise to *elaters*, while the others directly become
spore mother cells. In *Marchantia*, however, the sporogenous cells
greatly elongate, some remaining undivided to form elaters, the others
dividing transversely a number of times to form vertical rows of spore

mother cells (Fig. 140). As in *Riccia*, tetrads are formed and the walls of the spores thicken. The elaters are long, slender cells, pointed at each end, their walls developing spiral thickenings as the protoplasm disappears (Fig. 140*D*). Elaters are hygroscopic and perform squirming movements that assist in the liberation of the spores. The capsule wall is one layer of cells thick except in the apical region. In *Reboulia*,

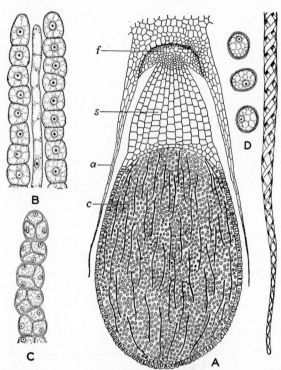

Fig. 140. Sporophyte of *Marchantia polymorpha*. *A*, longitudinal section of nearly mature sporophyte, showing the foot (*f*), seta (*s*), capsule (*c*), and ruptured calyptra (*a*); *B*, two rows of spore mother cells and portion of an undeveloped elater; *C*, a row of spore tetrads; *D*, three mature spores and the end of an elater; *A*, ×60; *B*, *C*, *D*, ×600.

Asterella, and related forms local thickenings are not formed on the cells of the capsule wall and dehiscence takes place by means of an apical lid. In nearly all the other genera, however, the cells of the capsule wall bear annular thickenings, dehiscence occurring by irregular clefts.

Summary. The Marchantiales are a group in which the gametophyte, while remaining simple in form, has achieved a high degree of structural complexity. In all members of the order the gametophyte is thalloid and grows by means of a cuneate apical cell. It is nearly always differentiated into an upper epidermis with air pores, a dorsal photosynthetic region with air chambers, and a compact, colorless ventral region. The gameto-phyte reaches an extreme of complexity in forms with compound air pores and air chambers having green filaments. It bears both smooth and tuberculate rhizoids. In the lower members the sex organs are borne directly on the thallus, sunken in the dorsal surface, but throughout the group there is a marked tendency to restrict and specialize the regions producing sex organs, resulting in the development of complex receptacles. The female receptacles, and sometimes the male as well, are stalked. The antheridia, when mature, are elongated organs lying in a deep chamber. Their early development is characterized by a series of trans-verse divisions. The neck of the archegonium shows six cells in cross section.

In the lower members the sporophyte is a spherical, undifferentiated spore case, all the inner cells forming spores. In the higher members the sporophyte is elongated and differentiated into a foot, seta, and capsule. The capsule contains both spores and sterile cells, the latter practically always developed as elaters. Thus, throughout the group, there is a marked tendency to divert potentially sporogenous tissue to functions other than spore production. The seta is comparatively short. The cap-sule is spherical or nearly so, its wall being composed of a single layer of cells (the apex usually thicker). Dehiscence, lacking in *Riccia*, nearly always occurs by irregular clefts or an apical lid. The Marchantiales are a group in which a complex gametophyte is combined with a relatively simple sporophyte.

2. Sphaerocarpales

The Sphaerocarpales comprise a small order of 3 genera and 25 species. *Sphaerocarpus* is a widely distributed genus but *Geothallus*, represented by a single species, has been found only near San Diego, California. Both of these forms grow on moist earth. *Riella* is an aquatic form occurring in Europe, Africa, California, and western Texas.

Gametophyte. The gametophyte of the Sphaerocarpales displays none of the internal differentiation seen in the Marchantiales. It consists of a simple plate-like thallus that differs somewhat among the three genera. In *Sphaerocarpus* the thallus is small, flat, and often orbicular, with an entire or more or less lobed margin. It has a broad indistinct midrib, several layers of cells in thickness, that merges gradually into the one-layered wings (Fig. 141). In *Geothallus* the thallus is larger and consists of an elongated thickened axis giving rise to crowded leaf-like outgrowths on either side, these mostly one layer of cells thick. A large portion of the axis becomes converted into a fleshy tuber that lives over into the next growing season. In both *Sphaerocarpus* and *Geothallus* the thallus may be either simple or dichotomously branched. The lower surface lacks scales but bears numerous colorless rhizoids of the smooth-walled type. Growth of the thallus results from the activity of a cuneate apical cell.

In general appearance *Riella* is unlike any other liverwort. It is a submerged aquatic, usually growing erect in standing water. It has a stem-like axis that bears a dorsal leaf-like wing or, in the Algerian *Riella bialata*, two wings. The wing is mostly one layer of cells thick. It is frequently undulate and sometimes spirally twisted. The axis is commonly several times dichotomous. It produces rhizoids near the base.

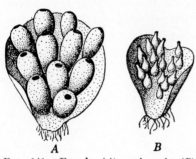

Sex Organs. The antheridia and archegonia are borne directly on the thallus, each enclosed in a special involucre that is open above. They arise in acropetal succession from dorsal segments of the apical cell. In *Riella* both kinds of sex organs may occur on the same plant, although generally, as in *Sphaerocarpus* and *Geothallus*, they are borne on separate plants.

FIG. 141. Female (*A*) and male (*B*) gametophytes of *Sphaerocarpus californicus*, ×6. (*From Gilbert M. Smith.*)

In *Sphaerocarpus* the sex organs are closely crowded on the dorsal surface of the thallus. The male plants, often purplish, are minute and much smaller than the female plants (Fig. 141). The antheridial involucres are flask-shaped and each contains an ovoid short-stalked antheridium. In development, two transverse walls appear in the outer cell arising from a transverse division of the papillate initial (Fig. 142*A*, *B*). In the upper two segments vertical walls are formed at right angles to each other and then periclinal walls cut off a layer of outer sterile cells from a central group of spermatogenous cells (Fig. 142*C–E*). Further development takes place as in the Marchantiales. The archegonial involucres, each enclosing an archegonium, are tubular or nearly spherical. The archegonium develops as in the Marchantiales (Fig. 143). It has two to four neck canal cells, its neck showing six cells in cross section. Following fertilization, the calyptra becomes two-layered. It is soon ruptured by the sporophyte.

In *Geothallus* the sex organs are borne and develop as in *Sphaerocarpus*, but are much less numerous and the male plants are only slightly smaller than the female. In *Riella* the antheridia occur in a series along the margin of the wing, each enclosed in a pocket. The archegonia are arranged serially on the axis, each surrounded by a flask-shaped involucre.

Sporophyte. The sporophyte of the Sphaerocarpales is more advanced than that of *Riccia* but simpler than that of nearly all the other Marchantiales. It has a foot, capsule, and very short seta (Fig. 144*A*). In

Sphaerocarpus the first division of the fertilized egg is transverse, the capsule arising from the outer segment and the foot and seta from the inner segment, as in the Marchantiales. Each segment again divides transversely at least once before vertical walls come in. The foot becomes bulbous and the capsule spherical. In all genera some of the sporogenous cells develop into spore mother cells and others into small

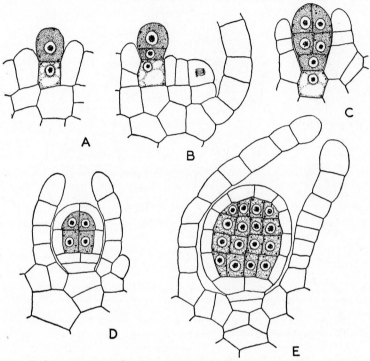

Fig. 142.   Early stages in the development of the antheridium of *Sphaerocarpus texanus*, ×500.   *A*, division of initial into inner and outer cell; *B*, first division of outer cell; *C*, formation of vertical walls; *D*, formation of periclinal walls; *E*, later stage, showing sterile jacket surrounding spermatogenous cells, with stalk below.

sterile cells that do not become elaters (Fig. 144*B*).   Instead, they function as nutritive cells, being finally absorbed by the spores.   As in the Marchantiales, the spore mother cells are not lobed.   The capsule has no regular dehiscence.   Its wall consists of a single layer of cells without local thickenings.

Sex Determination.   The mechanism of sex determination in *Sphaerocarpus* is of particular interest because here the occurrence of sex chromosomes in plants was first observed.   In addition to seven ordinary chromosomes, the cells of the female gametophyte have a very large X chromosome, while those of the male gametophyte have a very small

Y chromosome. Consequently all the eggs carry an X chromosome, all the sperms a Y chromosome, and the zygote is always XY. This develops into a sporophyte with eight pairs of chromosomes, seven ordinary pairs and the XY pair. When meiosis occurs at sporogenesis, two of the spores in each tetrad have an X chromosome and two have a Y chromosome. The spores with an X chromosome always develop into female gametophytes and those with a Y chromosome into male plants.

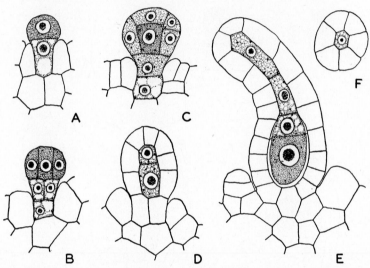

Fig. 143.   Development of the archegonium of *Sphaerocarpus texanus*, ×500.   *A*, division of initial into inner and outer cell; *B*, appearance of three vertical walls in the outer cell; *C*, formation of cover cell and central cell; *D*, formation of primary neck canal cell and primary ventral cell; *E*, nearly mature archegonium with egg, ventral canal cell, and two neck canal cells; *F*, cross section of neck.

Summary. The Sphaerocarpales are an aberrant group of liverworts showing a distinct relationship to the Marchantiales on the one hand and to the Jungermanniales on the other. They resemble the Jungermanniales in the form and structure of the gametophyte, but are like the Marchantiales in the structure and development of the sex organs and in the structure of the sporophyte. As in the Marchantiales, the apical cell is cuneate, the neck of the archegonium has six cells in cross section, and the spore mother cells are not four-lobed. The development of the antheridium shows a closer resemblance to the Marchantiales than to the Jungermanniales. The sporophyte consists essentially of a foot and capsule, the latter indehiscent and with a wall composed of a single layer of cells. In addition to the spores, the capsule contains sterile nutritive cells but no elaters. The most distinctive feature of the Sphaerocarpales is the presence of a special involucre around each antheridium and each archegonium. On the whole, they are a primitive group, with a simple gametophyte and a sporophyte only slightly more advanced than that of *Riccia*.

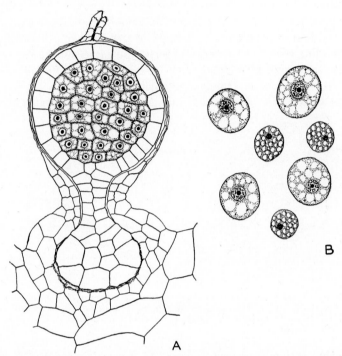

Fig. 144. Sporophyte of *Sphaerocarpus texanus*, ×250. *A*, early stage, showing foot, seta, and capsule with sporogenous tissue; *B*, spore mother cells and smaller, starch-filled nutritive cells.

3. Jungermanniales

The Jungermanniales are by far the largest order of Hepaticae, embracing 150 genera and approximately 5,500 species. They are most abundant in tropical regions, where they grow on the ground, on decaying logs, and as epiphytes on the stems and leaves of trees. They require abundant moisture and good drainage. Although much less numerous than in the tropics, the group is well represented in temperate regions also. The Jungermanniales comprise two great series, the Anacrogynae and the Acrogynae. These will be considered separately.

1. ANACROGYNAE

In the "anacrogynous" Jungermanniales all the archegonia originate behind the apical cell, none ever arising from the apical cell itself (Fig. 145*A*). Thus the archegonia and sporophytes are always dorsal. Most of the Anacrogynae are thallose, but some are leafy. They include 20 genera and about 500 species. The principal genera, all widely distributed, are *Riccardia, Metzgeria, Pallavicinia, Symphyogyna, Pellia*, and *Fossombronia*. The largest genus, *Riccardia*, has over 100 species.

Gametophyte. The Anacrogynae have a dorsiventral gametophyte that is thalloid in most forms but more or less leafy in others (Fig. 146). While tending toward a diversity of form, the gametophyte has remained structurally simple, displaying little or no internal differentiation. In fact, it is composed of compact, almost uniform tissue. The gametophyte is sometimes unbranched, but generally branches dichotomously

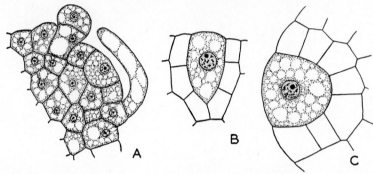

Fig. 145. *Fossombronia cristula.* *A*, longitudinal section through apical region of thallus, showing the apical cell, a young archegonium, and a mucilage hair, ×500; *B*, horizontal longitudinal section of apical cell, ×600; *C*, vertical longitudinal section of apical cell, ×600. (*After Haupt.*)

or, in some forms, by means of ventral adventitious shoots. Growth takes place through the activity of an apical cell that is prevailingly *dolabrate* (hatchet-shaped), cutting off segments on two sides, alternately left and right (Fig. 145). Rhizoids, usually formed in abundance, are all of the smooth-walled type. Ventral scales are rarely present.

The gametophyte of *Pellia* is one of the simplest in the Bryophyta. It consists of a thin, flat thallus, wavy along the margin, and with a broad indistinct midrib gradually passing into lateral wings composed of a single layer of cells (Fig. 146*A*). Some of the species of *Riccardia* have a similar thallus, while others have one like that of *Metzgeria*, with a narrow distinct midrib sharply marked off from the wings. A distinct midrib is also present in *Pallavicinia* and *Symphyogyna*, but in both of these genera some species have an entire or wavy margin, others a margin that is deeply lobed (Fig. 146*B*, *C*). *Fossombronia* represents an advanced condition, the wings of the thallus being dissected into two lateral rows of leaf-like segments, the midrib forming a stem. This series leads directly into the Acrogynae, where differentiation of the plant body into a leafy axis reaches its highest expression.

Vegetative propagation in the Anacrogynae occurs by death of the older parts of the thallus, resulting in the isolation of branches. Also, gemmae are produced in certain genera, such as *Riccardia* and *Metzgeria*, while others produce tubers that live over from one growing season to the next.

Sex Organs. The antheridia and archegonia are borne either on the same gametophyte or on separate gametophytes, according to the species. They are always dorsal in position, generally occurring singly or in groups

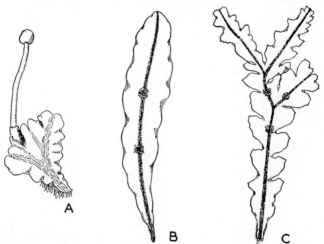

Fig. 146. Thallus of *Pellia epiphylla* (*A*) with a mature sporophyte, of *Pallavicinia lyellii* (*B*) with two groups of archegonia, and of *Symphyogyna brongniartii* (*C*) with three groups of archegonia, twice natural size.

on the main thallus or, less frequently, on special short branches that in *Riccardia* are lateral and in *Metzgeria* are ventral in origin. The sex organs, unlike those of the Marchantiales, are never borne on stalked receptacles. The archegonia are usually protected by an involucre. The antheridia are protected in various ways: in *Metzgeria*, by incurving of the thallus; in *Riccardia* and *Pellia*, by upgrowth of adjacent tissues; in *Pallavicinia* and *Symphyogyna*, by a special involucre.

In the Jungermanniales the development of the antheridium is characteristic, differing considerably from that seen in the Marchantiales and Sphaerocarpales. The antheridium arises as a papillate initial that undergoes a transverse division (Fig. 147*A*). Another transverse wall usually appears in the outer cell, but the third wall is a median vertical one (Fig. 147*B*, *C*). In each of the two terminal segments thus formed a periclinal division takes place. Two additional periclinal walls then come in at right angles to the first ones, intersecting both these and the median wall. As a result, four primary wall cells are cut off from two central spermatogenous cells (Fig. 147D, E). Further development of the antheridium corresponds to that of the Marchantiales. The mature antheridium is generally spherical and either long-stalked or short-stalked.

In all the Anacrogynae, as previously stated, the formation of archegonia never involves the apical cell, all of them arising from its segments (Fig. 145A). The development of the archegonium is essentially like

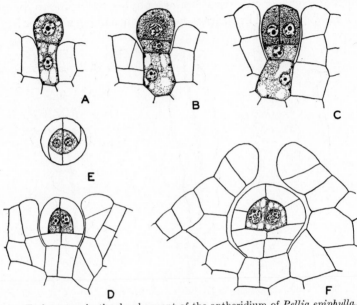

FIG. 147.   Early stages in the development of the antheridium of *Pellia epiphylla*, ×400. *A*, division of initial into an inner and outer cell; *B*, division of outer cell into a stalk cell and primary antheridial cell; *C*, vertical division of antheridial cell; *D*, appearance of periclinal walls; *E*, cross section of same; *F*, later stage, showing two primary spermatogenous cells surrounded by sterile jacket, with stalk below.

that of the Marchantiales and Sphaerocarpales, but the venter is usually more slender and the neck shows but five cells in cross section (Fig. 148). The number of neck canal cells is variable, but is commonly 6 or 8.   In such forms as *Pallavicinia* and *Pellia*, however, this number may reach 18. The calyptra, developed from the venter of the archegonium, may become massive, as in *Riccardia*, *Metzgeria*, and *Symphyogyna*.   In addition to the involucre, a pseudoperianth is formed in *Pallavicinia*, becoming conspicuous after fertilization.

Sporophyte.   The sporophyte of the Jungermanniales is more advanced than that of the Marchantiales and Sphaerocarpales in that a greater amount of sterile tissue is formed.   Following the first division of the fertilized egg, which is transverse, the lower cell often does not contribute to the embryo proper, but forms an appendage to it.   This may become haustorial, as in *Riccardia*.   The upper cell undergoes several transverse divisions before vertical walls appear, so that the embryo becomes elongated (Fig. 149*A–C*). A foot, seta, and capsule, always present, are differentiated early. The formation of periclinal walls in the upper part of the embryo delimits the amphithecium from the endothecium, the

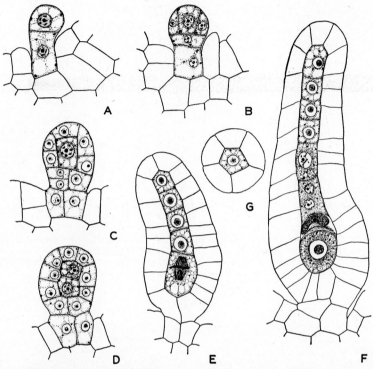

Fig. 148. Development of the archegonium of *Pellia epiphylla*, ✕400. *A*, division of initial; *B*, appearance of vertical walls in outer cell; *C*, formation of cover cell and central cell; *D*, formation of primary neck canal cell and primary ventral cell; *E*, formation of four neck canal cells and division of primary ventral cell; *F*, nearly mature archegonium with egg, ventral canal cell, and six neck canal cells; *G*, cross section of neck.

former giving rise to the capsule wall, the latter to the sporogenous tissue (Fig. 149*D*).

The seta undergoes considerable elongation, especially upon the ripening of the spores. The capsule is highly developed, producing both spores and elaters. It may be spherical, as in *Pellia*, or more or less elongated, as in *Pallavicinia*. In some genera an elaterophore is developed inside the capsule. It may be either apical, as in *Riccardia* and *Metzgeria*, or basal, as in *Pellia* (Fig. 150). The elaterophore consists of a group of sterile cells to which some of the elaters are attached. The fixed elaters generally are shorter than the free elaters and often have a greater number of spiral bands. The spore mother cells, unlike those of the Marchan-

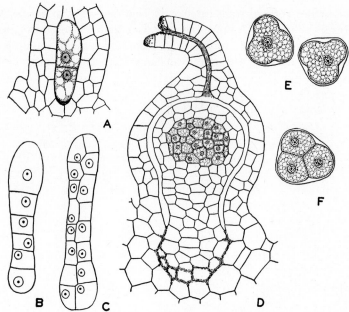

FIG. 149. Development of the embryo of *Fossombronia cristula*. *A*, two-celled embryo within calyptra, ×350; *B* and *C*, later stages, ×350; *D*, older embryo within calyptra, showing the foot, seta, and capsule with sporogenous tissue differentiated, ×250; *E*, two spore mother cells, ×500; *F*, a spore tetrad, ×500. (*After Haupt.*)

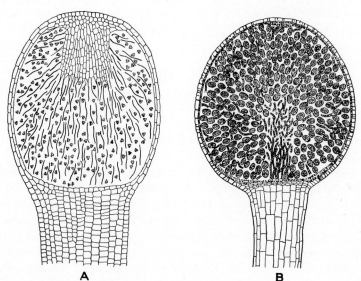

FIG. 150. Longitudinal section of the capsule of *Riccardia* (*A*), with apical elaterophore, and of *Pellia* (*B*), with basal elaterophore; *A*, ×40; *B*, ×28.

tiales and Sphaerocarpales, become four-lobed just previous to the formation of tetrads (Fig. 149*E*, *F*). The capsule wall is two or more layers of cells in thickness, or only one layer by resorption of the inner layer at maturity. Annular thickenings are generally present on one or both layers, but are constantly absent in a relatively few forms, such as *Pallavicinia* and *Symphyogyna*. Dehiscence of the capsule is nearly always effected by splitting into four valves.

2. Acrogynae

In the "acrogynous" Jungermanniales archegonia may arise from segments of the apical cell, but sooner or later the apical cell itself becomes an archegonium. The terminal position of the archegonia and sporophytes is in marked contrast to their dorsal position in the Anacrogynae. Practically all members of the group are leafy. The Acrogynae are a well-defined assemblage, comprising 130 genera and about 5,000 species. Notwithstanding its size, the group is fairly uniform in regard to general morphological features. Some of the largest genera are *Nardia*, *Plagiochila*, *Lophocolea*, *Radula*, *Porella*, *Frullania*, *Cephalozia*, *Scapania*, and *Lejeunia*.

Gametophyte. The gametophyte of the Acrogynae is a dorsiventral, branching, leafy axis. Only a few genera are thalloid and even these produce leafy fertile shoots. *Herberta* and a few other genera have an erect stem bearing three rows of similar, radially arranged leaves. The other Acrogynae have a prostrate stem bearing two rows of dorsal leaves and generally a row of ventral leaves (Fig. 151*A*, *B*). The ventral leaves, which are reduced, are known as *amphigastria*. In a number of genera amphigastria are not present. The dorsal leaves overlap and are generally bilobed, the lobes being unequal in size or, in a few cases (*e.g.*, *Lophocolea*), equal. The leaves nearly always consist of a single plate of cells and, with rare exceptions, are without a midrib. The stems are composed of essentially uniform tissue. Rhizoids are usually abundant on the lower side of the stem. They are chiefly anchoring in function, as much water absorption takes place directly through the leaves.

In practically all the Acrogynae the gametophyte grows by means of a *tetrahedral* apical cell (Fig. 151*C*). This has the form of a triangular pyramid, cutting off segments on three sides. The two rows of dorsal segments give rise, in part, to the dorsal leaves and the single row of ventral segments, in part, to the amphigastria. Branching in the Acrogynae is varied but most commonly is *monopodial*, with a main axis and lateral branches. Vegetative propagation is well developed. Often branches break off and give rise to new plants. One-celled or two-celled gemmae are frequently borne on the margins or at the apices of leaves, while multicellular discoid gemmae are produced in some forms.

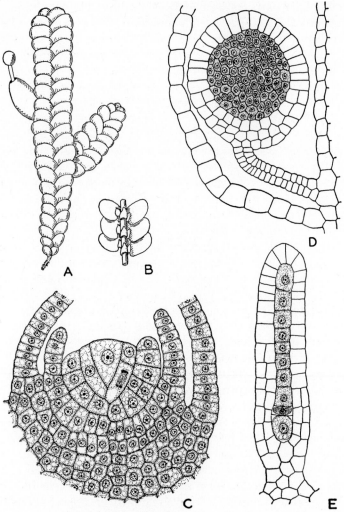

Fig. 151. *Porella bolanderi.* *A*, dorsal view of gametophyte with nearly mature sporophyte, ×30; *B*, ventral view of same, showing row of reduced ventral leaves and dorsal
leaves with small ventral lobes; *C*, horizontal longitudinal section of tip of gametophyte,
showing apical cell and developing leaves, ×400; *D*, longitudinal section of antheridium,
×250; *E*, longitudinal section of nearly mature archegonium, showing egg, ventral canal
cell, and eight neck canal cells, ×400.

Sex Organs.   The antheridia and archegonia may occur on the same
plant or on separate plants, depending on the species.   They are never
sunken in the tissues of the gametophyte.   The antheridia arise in the
leaf axils, very commonly in groups of two to four; but sometimes they
are solitary, as in *Porella,* or in groups of more than four.   Often the
antheridia are accompanied by paraphyses.   In *Lophozia, Nardia,* and

other simple forms the antheridia are borne on unmodified shoots, but in *Porella* and most members of the group they occur on special, short, lateral branches. The antheridia are globular and mostly long-stalked, developing as in the Anacrogynae except that the wall usually becomes several layers of cells in thickness (Fig. 151*D*).

The archegonia are generally borne on short lateral branches and are always terminal. They occur singly or in a small group. They are commonly intermixed with paraphyses, usually surrounded by a perianth and

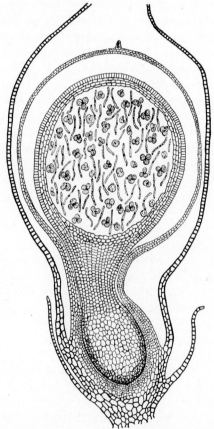

Fig. 152. Longitudinal section of sporophyte of *Porella*, showing capsule with spore mother cells and young elaters, ×40.

often also by an involucre lying outside the perianth. Both of these envelopes are formed of united leaves. The archegonia develop as in the Anacrogynae. In *Porella* six to eight neck canal cells are formed (Fig. 151*E*).

Sporophyte. The sporophyte of the acrogynous Jungermanniales is similar to that of the anacrogynous forms in that the seta is considerably elongated and relatively little of the embryonic tissue becomes sporogenous (Fig. 152). The embryogeny is known only in a few species. The lower cell arising from the first transverse division of the fertilized egg may become an appendage to the foot in some forms but not in others. Elaters are always present, but there is no elaterophore, except in *Gottschea*, which has a basal one. The spore mother cells are conspicuously four-lobed. The capsule wall is usually two layers thick, sometimes more, the inner layer generally having spiral thickenings. Dehiscence occurs by means of four valves, as in the Anacrogynae.

Summary. In contrast to the Marchantiales, the Jungermanniales have a gametophyte that, while remaining simple in structure, is more or less differentiated in form. In the lower members the gametophyte is a simple thallus, becoming in the higher members a leafy stem. The apical cell is dolabrate in most of the Anacrogynae, tetrahedral in the Acrogynae. In the Anacrogynae the sex organs are nearly always borne singly or in groups on the dorsal surface of the gametophyte, sometimes on special branches, but never on stalked receptacles. In the Acrogynae the antheridia are axillary, the archegonia terminal. The early development of the antheridium is characteristic, the formation of two transverse walls in the initial cell being followed by a median vertical wall in the terminal segment. The neck of the archegonium shows five cells in cross section.

The sporophyte always consists of a foot, seta, and capsule. There is much sterilization of potentially sporogenous tissue, the development of the seta being especially marked. The capsule, varying in form from spherical to cylindrical, produces both spores and elaters. It nearly always dehisces by means of four valves. The capsule wall consists of two or more layers of cells. The spore mother cells are deeply four-lobed. In the Jungermanniales a relatively simple gametophyte is combined with a complex sporophyte.

4. Anthocerotales

The Anthocerotales constitute an isolated order of 4 genera and over 100 species. They are so distinct that they are often set apart from the other liverworts as a distinct class of bryophytes. *Anthoceros*, with 60 species, and *Notothylas* are widely distributed in both temperate and tropical regions, while *Megaceros* and *Dendroceros* are chiefly confined to the tropics. *Dendroceros* is epiphytic on tree trunks, stems, and leaves, while the other members grow mainly on damp earth.

Gametophyte. The gametophyte of the Anthocerotales is a dorsiventral plate-like thallus often growing in an irregularly dichotomous manner (Fig. 153). It is frequently more or less lobed, but does not have any leaves. In *Dendroceros* the thallus is narrow, consisting of a thickened midrib and lateral wings composed of a single layer of cells. In the other genera the thallus is several layers of cells thick and without a mid-rib. There is no internal differentiation of tissues. The cells are peculiar in having, as a rule, a single large chloroplast with a conspicuous pyrenoid, a feature of most green algae but not of any other bryophyte. In some members of the group two or more chloroplasts are present.

The thallus grows by means of a cuneate (wedge-shaped) apical cell, as in the Marchantiales. There are no air chambers or air pores, but some species of *Anthoceros* and *Dendroceros* have intercellular mucilage cavities that open by clefts to the ventral surface, and in these cavities colonies of *Nostoc* may live. Smooth rhizoids are present, but there are no ventral scales. In some species of *Anthoceros* vegetative propagation is accomplished by the isolation of branches, in other species (*e.g.*, *Anthoceros hallii*) by the formation of small tubers that rest in the soil until the next growing season.

Sex Organs. In most of the Anthocerotales the antheridia and archegonia are borne on the same plant but in separate groups, the antheridia appearing first. Both kinds of sex organs are embedded in the dorsal surface of the thallus and develop endogenously.

The antheridium initial is a superficial cell arising close to the growing apex. It does not become papillate, as in the other Hepaticae, but divides transversely, the inner cell giving rise to the antheridium. Between the two cells a mucilage-filled cleft appears that later becomes the antheridial chamber, the roof of which is formed by the derivatives of the outer

Fig. 153. *Anthoceros fusiformis*, with three sporophytes arising from the gametophyte, ×3.

cell. In the inner cell two vertical walls at right angles to each other now appear, followed by two transverse walls (Fig. 154*A*). As a result, three tiers are formed with four cells in each tier. The stalk is derived from the lowest tier. Periclinal walls in the two upper tiers separate the outer sterile jacket from the inner spermatogenous cells (Fig. 154*B, C*). Further development follows the usual liverwort pattern.

The mature antheridia are spherical or nearly so, generally long-stalked, and often bright orange-yellow. When the sperms are ripe, the roof of the antheridial chamber bursts. In *Notothylas* and most species of *Anthoceros* two or four antheridia develop in the same chamber, all coming from the inner segment of the same initial cell. This divides by a

188 PLANT MORPHOLOGY

vertical wall, or by two vertical walls at right angles to each other, each
segment giving rise to an antheridium. Frequently additional antheridia
are budded off from the base of the others.

The archegonium initial is a superficial cell that, like the antheridium

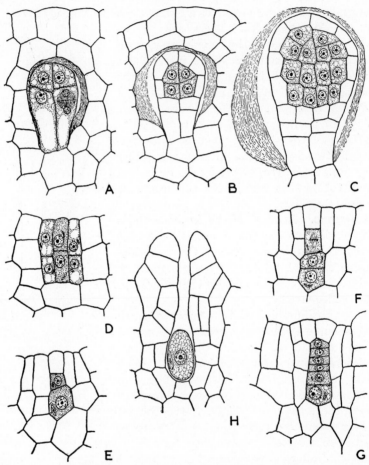

Fig. 154. Sex organs of *Anthoceros*, ×500. *A, B, C,* stages in development of the antheridium; *D,* young archegonium showing transverse division of axial cell; *E,* formation of
cover cell, primary neck canal cell, and primary ventral cell; *F,* division of primary neck
canal cell and formation of ventral canal cell and egg; *G,* later stage with four neck canal
cells; *H,* mature archegonium with egg ready for fertilization. (*A* to *C, Anthoceros pulcher-
rimus; D* to *H, Anthoceros fusiformis.*)

initial, does not become papillate. The usual three vertical walls appear,
cutting off the wall cells from the primary axial cell. The latter divides
transversely (Fig. 154*D*), while a second transverse division occurs in the
outer cell, resulting in a row of three cells (Fig. 154*E*). These are the

cover cell, primary neck canal cell, and primary ventral cell. The cover cell later divides by one or two vertical walls; the primary neck canal cell gives rise to four or sometimes six neck canal cells; and the primary ventral cell produces the ventral canal cell and the egg (Fig. 154*F*, *G*). Just previous to fertilization the cover cells and canal cells break down, leaving the egg in a cavity below the surface of the thallus (Fig. 154*H*).

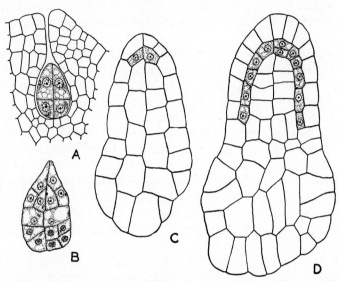

Fig. 155. Embryos of Anthocerotales, ×300. *A*, young embryo of *Anthoceros fusiformis;* *B*, slightly older embryo of *Anthoceros punctatus*, showing differentiation of amphithecium and endothecium; *C*, embryo of *Megaceros*, showing two sporogenous cells cut off from amphithecium; *D*, later stage, showing further development of sporogenous tissue.

Sporophyte. In *Anthoceros* the first division of the fertilized egg is vertical, the second transverse, and the third vertical at right angles to the plane of the first division (Fig. 155*A*). A fourth division occurs transversely in the upper part of the embryo, resulting in three tiers of four cells each. The upper tier produces the capsular region, the middle tier an intermediate zone, while the lower tier forms the foot. In the development of the capsular region, which occurs very early, the amphithecium is cut off from the endothecium by periclinal walls (Fig. 155*B*). The latter forms the *columella*, an axis of sterile tissue. The amphithecium soon becomes two-layered, the inner layer giving rise to the sporogenous tissue and the outer layer to the sterile wall (Fig. 155*C, D*). The derivation of the sporogenous tissue from the amphithecium rather than from the endothecium is very characteristic and stands in marked contrast to the condition in the other Hepaticae. In some species of *Notothylas*, however, the endothecium does not produce a sterile columella but, instead, gives rise to the sporogenous tissue.

The foot becomes bulbous and in many species penetrates the thallus by means of rhizoid-like papillae (Fig. 156). The intermediate zone is meristematic. It contributes somewhat to the development of the foot, but is chiefly concerned with the elongation of the capsular region. There is no seta. *Notothylas* has a short capsular region, the other genera a long one. The young sporophyte is protected by the surrounding tissue of the thallus, which grows upward with it to form a massive involucre. This is later ruptured by the elongation of the sporophyte, forming a basal sheath.

The columella consists of elongated cells. It may be regarded as representing the beginning of a conducting system. In *Anthoceros* the columella shows about 16 cells in cross section. In the young sporophyte the sporogenous tissue caps the columella in a dome-like manner. It soon becomes two-layered above and then gives rise to spore mother cells. Meanwhile new sporogenous tissue continues to be differentiated in the meristematic region lying just above the foot (Fig. 156B). Although, in *Anthoceros*, the sporogenous tissue generally becomes two-layered, it may remain one-layered, as in *Anthoceros hawaiiensis*, or may become three or four layers thick, as in *Anthoceros hallii* and *Megaceros*. In *Notothylas* the amount of sporogenous tissue is greatly increased; in some species a definite columella is not formed and the sporogenous tissue arises from both the amphithecium and endothecium, or from the endothecium alone.

The wall of the capsule becomes four to eight layers of cells thick. In *Anthoceros*, but not in the other genera, the outer layer, constituting the epidermis, develops stomata. These are not like the air pores seen in the gametophyte of the Marchantiales, but resemble the stomata of the higher plants. The wall layers beneath the epidermis develop chloroplasts and intercellular spaces, thus becoming a photosynthetic region.

The intermediate zone elongates constantly, adding to the capsular region from below. Thus spores continue to be produced over a long period. It is noteworthy that the Anthocerotales are the only bryophytes whose sporophyte displays indeterminate growth. Some of the sporogenous cells become sterile, small groups of these alternating with groups of spores and so tending to break up the spore mass into separate units. As a rule, these sterile cells give rise to peculiar short elaters that are often branched. In *Anthoceros* the elaters, where present, are smooth-walled; in *Notothylas* they have short, curved, thickened bands on their walls; in *Megaceros* and *Dendroceros* the elaters have spiral thickenings like those of other liverworts. The capsule dehisces by splitting into two valves.

Summary. The Anthocerotales are of phylogenetic interest in that they may represent a stage of progress through which the higher plants have passed in the course of their evolution. As in the Jungermanniales, the gametophyte is simple and the sporophyte complex, but the complex-

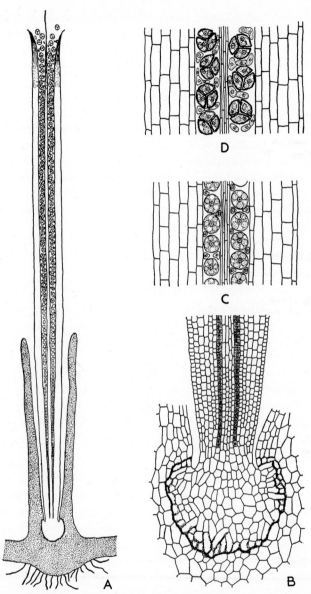

Fɪɢ. 156.   Longitudinal sections of the sporophyte of *Anthoceros laevis*.   A, entire sporophyte with foot embedded in the gametophyte, ×20; B, basal region, showing origin of
sporogenous tissue, ×100; C, higher level, showing spore mother cells, ×100; D, level where
spore tetrads are forming, ×100.

ity is of an entirely different kind. The gametophyte is a flat thallus without structural differentiation. It grows by means of a cuneate apical cell. The sex organs are endogenous. The antheridium is formed from the inner half of the initial cell and the sequence of early wall formation is distinctive. The archegonium represents a new departure in that the primary neck canal cell is cut off from the outer segment arising from a transverse division of the initial.

The sporophyte consists of a foot and a cylindrical capsule. It displays a great development of sterile tissue. The presence of green tissue, stomata, and rhizoid-like processes suggests that the sporophyte is becoming independent. The breaking up of the sporogenous tissue into smaller units may represent an initial stage in the formation of sporangia. The establishment of a sterile axis by the transfer of sporogenous tissue from the endothecium to the amphithecium may represent the beginning of a conducting system. A meristematic region in the sporophyte results in its continued growth. Dehiscence of the capsule is accomplished by means of two valves.

2. MUSCI

The mosses constitute the larger and more highly developed class of bryophytes, numbering about 14,000 species. They are widely distributed and, although abundant in arctic and alpine regions, are represented in nearly all habitats except the ocean. The fossil history of the group is very fragmentary, there being few reliable evidences of its existence earlier than the Tertiary. The gametophyte is leafy and, in contrast to that of the liverworts, is typically radial rather than dorsiventral. The leaves generally have a midrib. The rhizoids are septate and usually branched. The Musci comprise three orders, the Sphagnales, Andreaeales, and Bryales.

1. Sphagnales

The Sphagnales, or bog mosses, are a group of about 350 species, all belonging to the genus *Sphagnum*. They are relatively large, pale mosses generally living in bogs at high altitudes and high latitudes. Because their accumulated remains form peat, they are often called peat mosses.

Gametophyte. Upon germination, the spore produces a short filament that, in turn, gives rise to a flat green thallus (Fig. 157*A*). This consists of a single layer of cells bearing numerous septate rhizoids. The thallus gives rise to an erect leafy branch and then disappears (Fig. 157*B*). The erect shoot develops rhizoids below and becomes the mature gametophyte. The rhizoids soon die but the shoot continues to grow from year to year (Fig. 158*A*). Branching in *Sphagnum* is very profuse, there being branches of limited growth crowded near the apex of the main stem and others occurring in tufts farther down. The stem grows by means of a tetrahedral apical cell, and from each of its three rows of segments a row of leaves arises, these being spirally arranged.

The leaves are composed of a single layer of cells and lack a midrib. They are peculiar in structure, some cells being enlarged, rhomboidal, and hyaline, while others are small, narrow, and green (Fig. 158*E*). The green cells form the meshes of a network enclosing the hyaline cells. The latter are dead cells filled with water; their walls bear large circular pores

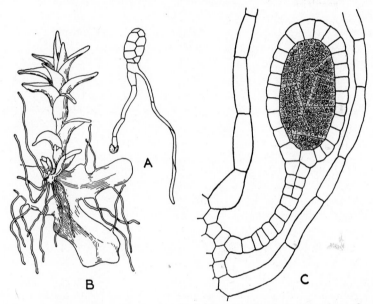

Fig. 157. *Sphagnum.* *A*, young gametophyte, showing filament arising from the spore, a rhizoid, and the thallus beginning to develop by an apical cell; *B*, mature thallus, with rhizoids, producing a leafy shoot; *C*, an antheridium arising between two leaves, ×250. (*A and B, after Schimper.*)

and usually spiral thickenings as well. The leaves have an extraordinary power of absorbing and retaining water. At first the leaf cells are uniform, but later from each a narrow cell is cut off on two sides, as represented by Fig. 158*B–D*.

The stem of *Sphagnum* is differentiated into three regions: (1) a cortex of dead hyaline cells that absorb and store water; (2) a cylinder of small elongated cells with thick walls; and (3) a pith-like axis. Vegetative propagation occurs by branching and death of the older parts of the plant. This is the principal method of reproduction.

Sex Organs. Depending on the species, *Sphagnum* is either monoecious or dioecious. The antheridia appear on special, short, lateral branches that arise near the apex of the main shoot. They are solitary in the leaf axils, unaccompanied by paraphyses, and arise in acropetal succession. The initial is a superficial cell that undergoes several transverse divisions, resulting in a short filament. Then the terminal cell functions as a dolabrate apical cell (one with two cutting faces), the lower segments forming the stalk and the upper ones the rest of the antheridium. The spermatogenous tissue is differentiated from the jacket cells by the formation of periclinal walls. The mature antheridia are long-stalked and

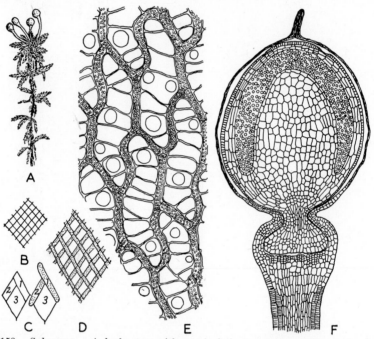

FIG. 158. *Sphagnum. A*, leafy stem with terminal cluster of sporophytes, natural size; *B*, surface view of portion of very young leaf, ×260; *C*, diagram showing how the leaf cells divide, cutting off cells marked 1, and then cells marked 2; *D*, appearance of leaf after these cells have been cut off; *E*, surface view of portion of mature leaf, showing the narrow elongated cells with chloroplasts and the larger hyaline cells with pores and slender bands of thickening, ×300; *F*, longitudinal section of nearly mature sporophyte, showing the capsule, neck-like seta, and the foot, ×24. (*After Chamberlain.*)

nearly spherical, opening irregularly to discharge their sperms (Fig. 157*C*).

The archegonia appear at the apex of short branches that, like the antheridial branches, arise at the upper end of the main shoot. They are borne in groups of one to five, without paraphyses, and are stalked and free. An archegonium arises directly from the apical cell, as in the acrogynous Jungermanniales, and then several others may arise from the last-formed segments of the apical cell. After a short filament has been produced by the formation of walls that may be either transverse or oblique, the usual three vertical walls appear in the terminal cell, cutting

off three primary wall cells from the primary axial cell (Fig. 159*A*).   The
axial cell, by a transverse division, gives rise to the cover cell and central
cell (Fig. 159*B*).   The development of the axial row is similar to that of
the Jungermanniales.   The central cell divides to form the primary neck
canal cell and primary ventral cell (Fig. 159*C*).   The neck canal cells,

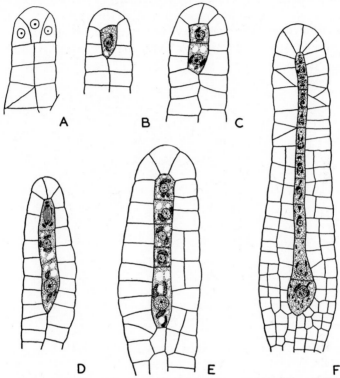

FIG. 159.   Development of the archegonium of *Sphagnum subsecundum*.   *A*, formation of
primary axial cell; *B*, formation of cover cell and central cell; *C*, formation of primary neck
canal cell and primary ventral cell, the cover cell divided vertically; *D*, archegonium with
primary ventral cell and two neck canal cells; *E*, later stage with four neck canal cells; *F*,
archegonium with egg, ventral canal cell, and nine neck canal cells; *A* to *E*, ×525; *F*,
×300.   (*After Bryan*.)

numbering eight or nine, all arise directly from the primary neck canal
cell, while the ventral canal cell and egg, approximately equal in size, are
produced by a transverse division of the primary ventral cell (Fig.
159*D–F*).   The mature archegonium has a long stalk, a massive venter,
and a long twisted neck.

   Sporophyte.   The fertilized egg of *Sphagnum* undergoes a series of
transverse divisions that result in the formation of a short filament of six
or seven cells (Fig. 160).   Vertical walls then appear and the embryo
becomes cylindrical.   It next becomes differentiated into an upper fertile

region (the capsule), a middle region (the neck), and a basal portion (the foot). As in *Anthoceros*, a columella is formed from the endothecium, the sporogenous tissue being cut off from the amphithecium and capping the columella like a dome. The sporogenous tissue becomes two to four layers of cells in thickness, while the outer portion of the amphithecium forms the capsule wall, eventually composed of five to seven layers of cells. This becomes a region of green tissue with intercellular spaces, the outer layer developing rudimentary stomata. The sporogenous tissue is surrounded by a definite nutritive layer, the *tapetum*. As in the other

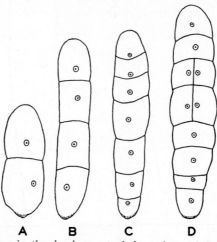

Fig. 160. Early stages in the development of the embryo of *Sphagnum subsecundum*, ×200. *A*, two-celled stage; *B*, four-celled stage; *C*, seven-celled stage; *D*, appearance of vertical walls. (*After Bryan.*)

Musci, no elaters are formed, all the sporogenous cells becoming spore mother cells.

The foot becomes large and bulbous, but the seta does not develop beyond the neck-like stage (Fig. 158*F*). The seta is replaced functionally by the *pseudopodium*, a leafless stalk developed from the stem of the gametophyte, in the tip of which the foot of the sporophyte is embedded. The pseudopodium elongates rapidly after the spores have ripened, carrying the capsule upward. When mature, the capsule is globular and dark brown or black. It dehisces by means of a lid or operculum, as in the Bryales. The spores are discharged with force. As in the Hepaticae, the sporophyte remains enclosed by the calyptra until the spores are ripe.

Summary. The Sphagnales are a synthetic group, combining characters found both in liverworts and mosses. A thallus like that of the anacrogynous Jungermanniales gives rise to an erect leafy shoot that becomes the mature gametophyte. This shows some internal differentiation, both in the leaves and stem. The antheridia are spherical and axillary, as in the acrogynous Jungermanniales, but in development resemble the Bryales. In position, origin, and development the archegonia show a resemblance to those of the acrogynous Jungermanniales, except that, when mature, the venter is massive, as in the Bryales. The general organization of the sporophyte is like that of the Anthocerotales, the sporogenous tissue being dome-shaped and derived from the amphithecium; but there is no meristematic region. The seta is replaced functionally by a pseudopodium. The capsule contains green tissue and rudimentary stomata. It dehisces by an operculum, as in the Bryales.

2. Andreaeales

This order comprises a single genus, *Andreaea*, of about 125 species. They are small, tufted, dark-colored mosses growing on rocks in dry situations, especially in cold regions. In warmer regions they are restricted to high mountains.

Gametophyte. In the germination of the spore, its protoplast produces inside the spore wall a mass of cells called the *primary tubercle*. After rupturing the wall, one or more of its superficial cells give rise to branching filaments. These correspond to the protonema of the Bryales. Some of the filaments turn brown and function as rhizoids, while others may give rise either to flat thalli or cylindrical masses. A leafy shoot is then organized (Fig. 161). It may arise from the flat thallus, from the cylinder, or directly from the protonema. The stem, which is prostrate, exhibits *sympodial* branching (like dichotomy, but with unequal branches). It produces many rhizoids. The stem is without a central strand, consisting of uniform, thick-walled cells. It grows by means of a tetrahedral apical cell. The leaves, formed in three rows, are generally without a midrib, being composed usually of thick-walled cells.

Sex Organs. *Andreaea* is generally monoecious, the antheridia and archegonia occurring in terminal groups on separate branches. The apical cell is involved in the formation of the sex organs. In development, the antheridium corresponds very closely to that of *Sphagnum* and similarly, when mature, is long-stalked and nearly globular. The archegonia develop as in the Bryales, the cover cell contributing to the row of neck canal cells.

Sporophyte. The first division of the fertilized egg is transverse, the inner segment forming the foot and the outer segment the rest of the sporophyte. A dolabrate apical cell is organized in the outer segment and about a dozen cells are formed before vertical walls come in. The sporogenous tissue is cut off from the endothecium as the outermost layer of cells and caps the columella as a dome. It eventually becomes two-layered. As in *Sphagnum*, a pseudopodium is formed, the seta remaining undeveloped. The calyptra encloses the sporophyte until it is nearly mature.   The capsule is without an operculum, dehiscence taking place by means of four longitudinal slits, but these usually do not extend to the apex of the capsule (Fig. 161).

Summary. Like the Sphagnales, the Andreaeales are a synthetic group. The gametophyte begins either as a thallus, as in the Sphag-

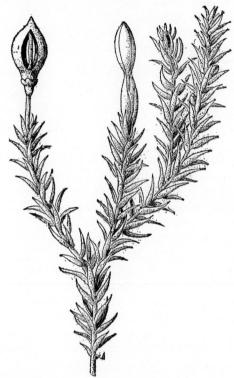

FIG. 161.   Gametophyte of *Andreaea petrophila* with mature and immature sporophytes, ×3.   (*From Gilbert M. Smith.*)

nales, as a filamentous protonema, as in the Bryales, or as a cylindrical body.   The antheridia are terminal, as in the Bryales, but are long-stalked and globular, as in the Sphagnales.   The archegonia develop like those of the Bryales.   The sporogenous tissue is derived from the endothecium, a feature of the Bryales, but caps the columella in a dome-like manner, a feature of *Sphagnum*.   Similarly, as in *Sphagnum*, a pseudopodium is developed.   The capsule dehisces by means of four valves, as in the Jungermanniales.

3. Bryales

The Bryales, or true mosses, are the culminating order of bryophytes. They constitute a highly specialized, as well as a very distinct group, displaying remarkable uniformity with respect to basic morphological features. The Bryales are by far the largest group of bryophytes, numbering about 13,500 species included in 80 families. Although world-wide in distribution, they are particularly abundant in moist northern regions. They grow on rocks, tree trunks, fallen logs, and on the ground, often forming extensive mats. Some grow in dry situations, while a few are aquatic. Some of the largest genera are *Fissidens, Leucobryum, Barbula, Tortula, Grimmia, Funaria, Bryum, Mnium, Bartramia, Hypnum, Polytrichum*, and *Pogonatum*.

Gametophyte. In nearly all the Bryales the spore produces a *protonema*—a green, branching, septate filament (Fig. 162). Some of the

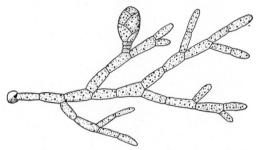

Fig. 162. Moss protonema arising from a spore and bearing a bud from which an erect leafy shoot will arise, ×100.

branches penetrate the soil, turn brown, and become rhizoids. The protonema, which is the morphological equivalent of the thallus of *Sphagnum*, gives rise to an erect leafy stem, the *gametophore*. This arises as a bud on the protonema and, in most genera, grows by means of a tetrahedral apical cell. After formation of the leafy shoot or, more commonly, of several or many leafy shoots, the protonema usually disappears; but it may persist, turn brown, and contribute to the mass of rhizoids that arise from the lower end of the stem. Branching of the stem, where it occurs, is nearly always monopodial (with a true main axis). Generally the leaves are spirally arranged and borne in three vertical rows (Fig. 163). Usually they consist of a single layer of cells, except for a slightly thickened midrib, which is nearly always present. The stems of such mosses as *Mnium* and *Polytrichum* contain a strand of elongated thick-walled cells, but the stem tissue of most mosses is uniformly thin-walled.

Vegetative propagation in the Bryales is highly developed and varied. It may occur by isolation of branches following death of the older parts of the plant, by small multicellular gemmae, by resting buds (bulbils) on the protonema, or by the formation of a protonema from almost any part of the plant.

Sex Organs. In many mosses sex organs are rarely produced, reproduction taking place chiefly by vegetative means. The sex organs occur
in terminal groups (Fig. 163). In the "acrocarpous" forms they are
borne at the apex of the main stem or its principal branches; in the
"pleurocarpous" forms they occur at the apices of short lateral branches.
The sex organs are usually surrounded by a sheath or rosette of modified
leaves forming the *perichaetium*. According to the species, mosses may be

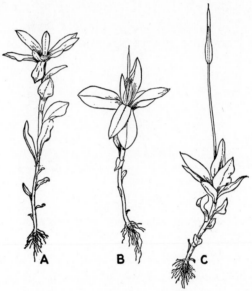

FIG. 163.   Leafy shoots of *Funaria hygrometrica*, ×3.   *A*, male plant with terminal cluster
of antheridia; *B*, female plant with an archegonium in which an embryo sporophyte has
started to develop; *C*, older stage, the sporophyte elongating and carrying the calyptra
upward.

either monoecious or dioecious. If monoecious, the antheridia and archegonia usually occur in the same cluster. Multicellular paraphyses are
commonly present. Both kinds of sex organs arise from segments of the
apical cell, in many cases from the apical cell itself. The formation of
sex organs limits growth of the vegetative axis.

The antheridium arises from a superficial cell that becomes papillate.
Several transverse divisions may take place and then the terminal cell
becomes a dolabrate apical cell (one with two cutting faces), cutting off
a series of segments (Fig. 164*A*). Periclinal walls in the younger segments delimit the jacket cells from the primary spermatogenous cells
(Fig. 164*B*, *C*). As additional divisions occur, the antheridium becomes
club-shaped, with a stalk of variable length (Fig. 164*D*). A large number of sperm mother cells are formed, each giving rise to two sperms.

When mature, the antheridium ruptures at the apex, the sperms being discharged in a mass.

The archegonium also develops by means of a dolabrate apical cell, but only a comparatively few segments are cut off (Fig. 165*A*). In the terminal cell then appear the three characteristic walls that differentiate the primary wall cells from the primary axial cell (Fig. 165*B*). A transverse

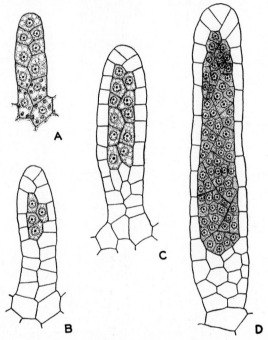

Fig. 164. Development of the antheridium of *Mnium affine*, ×400. *A*, young stage; *B*, beginning of differentiation of primary spermatogenous cells; *C*, slightly older stage; *D*, antheridium showing subdivision of spermatogenous tissue.

division of the axial cell results in the formation of the cover cell and central cell, the latter soon giving rise to the primary neck canal cell and primary ventral cell (Fig. 165*C, D*). Later development is characteristic in that the cover cell cuts off lateral segments that add to the neck cells and inner segments that contribute to the neck canal cells. Thus the upper neck canal cells are derived from the cover cell, the lower ones from the primary neck canal cell, while the ventral canal cell and egg, as usual, arise from the primary ventral cell (Fig. 165*E–H*). The mature archegonium has a long stalk, a massive venter, and many neck canal cells—sometimes up to 50 or 60.

Sporophyte. In the Bryales the sporophyte reaches a high degree of specialization. During its early development a large calyptra is formed

from the stalk and venter of the archegonium.   This is soon ruptured and
carried upward on the top of the sporophyte as a conspicuous hood, which
may remain until the sporophyte is mature (Fig. 163*C*).

   The first division of the fertilized egg is transverse or oblique.   Each

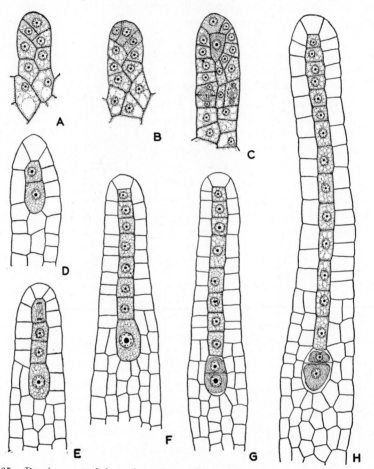

Fig. 165.   Development of the archegonium of *Mnium affine*, ×400.   *A*, young stage; *B*,
formation of primary axial cell; *C*, formation of cover cell and central cell, the former
divided by a radial wall; *D*, formation of primary neck canal cell and primary ventral cell;
E, archegonium with primary ventral cell and three neck canal cells; *F*, later stage with
seven neck canal cells; *G*, archegonium with egg, ventral canal cell, and eight neck canal
cells; *H*, later stage.

segment becomes an apical cell through the activity of which a slender
elongated embryo is developed (Fig. 166).   Apical growth continues for a
long time.   Finally, at the upper end of the embryo, after the appearance
of two sets of four vertical walls, periclinal divisions cut off the amphithecium from the endothecium.   The amphithecium gives rise to several

layers of cells. The sporogenous tissue is cut off from the endothecium as the outermost layer of cells, the remainder form-ing a sterile columella. The sporogenous tissue is not continuous over the columella as a dome, but has the form of a hollow cylinder. It may extend to the base of the capsule, as in *Polytrichum*, or may not. The sporogenous tissue usually becomes two-layered, all its cells giving rise to spore mother cells.

As seen in longitudinal section, the mature cap-sule is very complex, being made up of an epider-mis with stomata, several wall layers of colorless cells, an air-chamber region consisting of green tissue, an outer tapetum, the sporogenous tissue, an inner tapetum, an inner air-chamber region (present only in highly specialized forms, such as *Polytrichum*), and a central columella (Fig. 167).

The *operculum*, which forms the upper part of the capsule, is complex in its development (Fig. 168). It is often dif-

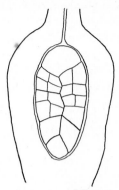

Fig. 166. Embryo of *Funaria hygrometrica* enclosed by the calyp-tra, × 500. (*After Sachs.*)

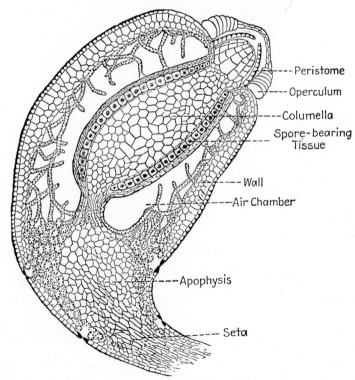

Peristome
Operculum
Columella
Spore-bearing Tissue
Wall
Air Chamber
Apophysis
Seta

Fig. 167. Longitudinal section of the capsule of *Funaria hygrometrica*. (*From Sinnott.*)

ferentiated into an upper *annulus*, consisting of several series of large thin-walled cells, and a lower *rim*. When the capsule is mature, the annulus collapses and the operculum comes off, exposing the *peristome*. This consists of one or two rings of tooth-like projections that are anchored to the rim. The usual number of teeth is 16, but they may occur in some other multiple of 4. The teeth, which are hygroscopic, assist in spore dispersal, bending inward and outward. In a few genera,

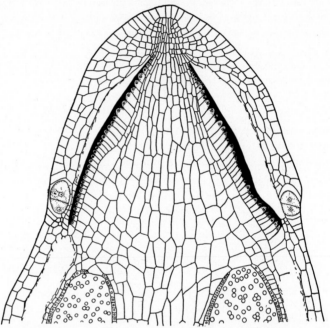

Fig. 168. Longitudinal section of the upper part of the capsule of *Mnium*, showing the operculum and two teeth of the peristome, ×90. (*After Chamberlain.*)

said to be "cleistocarpous," an operculum and a peristome are lacking, the capsule wall rupturing irregularly in dehiscence. In the other genera, which are "stegocarpous," an operculum and a peristome are present.

Often the lower portion of the capsule does not produce spores, but forms a chlorophyll-bearing region, called the *apophysis*, in which stomata are present (Fig. 167). In many mosses the apophysis is ring-like. The seta of mosses is nearly always very long. It has a central strand of elongated cells, but these are not conductive in function. The foot is simple.

Summary. The Bryales are the most highly developed group of bryophytes. The gametophyte consists of a protonema giving rise to a leafy shoot, the latter being differentiated in form and somewhat in structure. The antheridia are terminal and club-shaped, developing by means of a dolabrate apical cell, as in all the Musci. The archegonia have a long stalk, a massive venter, and a long twisted neck. The number of neck canal cells is greater than in any other group of plants. The sporophyte displays the greatest amount of sterilization of potentially sporogenous tissue seen in the Bryophyta. The sporogenous tissue arises from the outer part of the endothecium and has the form of a hollow cylinder. The seta is elongated, no pseudopodium being formed. The capsule shows an extraordinary degree of specialization, both in the organization of an operculum, peristome, and apophysis, and in its internal differentiation of tissues. It contains both green tissue and stomata.

COMPARISON OF LIVERWORTS AND MOSSES

The most important distinguishing characters of the Hepaticae (liverworts) and Musci (mosses) are as follows:

HEPATICAE	MUSCI
Gametophyte almost invariably dorsiventral; thalloid or leafy	Gametophyte typically radial; leafy
Leaves, where present, without a midrib	Leaves generally with a midrib (except in *Sphagnum* and *Andreaea*)
Rhizoids unicellular and mostly unbranched	Rhizoids septate, mostly branched
Protonema, where present, small and transitory	Protonema usually conspicuous, relatively persistent
Sporophyte remaining enclosed by the calyptra, or breaking through only when spores are ripe	Sporophyte breaking through the calyptra at an early stage of development (except in *Sphagnum*)
Elaters usually present	Elaters absent

GENERAL CONCLUSIONS

The bryophytes, undoubtedly derived from aquatic ancestors, are the simplest group of green plants growing on land. Their position in the plant kingdom is an expression of the degree of evolutionary progress they have made, but is not necessarily an indication of their phylogenetic relationship to the higher plants. One theory holds that the bryophytes are an ancient stock from which the pteridophytes have been derived. Another theory contends that the pteridophytes have originated directly and independently from the algae and that, therefore, the bryophytes represent a blindly ending line of descent. But even if the latter view should prove to be the correct one, the first land plants may have passed through a general stage of development similar to that reached by the bryophytes of the present.

The bryophytes differ from the algae in the possession of archegonia, multicellular antheridia, and an established heteromorphic alternation of generations. Because the liverworts are simpler than the mosses, it seems very probable that they are more primitive and thus more ancient than the mosses. Both groups may have had a common origin, but it is more likely that the mosses were derived directly from the liverworts. Each has subsequently pursued its own course of evolution, the mosses having advanced considerably beyond the liverworts.

The Land Habit. The establishment of the land habit was one of the most important events in the history of plant life, for it made possible all subsequent progress. Its advantage lies in the greater opportunity for photosynthesis in the presence of more light. Its disadvantage lies in the danger of excessive transpiration. The first land plants may have arisen from some green alga consisting of a simple plate of cells, perhaps from a form somewhat like *Coleochaete*. Adjustment to the land environment must have involved structural changes facilitating the absorption of water from the soil and the retention of water by parts exposed to the air. This adjustment on the part of bryophytes is manifested chiefly by the development of compact bodies, absorptive filaments (rhizoids), jacketed sex organs, heavy-walled aerial spores, and, in some cases, by an epidermis with air pores, in others, by primitive conducting cells.

Because the simplest liverworts are thalloid, it is reasonable to suppose that they have given rise to the leafy forms. An alternative view is that the leafy body is primitive, the thalloid type having been derived from it by reduction. Since an erect leafy body permits the exposure of a greater photosynthetic surface to the light than is afforded by a flat thallus, it would seem to represent a more advanced state of adaptation to the land habit.

The Gametophyte. The bryophytes are a group in which the gametophyte is the dominant generation. It is always a green, independent plant body. In its simplest form it is a flat thallus, one to several layers of cells thick, and without any internal differentiation of tissues. Such a gametophyte is seen in *Sphaerocarpus, Pellia, Notothylas*, and a number of other Hepaticae. It may be regarded as having given rise to two divergent lines of descent: (1) a line in which the gametophyte, remaining thalloid, has undergone differentiation in structure; (2) a line in which the gametophyte has remained simple structurally but has become differentiated in form, finally becoming a leafy shoot. The first line of evolution has been followed by the Marchantiales, the second by the Jungermanniales. In the Musci the gametophyte reaches its highest development, the erect leafy shoot of the higher mosses, with its radial symmetry, showing differentiation in both form and structure.

The Sporophyte. The simplest sporophyte among the bryophytes is that of *Riccia*, where, except for the single layer of wall cells, all the cells are sporogenous. If this sporophyte be regarded as primitive rather than reduced, all subsequent progress has resulted from sterilization of potentially sporogenous tissue and its diversion to other functions. This is seen in the development of a foot and seta, as well as in the formation of elaters. The foot absorbs food from the gametophyte. The seta places the capsule in a favorable position with reference to spore dispersal. Except in *Riccia*, the Sphaerocarpales, and a few other forms, a seta is found in all bryophytes. Its absence in the Anthocerotales is correlated with the indeterminate growth of the elongated capsule and in the Sphagnales and Andreaeales with the presence of a pseudopodium, the functional equivalent of a seta. The development of a definite means of dehiscence, seen in nearly all bryophytes except *Riccia* and the Sphaerocarpales, represents an advanced feature. Elaters are present in almost all liverworts but not in any of the mosses, where spore dispersal is aided by other means, as by a peristome.

Further progress of the sporophyte has come about through additional sterilization and earlier diversion of potentially sporogenous tissue. Thus an elaterophore is developed in some of the Jungermanniales. The formation of a columella in the center of the capsule and of additional sterile tissue in its outer portion is an advanced feature of the Anthocerotales and Musci. The failure of a columella to develop in certain members of each group indicates that the entire central region of the capsule was originally sporogenous. The sporophyte reaches its highest development in the Bryales, where the most extensive amount of sterilization seen in all bryophytes has resulted in a greatly elongated seta and a capsule of extreme complexity.

The bryophytes show two well-marked lines of evolution with respect to the sporophyte. The one, emphasizing spore dispersal, ends blindly with the mosses. The other, in which the sporophyte attains partial independence and exhibits indeterminate growth, culminates in *Anthoceros*.

Plan of the Mosses. In the mosses photosynthesis and fertilization are functions of the gametophyte, the sporophyte being concerned mainly with the production and dispersal of spores. An erect leafy gametophyte, best developed in this group, favors photosynthesis but at the same time hinders fertilization, since the sex organs are carried upward where it is difficult for swimming sperms to function. The moss sporophyte is highly specialized for spore dispersal, but without fertilization there can be no sporophyte. It is evident, therefore, that combining photosynthesis with fertilization as functions of the gametophyte is an unprogressive tendency, because these two functions have different requirements. It follows that the mosses must be regarded as a blindly ending evolutionary line.

Plan of Anthoceros. In the Anthocerotales the sex organs are borne on a flat thallus, and so fertilization is easily accomplished. Although still largely dependent upon the gametophyte, the sporophyte develops much green tissue and so exhibits a marked tendency toward independence. The combining of photosynthesis with spore dispersal as functions of the sporophyte permits of further progress, since both, favored by a tall body, have the same requirements. The plan of *Anthoceros* is the one carried forward by the higher plants, where the sporophyte is dependent upon the gametophyte only during early life. Thus *Anthoceros* displays a strong tendency that, if present in the ancestors of the pteridophytes, may have led to their origin.

CHAPTER VI

PTERIDOPHYTA

The pteridophytes are a comparatively small group of plants today, but in past geologic times they were much more numerous. They are represented by over 9,000 living species, very unequally divided among the four classes Psilophytinae, Lycopodiinae, Equisetinae, and Filicinae. Most pteridophytes are terrestrial plants, but some are epiphytic and a few are secondarily aquatic. They grow in a wide variety of habitats.

Pteridophytes may be characterized as vascular plants without seeds. Like the bryophytes, they display a distinct alternation of generations. Their great advance lies in the development of an independent sporophyte with complex roots, stems, and leaves, and one in which a prominent vascular system is present. The sporophyte has now become the dominant generation, the gametophyte always being small and inconspicuous.

The sporophyte presents a great range in size and habit, although one not so extreme as in the spermatophytes. Nearly all existing pteridophytes are herbaceous or somewhat woody, the tree ferns being a notable exception. Branching of the stem, where present, is dichotomous in some members, monopodial in others. Elongation of the root and stem generally occurs through the activity of an apical cell; in some forms this is replaced by a meristem. The spores are produced in sporangia, which are usually borne in connection with the leaves. Most living pteridophytes are *homosporous*, all the spores being alike. Some are *heterosporous*, with spores of two different kinds, these always being produced in separate sporangia. As in all bryophytes and spermatophytes, the reduction in chromosome number occurs in connection with the formation of spores. Consequently the sporophyte is the diploid generation, while the gametophyte, produced by a spore, is the haploid generation.

In the homosporous pteridophytes the gametophyte is either a simple green thallus or a tuberous body that is subterranean, colorless, and saprophytic. In the heterosporous forms the gametophytes are sexually differentiated and greatly reduced in structure, developing entirely or largely within the spore wall. The sex organs of pteridophytes are essentially similar to those of bryophytes, but are simpler. Generally both the antheridia and archegonia are embedded structures. Swimming sperms are universally present. Following fertilization, the embryo develops within the venter of the archegonium, which forms the calyptra. The young sporophyte lives on the gametophyte until able to maintain itself as an independent plant.

THE VASCULAR SYSTEM

The vascular system of pteridophytes and spermatophytes is made up mainly of two kinds of complex tissues: *xylem* and *phloem*. Each of these consists of several different kinds of elements. Xylem conducts water and dissolved substances absorbed from the soil, while phloem carries food away from the leaves and other organs where it is synthesized. The unit of the xylem is the *tracheid*—a slender, elongated, thick-walled cell generally pointed at each end and without living contents when mature. The most important element of the phloem is the *sieve tube*—an elongated, thin-walled, living cell whose end walls, and often side walls as well, have many fine pores (Fig. 314*A*, *B*).

The cell walls of tracheids are thickened with lignin, which is deposited on the inner surface to form a spiral, rings, parallel bars, or an irregular network, in accordance with which spiral, annular, scalariform, and reticulate types are recognized. Most commonly the lignin is so abundant that the walls are pitted, the pits being unthickened areas. *Vessels* resemble tracheids except that each represents a longitudinal row of cells whose end walls break down. Vessels are of rare occurrence in pteridophytes but are the chief xylem elements of angiosperms (Fig. 314*C–E*).

In addition to tracheids and/or vessels, xylem may contain parenchyma. Phloem may contain parenchyma in addition to sieve tubes. *Fibers*, which are elongated, thick-walled, nonconducting cells, may also form part of the xylem or phloem (Fig. 314*F*).

Development of Xylem. A short distance behind the apex of the root and shoot, which is composed of embryonic tissue, the first xylem is differentiated. This is known as *protoxylem*. The next xylem to lignify is called *metaxylem*. The position of the metaxylem with reference to the protoxylem is of considerable importance. There are three conditions, as follows:

(1) If the lignification begins at the outside (periphery) of the root or stem and proceeds toward the center, in a centripetal direction, the development is *exarch*. This type is characteristic of all roots and of the stems of lycopods (Figs. 176, 188, 220, 227, and 311). (2) If the lignification spreads out in all directions, so that the metaxylem surrounds the protoxylem, the development is *mesarch*. This type is characteristic of the stems of ferns (Fig. 239). (3) If the lignification begins near the center of the stem and proceeds outward, in a centrifugal direction, the development is *endarch*. Only a few pteridophytes have reached this condition, but it is almost universal in the stems of spermatophytes.

Protoxylem consists mainly of spiral and annular tracheids, while metaxylem is generally made up of scalariform or of pitted tracheids. Scalariform tracheids, in which the bands of thickening resemble the rungs of a ladder, are most common in pteridophytes and pitted tracheids in spermatophytes. *Primary xylem*, consisting of all wood differentiated directly from embryonic cells of a terminal meristem, includes both protoxylem and metaxylem. *Secondary xylem* is wood that arises through the activity of a cambium. It occurs in only a few living pteridophytes, but is characteristic of nearly all spermatophytes except the monocotyledonous angiosperms.

Types of Steles. The vascular tissues lie within the *stele*,[1] which in roots and stems generally forms a central core. This is surrounded by a cylindrical region, the *cortex*, outside of which lies a layer of cells constituting the *epidermis*. The innermost layer of the cortex is the *endodermis*. Four main types of steles occur in vascular plants and all of them are found in pteridophytes. These are as follows:

(1) The *protostele* is the simplest and most primitive type. Here the xylem forms a solid central strand surrounded by phloem, no pith being present (Figs. 176, 188, 200, 235, and 311). (2) The *amphiphloic siphonostele* has the xylem in the form of a hollow cylinder enclosing pith, with phloem both inside and outside the xylem (Figs. 236 and 249). (3) The *ectophloic siphonostele* also has the xylem surrounding pith, but there is no internal phloem (Figs. 221, 237, 269, 285, 294, and 315). (4) The *dictyostele* is the most advanced type. Here the vascular cylinder is broken up into a network of separate strands that, as seen in cross section, may be either arranged in a circle or scattered (Figs. 238 and 316).

The arrangement of xylem and phloem with reference to each other follows four general types, three of which occur in pteridophytes. (1) In the *radial* arrangement, which is most primitive, the xylem and phloem are in separate strands and occupy alternating radii (Figs. 171, 176, 220, 227, and 311). The xylem may or may not meet in the center. (2) In the *amphicribral* arrangement the phloem completely surrounds the xylem (Figs. 188 and 239). (3) In the *collateral* arrangement the xylem and phloem lie side by side on the same radius, with the phloem external to the xylem (Figs. 221, 294, and 315). Where the phloem occurs both outside and inside the xylem, the arrangement is *bicollateral*. (4) In the *amphivasal* arrangement the xylem surrounds the phloem. This is an advanced type occurring only among the monocotyledonous angiosperms (Fig. 317).

In practically all vascular plants the root is an exarch radial protostele. Stems display a great variety of vascular structure. Those of lycopods are much like roots and so are very primitive. The stems of ferns display all four stelar types, the amphiphloic siphonostele and the dictyostele

---

[1] Practically all stems have a single stele, and thus are sometimes designated as *monostelic*. *Polystelic* stems, containing more than one stele, are very rare (see p. 231).

being most common.   Most fern stems have mesarch amphicribral bundles.   The characteristic stem of seed plants is an ectophloic siphonostele with endarch collateral bundles, a type that is uncommon in pteridophytes.

Traces and Gaps.   In all vascular plants the conducting system is essentially continuous throughout the plant body.   A strand of conducting tissue extending from the stele of the stem through the cortex to a leaf is called a *leaf trace*.   A strand connecting the vascular tissue of the stem with that of a branch is a *branch trace*, while a *root trace* occurs where a root arises from a stem or from another root.   A *gap* is a break or interruption in a siphonostele caused by the departure of a leaf trace or a branch trace (Fig. 221).   It consists of parenchyma.   Gaps are not formed by root traces.   Branch gaps are present in all siphonostelic stems, but leaf traces occur only in ferns and seed plants.

1. PSILOPHYTINAE[1]

The Psilophytinae comprise a group of primitive pteridophytes that were abundant and widespread during the Devonian, but are represented today by only two genera of somewhat restricted distribution (Fig. 258). They are all rootless plants and either leafless or provided with small, simple, spirally arranged leaves.   The sporangia are solitary and terminal on branches that are elongated or, in modern forms, greatly reduced. The Psilophytinae comprise two orders, the extinct Psilophytales and the existing Psilotales.

1. Psilophytales

The Psilophytales are the oldest and most primitive of all known vascular plants.   They appeared in the late Silurian and flourished during the early and middle Devonian.   Their remains have been found in many parts of the world, but the best-preserved material has come from Scotland.   The chief genera are *Rhynia, Hornea, Psilophyton*, and *Asteroxylon*.

The Psilophytales were small herbaceous plants that lived on land. Few exceeded 60 cm. in height.   The sporophyte consisted of a rhizome bearing slender, erect, dichotomously branched shoots (Fig. 169).   The stems of *Asteroxylon* were covered with small simple leaves, but the three other genera were leafless.   In some species of *Psilophyton* the stems were spiny.   Apparently true roots were not present, but in some genera the rhizome bore numerous rhizoids.   In *Psilophyton* the tips of the branches were circinately coiled, as in the young leaves of ferns.   In all members of the group the stem was a protostele, a narrow zone of phloem enclosing a central mass of xylem.   Around the stele was a wide cortex surrounded by a cutinized epidermis with typical stomata.   The presence of stomata

---

[1] Also called Psilopsida.

on the erect stems demonstrates that they were aerial and green. In *Asteroxylon* the xylem was deeply lobed. The conducting tissues were very simple. There was no secondary thickening. The leaves, where present, were without veins, although the base of each leaf was con-

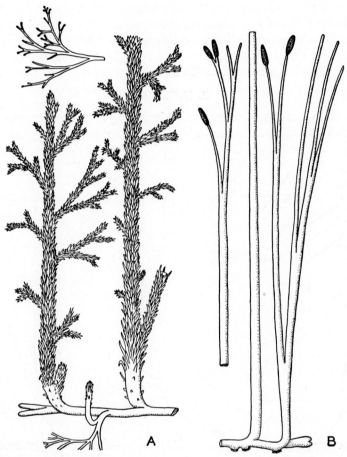

FIG. 169. Psilophytales from the Devonian of Scotland. *A, Asteroxylon mackiei; B, Rhynia major.* (*After Kidston and Lang.*)

nected with the stele by a strand of vascular tissue constituting a leaf trace.

The sporangia were borne singly at the ends of the branches and not in association with the leaves. They were relatively large (in some species up to 12 mm. long, but usually smaller), cylindrical, and homosporous. The sporangium wall was several layers of cells in thickness. As in other pteridophytes, the spores were formed in tetrads. In *Hornea* the sporogenous tissue was dome-shaped, capping a sterile columella, as in *Anthoc-eros* and *Sphagnum.* Nothing is known of the gametophyte generation.

Some botanists see in the simpler Psilophytales a resemblance to the liverwort *Anthoceros* and regard this group as a connecting link between the bryophytes and pteridophytes. Others feel that a closer relationship exists between the Psilophytales and the algae and that the Psilophytales were derived directly from alga-like ancestors. But, regardless of their origin, there is general belief that the group may have been ancestral to the other great pteridophyte lines—the lycopods, horsetails, and ferns—all of which are represented in the later Devonian deposits (Fig. 258).

2. Psilotales

The Psilotales are a modern order including only two genera. *Psilo-tum,* with two species, occurs in tropical and subtropical regions in both

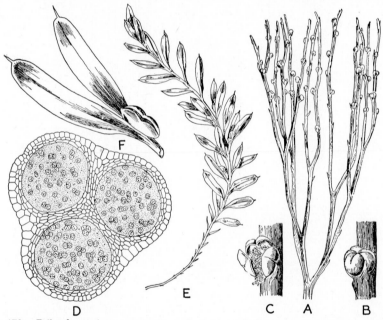

Fig. 170. Psilotales. *A,* upper portion of shoot of *Psilotum nudum* with sporangia, slightly reduced; *B,* closed sporangium of same, enlarged; *C,* open sporangium; *D,* cross section through an unripe sporangium, showing three locules containing spore mother cells; *E,* shoot of *Tmesipteris tannensis,* slightly reduced; *F,* a sporophyll of same, enlarged. (*After Wettstein.*)

the Eastern and Western Hemispheres. *Tmesipteris,* with a single species, is confined to Australia, New Zealand, the Philippine Islands, and parts of Polynesia. The Psilotales were formerly classified with the Lycopodiinae, but they are now generally regarded as being more closely related to the extinct Psilophytales.

Sporophyte. The sporophyte consists of a rhizome bearing rhizoids and giving rise to slender, green, aerial stems (Fig. 170*A*, *E*). A peculiar feature is the absence of roots. The aerial stems of *Psilotum* branch dichotomously and generally grow erect upon the ground, but are sometimes epiphytic and drooping. They reach a length of 20 to 100 cm. The leaves are few, scale-like, and without veins. *Tmesipteris* may grow as an erect terrestrial plant but is generally epiphytic and pendulous,

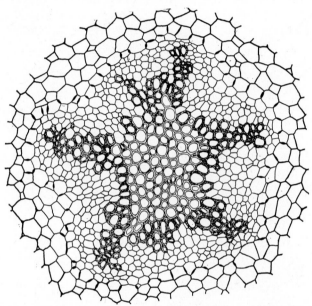

Fig. 171. Cross section of the central portion of the aerial stem of *Psilotum nudum*, ×100. The protoxylem lies at the tips of the xylem rays, the phloem between them. The center of the stele is occupied by a group of fibers.

especially on tree ferns. The stem is unbranched, rarely showing a single dichotomy. It reaches a length of 5 to 25 cm. The leaves are narrow, 12 to 18 mm. long, and have a single vein. In both genera the leaves are more or less spirally arranged. The rhizome and aerial stem grow by means of a tetrahedral apical cell (having the form of a triangular pyramid).

Vascular Anatomy. In both genera the rhizome is a protostele. In the aerial stem the xylem forms a star-shaped mass enclosing a pith that, in *Psilotum*, is occupied by a group of fibers (Fig. 171). The rhizome is exarch in both genera, the first-formed xylem (*protoxylem*) lying outside the later-formed xylem (*metaxylem*). The aerial stem is exarch in *Psilotum* but mesarch in *Tmesipteris*, in the latter the metaxylem surrounding the protoxylem. The phloem, which lies outside the xylem, is poorly developed. There is no cambium. An endophytic fungus is present in the outer cortical region of the rhizome.

Sporangium. The sporangia are borne singly in the axils of the upper leaves, which are bifurcated in both genera, a sporangium arising at the point of forking (Fig. 170). Each sporangium is situated at the end of a short stalk. In *Tmesipteris* the large sporangium is divided transversely

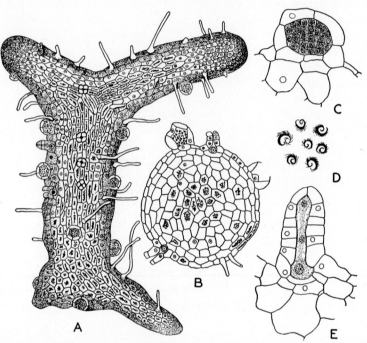

Fig. 172. Prothallium and sex organs of *Psilotum nudum*. *A*, surface view of an entire prothallium of rather small size, bearing rhizoids, antheridia, and archegonia, ×28; *B*, cross section of prothallium, showing two antheridia (one discharged), two archegonia, and endophytic fungus, ×38; *C*, a nearly mature antheridium, ×145; *D*, several sperms, ×450; *E*, a nearly mature archegonium, ×145. (*After Lawson.*)

by a sterile plate into two separate chambers, so that two sporangia seem to be present. In *Psilotum* the sporangium is three-chambered. The wall consists of several layers of cells. No tapetum is present, but among the spore mother cells are numerous sterile cells that are resorbed by the developing spores. Both genera of the Psilotales are homosporous. Dehiscence of the sporangium occurs by means of a longitudinal slit.

The nature of the sporangium-bearing structures of the Psilotales is not clearly understood. One interpretation is that the upper, forked leaves are bifid sporophylls bearing solitary adaxial sporangia that are bilocular in *Tmesipteris* and trilocular in *Psilotum*. Another view is that the whole structure is a sporangiophore bearing two leaves and a terminal sporangium; that the sporangiophore is not a lateral branch but a reduced member of a dichotomous branch of the main stem. The existing evidence favors this second interpretation. It is also not clear whether the sporangium should be regarded as a single sporangium or a *synangium*, which is a group of united sporangia. In early developmental stages each mass of sporogenous tissue has an independent origin, but it is uncertain whether or not the partitions represent sterile sporogenous tissue.

Gametophyte. The prothallia of both *Psilotum* and *Tmesipteris* are tuberous, subterranean, saprophytic bodies without any chlorophyll (Fig. 172*A*, *B*). They are light brown, cylindrical, simple at first but later branched, and up to 20 mm. in length. Long rhizoids uniformly cover the surface. An endophytic fungus is present. In *Psilotum*, but not in *Tmesipteris*, the largest prothallia sometimes possess a strand of conducting tissue consisting of a few tracheids. Both kinds of sex organs occur in abundance on the same prothallium. The antheridia are globular and projecting, each producing many multiciliate sperms (Fig. 172*C*, *D*). The antheridium initial, which is superficial, undergoes a periclinal division, the outer cell giving rise to the sterile jacket and the inner cell to the spermatogenous tissue. The archegonia are sunken in the prothallium, but the neck protrudes (Fig. 172*E*). Apparently two neck canal cells are present.

Embryo. The embryos of *Psilotum* and *Tmesipteris* are very similar. They are peculiar in that no suspensor, root, or leaf is present. The fertilized egg divides transversely, the outer cell giving rise to the stem and the inner cell to the foot. In *Tmesipteris* a second stem tip often appears near the base of the first one; later both may grow erect and produce leaves.

Summary. The stem of *Psilotum* is elongated and branched, the leaves scale-like and relatively few. The stem of *Tmesipteris* is also elongated but generally unbranched; the leaves are small and numerous. Roots are absent in both genera. The stem is differentiated into an underground and an aerial portion. The rhizome is an exarch protostele. The aerial stem, which is medullated, is exarch in *Psilotum* and mesarch in *Tmesipteris*. The arrangement of xylem and phloem is amphicribral. There is no cambial activity. The sporangia are borne singly in the axils of the upper leaves, each at the end of a short sporangiophore. There is no definitely organized strobilus. The sporangium is either bilocular (*Tmesipteris*) or trilocular (*Psilotum*), homosporous, and longitudinally dehiscent. A tapetum is not organized. The prothallia are subterranean and tuberous. The antheridia produce many multiciliate sperms. The archegonia have two neck canal cells. The embryo is without a suspensor. The Psilotales form an isolated order not closely related to other living pteridophytes.

2. LYCOPODIINAE[1]

The lycopods, numbering nearly 950 species, are an ancient group represented in our modern flora by only four surviving genera. They were abundant in the Devonian but reached their greatest display during the Carboniferous (Fig. 258), when some were trees 30 m. tall. Today all lycopods are herbaceous, generally growing close to the ground. They are characterized by leaves that are mostly small, simple, and spirally arranged and by sporangia that are always solitary, adaxial, and unilocular. There are four orders, the Lycopodiales, Selaginellales, Lepidodendrales, and Isoetales. Of these, the third is extinct.

Fig. 173. Two tropical species of *Lycopodium* from Costa Rica, about one-third natural size. *A, Lycopodium cernuum*, a terrestrial species with upright stems and nodding cones; *B, Lycopodium tubulosum*, a pendent epiphytic species with loosely organized cones at the ends of the branches.

1. Lycopodiales

Only two living genera belong to this order. *Lycopodium*, with 180 species, is widely distributed throughout the world but is most abundant

[1] Also called Lycopsida.

in the tropics.   *Phylloglossum* has a single species confined to Australia, Tasmania, and New Zealand.   Fossil forms known as *Lycopodites* have been found in Carboniferous and later formations.

Sporophyte.   The sporophyte of *Lycopodium* consists of a slender stem, generally branched, and bearing roots and numerous small leaves.   Most of the species are terrestrial plants either with erect stems or, more commonly, with elongated, trailing or subterranean stems giving rise to

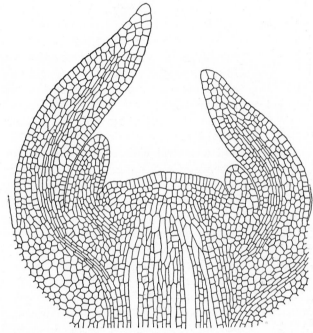

Fig. 174.   Median longitudinal section through the stem tip of *Lycopodium reflexum*, showing the apical meristem and developing leaves, ×100.

upright branches (Figs. 173*A*, 179, and 180).   Many of the tropical species are epiphytes with erect or pendent stems (Fig. 173*B*).   The terrestrial species grow close to the ground, few exceeding 30 cm. in height. Numerous roots penetrate the soil.   Generally both the roots and stems branch dichotomously, but in some species the branching of the stem is apparently monopodial, the branches arising laterally from a true main axis.   The leaves are small and often scale-like, simple, entire, and densely cover the branches.   They are generally borne in spiral arrangement.   Growth of the root and stem takes place by means of an apical meristem, no apical cell being present (Fig. 174).

Although *Phylloglossum* is much simpler than *Lycopodium*, it is generally regarded, not as a primitive form, but as one reduced from more highly developed ancestors.   The sporophyte is only 3 to 5 cm. high and consists of a short tuberous stem bearing a few small fleshy leaves that form a cluster around the stem apex (Fig. 175). As a rule, only a single root is present, but sometimes there are two or three roots. In some species of *Lycopodium* the sporophyte begins its development as a small tuberous body like that of *Phylloglossum*. This disappears after giving rise to the ordinary type of leafy stem with roots. In other species no embryonic body of this kind occurs in the life history.

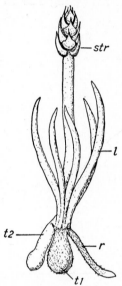

FIG. 175. Fertile plant of *Phylloglossum drummondii*, twice natural size; *str*, strobilus; *l*, leaves; *r*, root; *t1*, primary tuber; *t2*, secondary tuber.

Vascular Anatomy. Anatomically the roots and leaves of *Lycopodium* are essentially like those of other vascular plants. The leaves are only a few layers of cells in thickness and consist of uniform mesophyll enclosed above and below by an epidermis with stomata. Each leaf has a single median vein.

The stem structure of *Lycopodium* is very primitive. A cross section shows an outer cortex and a central cylindrical stele. Because of the absence of a pith, this type of vascular system is a protostele. In some species the xylem forms a star-shaped mass between the rays of which lies the phloem (Fig. 176). In other species, although fundamentally radial, a modification is seen in that the xylem and phloem are somewhat intermixed (Fig. 177), while in still others the two kinds of conducting tissues occur in alternating, transverse, parallel bands (Fig. 178). A protostele that is star-shaped in outline is often designated as an *actinostele;* one that is circular in outline is called a *haplostele;* while the type with separate, parallel plates of xylem is termed a *plectostele*. The radial type is most primitive and the banded type most advanced. This is shown by the development of the vascular system in a young plant, where, if the banded condition appears, it is always preceded by the radial condition. Also, in many species, the growing stem is radial at the tip and gradually becomes banded farther back.

All the vascular tissues are primary, there being no cambial activity. The smaller cells at the tips of the radiating arms of xylem are the first elements to lignify, subsequent lignification proceeding toward the center of the stem. Thus the development of the xylem is exarch, the protoxylem lying external to the metaxylem (Figs. 176, 177, 178). The protoxylem is composed of narrow, spiral, and annular tracheids, the metaxylem of larger, scalariform tracheids.

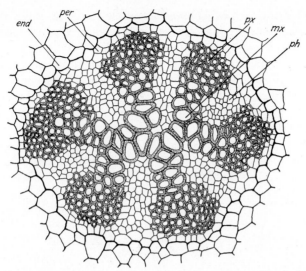

FIG. 176. Cross section of the central portion of the stem of *Lycopodium lucidulum*, showing the "radial" type of stele, ×250; *end*, endodermis; *per*, pericycle; *px*, protoxylem; *mx*, metaxylem; *ph*, phloem.

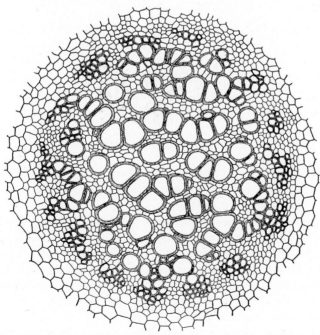

FIG. 177. Cross section of the central portion of the stem of *Lycopodium cernuum*, showing the "mixed" type of stele, ×70.

The stele is enclosed by a parenchymatous pericycle, one or more layers of cells in thickness, outside of which is an ill-defined endodermis, consisting of a layer of cells with cutinized walls (Fig. 176). As in all vascular plants, the conducting system is essentially continuous throughout the plant body. From the stele of the stem a strand of conducting tissue, called a *leaf trace*, extends through the cortex to enter each leaf and

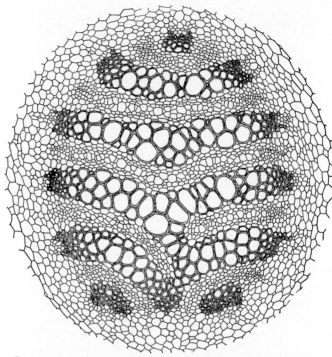

Fig. 178.   Cross section of the central portion of the stem of *Lycopodium complanatum*, showing the "parallel-banded" type of stele, $\times 130$.

become its vein.   Similarly each branch is connected with the stele of the main stem by a *branch trace* and each root by a *root trace*.   These traces are present in all vascular plants.

Like the stem, the root of *Lycopodium* is an exarch protostele, but nearly always shows the radial arrangement of xylem and phloem, even where the stem is of the mixed or parallel-banded type.   The striking similarity between the root and stem of *Lycopodium* bespeaks a very ancient origin for the genus, for in the higher groups of vascular plants the organization of the stem becomes increasingly more advanced, while that of the root remains unchanged.

The vascular system of *Phylloglossum* is poorly developed and shows evidences of reduction.   The tuber consists mainly of compact storage parenchyma with a small amount of xylem in its upper portion. Apparently no phloem is present. In sterile plants the vascular system is a protostele, but in fertile plants the xylem surrounds a central mass of parenchyma and is thus a siphonostele. The development of the xylem

FIG. 179. *Lycopodium reflexum*, an upright tropical species in which most of the leaves are sporophylls; about natural size.

is mesarch, the metaxylem arising both inside and outside the protoxylem. This is a more advanced condition than that seen in *Lycopodium*.

Sporangium. The sporangia of *Lycopodium* are borne singly in the leaf axils. Each sporangium is large and more or less kidney-shaped, with a very short stalk, a wall several layers of cells in thickness, and a central mass of small, yellow, thick-walled spores. When mature, it dehisces by means of a transverse slit. A leaf that bears a sporangium is termed a *sporophyll*.

In the simplest species of *Lycopodium* every leaf on the plant is a sporophyll, or at least potentially so, but in most species just the upper leaves bear sporangia, the lower leaves being sterile and functioning merely as foliage leaves (Figs. 179 and 180).   An aggregation of sporophylls is called a *cone* or *strobilus*.   The sporophylls may be loosely arranged but, more commonly, are compactly organized.   They may be similar to the

Fig. 180.   *Lycopodium obscurum*, a common species occurring throughout the northeastern United States, about one-half natural size.   Upright branches bearing terminal cones arise from long trailing stems.

foliage leaves but generally are smaller, of a different form, and without chlorophyll.

Because of this variation among the species of *Lycopodium*, it is not difficult to arrange a series representing progressive stages in the differentiation of the sporophylls and organization of a strobilus.   It seems reasonable to suppose that such a series represents the course of evolution that the more complex species have followed.   This is confirmed by other characters.   Thus most of the species without a definite strobilus have

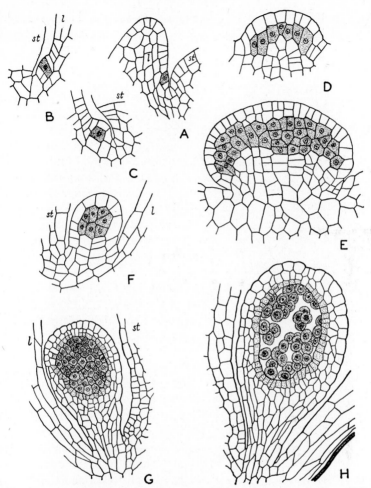

Fig. 181. Early development of the sporangium of *Lycopodium selago*. *A*, radial section of base of young sporophyll (*l*) arising from stem (*st*), showing initial cell (one of a transverse row); *B*, slightly later stage; *C*, division of initial into primary wall cell and primary sporogenous cell (latter shaded); *D*, tangential section of same; *E*, further development of sporogenous tissue; *F*, radial section of same; *G*, later stage, showing development of tapetum; *H*, sporangium showing stalk, wall, tapetum, and spore mother cells. (*After Bower*.)

dichotomously branched stems showing the radial type of stele, while many of the cone-bearing species have stems with monopodial branching and most of them show the parallel-banded type of stele.

The large solitary sporangium is always adaxial in its relation to the sporophyll and is also unilocular. The sporangium arises from a superficial group of initials consisting of a transverse row of 6 to 12 cells (Fig. 181*A*, *B*). In some species there may be two or three such rows. Each initial divides by a periclinal wall to form an outer and an inner row, the former constituting the *primary wall cells* and the latter the *primary sporogenous cells* (Fig. 181*C*, *D*). The sporangium wall becomes at least three layers of cells thick, the inner layer forming the *tapetum* (Fig.

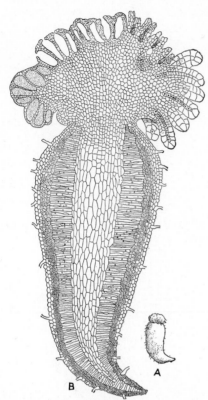

181*E–G*). This is a nutritive layer that, instead of disorganizing, as in the horsetails and ferns, remains intact for a long time. After the sporogenous cells have increased in number, spore mother cells are organized and from each a tetrad of spores arises (Fig. 181*H*). The development of the sporangium of *Lycopodium* takes place according to the *eusporangiate* method. This means that the sporogenous tissue is derived from the inner segment following the first periclinal division of the initial. All vascular plants, except the higher ferns, are eusporangiate.

In *Phylloglossum* the apex of the tuber gives rise to an erect naked stalk bearing a small terminal strobilus (Fig. 175). If no strobilus is formed, the stem tip produces a new tuber at the close of the growing season, but otherwise a secondary tuber appears adventitiously

Fig. 182. Gametophyte of *Lycopodium complanatum*. *A*, the entire gametophyte, twice natural size; *B*, longitudinal section with antheridia to the left, some of which have shed their sperms, and with archegonia to the right, in one of which an embryo has developed, ✕25. The shaded cells in the lower portion contain a fungus. (*After Bruchmann.*)

at the end of a short stalk. The strobilus consists of a few spirally arranged sporophylls, each bearing a solitary, unilocular, adaxial sporangium. The sporangium is short-stalked and kidney-shaped. It consists of a central mass of sporogenous tissue surrounded by a wall three layers of cells in thickness, the inner layer forming the tapetum. As in *Lycopodium*, dehiscence occurs by means of a transverse slit.

Gametophyte. The spores of *Lycopodium* are remarkably long-lived and often do not germinate for a number of years. Eventually they give rise to gametophytes, or *prothallia* as they are usually called. These are small tuberous bodies that vary widely in form, depending on the species, being turnip-shaped, cylindrical, flat, or irregularly bulbous.   In *Lycopo-dium cernuum*, a widespread tropical species, the prothallium is an erect cylindrical body only 2 or 3 mm. long.   It grows at the surface of the ground and consists of a colorless basal portion buried in the soil and a conspicuously lobed aerial crown that is green and bears the sex organs. The lower portion produces rhizoids and contains an endophytic fungus. The spores germinate promptly and the prothallium reaches maturity in a

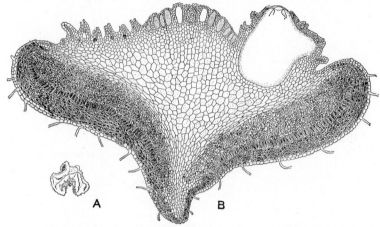

Fig. 183.   Gametophyte of *Lycopodium clavatum*.   *A*, the entire gametophyte, twice natural size; *B*, longitudinal section with antheridia in center and archegonia to the left and right, ×20.   In the embryo, shown in outline, a young shoot has developed above, a young root to the right, and a large foot below and to the left.   The shaded cells in the lower portion of the prothallium contain a fungus.   (*After Bruchmann.*)

single season.   Several other species of *Lycopodium*, as well as *Phylloglos-sum*, have a similar type of prothallium but some lack the fungus.

In most other species, including nearly all those of the North Temperate Zone, the prothallium is larger, commonly 12 to 18 mm. long, and entirely subterranean, colorless, and saprophytic (Figs. 182 and 183).   An endo-phytic fungus, restricted to the lower portion of the prothallium, is always present and seems to play an essential part in its nutrition.   The spores do not germinate for 3 to 8 years and the prothallium may not reach maturity for an equally long period, growth being extremely slow. The production of sex organs may continue for a number of years.   The gametophyte may be erect and somewhat turnip-shaped, as in *Lycopo-dium complanatum*, with the sex organs borne on an irregularly lobed crown that is not as well developed as in *Lycopodium cernuum* (Fig. 182). In certain other species, such as *Lycopodium clavatum*, the crown is reduced even more, the prothallium being flat and irregularly cup-shaped, with a depressed center surrounded by a broad rim (Fig. 183).   The sex organs are borne in the center.   This type of prothallium grows farthest below the surface of the ground and requires the greatest number of years to reach maturity.

It is an interesting fact that only species with a green aerial prothallium have a sporophyte that passes through a *Phylloglossum*-like stage in its early development. The prothallium of such species doubtless represents a primitive type from which the colorless subterranean prothallia have been derived. Their development may have been caused by delayed germination of the spores, resulting in their burial in the soil.

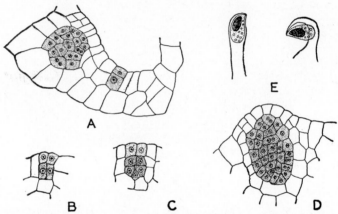

FIG. 184. Antheridial development in *Lycopodium clavatum*, ×150. *A*, to the right, a young antheridium after first division of initial cell; to the left, a much older stage; *B*, vertical division of primary wall cell and primary spermatogenous cell; *C*, further division of spermatogenous cells; *D*, nearly mature antheridium, showing wall and spermatogenous tissue; *E*, two sperms, ×625. (*After Bruchmann.*)

In fact, in some species, a spore will produce a green prothallium if it germinates on the surface of the ground and a colorless one if it germinates below the surface.

Both kinds of sex organs are borne in rather large numbers on the same gametophyte. The antheridia are either completely embedded or slightly projecting. They are globular, have a sterile jacket consisting of a single layer of cells, and produce many small, slightly curved, biciliate sperms (Fig. 184). In development, a superficial initial divides by a periclinal wall to form an outer *primary wall cell* and an inner *primary spermatogenous cell*. The former gives rise to the sterile jacket, the latter to the mass of spermatogenous tissue.

The archegonia are also embedded in the prothallium, only the neck protruding (Fig. 185). The initial is superficial and gives rise, by a periclinal division, to an outer *primary neck cell* and an inner cell that again divides to form the *central cell* and *basal cell* (Fig. 185*A*, *B*). The central cell gives rise to two cells, the outer one being the *primary neck canal cell* and the inner one the *primary ventral cell* (Fig. 185*C*). The primary neck canal cell, by additional transverse divisions, gives rise to a variable number of *neck canal cells*, while the primary ventral cell, by a single transverse division, produces the *ventral canal cell* and *egg* (Fig. 185*D–F*). In some species there are 4 to 6 neck canal cells. In *Lycopodium cernuum* the number has been reduced to 1, while in *Lycopodium complanatum* as many as 16 have been counted. The presence of numerous neck canal cells is a primitive feature not seen in other living pteridophytes.

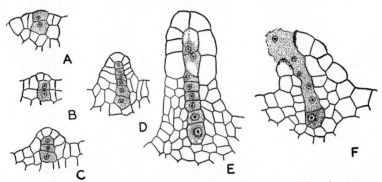

FIG. 185. Archegonial development in *Lycopodium clavatum*, ×150. *A*, young archegonium after first division of initial cell; *B*, vertical division of primary neck cell and transverse division of inner cell to form basal cell and central cell (both shaded); *C*, division of central cell to form primary neck canal cell and primary ventral cell; *D*, later stage, showing basal cell, primary ventral cell, and four neck canal cells; *E*, nearly mature archegonium with egg, ventral canal cell, and six neck canal cells; *F*, older stage, the canal cells breaking down. (*After Bruchmann.*)

Embryo. The fertilized egg divides transversely to form an outer suspensor cell and an inner embryonal cell (Fig. 186*A*). The suspensor cell may or may not divide again but usually elongates and pushes the embryo a short distance into the prothallium. The embryonal cell, by two vertical divisions at right angles to each other, gives rise to quadrants, each of which then divides transversely to form eight cells in two tiers (Fig. 186*B–E*). Of these, the tier lying next to the suspensor develops the foot, while the lower tier gives rise on one side to the stem and on the other side to the leaf (Fig. 186*F–I*). The foot is a temporary organ that absorbs food from the gametophyte. It persists until the sporophyte has become independent. The primary root is formed relatively late and arises from the same tissue that produces the leaf.

Summary. In *Lycopodium* an elongated, generally branched stem bears numerous small leaves. In *Phylloglossum* a short tuberous stem produces a few small leaves in a cluster. The vascular system of the stem of *Lycopodium* is a protostele, fundamentally radial in organization, with exarch development of xylem. Secondary thickening is absent. In the simplest species of *Lycopodium* all the leaves are sporophylls, but in the more advanced species a differentiation exists between sporophylls and foliage leaves, the former forming a more or less distinct strobilus. All the Lycopodiales are homosporous. Dehiscence of the sporangium occurs by means of a transverse slit. The gametophyte is a subterranean tuberous body, sometimes with an aerial portion. The antheridia develop

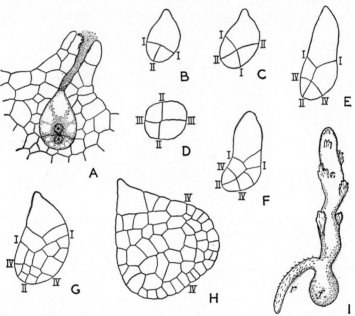

FIG. 186. Development of the embryo of *Lycopodium clavatum*. *A*, first division of the fertilized egg into suspensor and embryonal cells; *B*, second division of embryonal cell; *C*, second division of suspensor cell; *D*, cross section, showing third division of embryonal cell; *E*, transverse division (IV) of four cells derived from the embryonal cell; *F, G, H*, later stages; *I*, young sporophyte, showing foot (*f*), primary root (*r*), and stem bearing scale leaves. (*After Bruchmann.*)

endogenously and produce many small biciliate sperms similar to those of bryophytes. The archegonia are primitive, being characterized by a large number of neck canal cells. The embryo has a suspensor. On the whole, the Lycopodiales are a very primitive group of pteridophytes.

2. Selaginellales

The Selaginellales include a single genus, *Selaginella*, with nearly 700 species. The great majority of these are tropical or subtropical in distribution, but a few occur in temperate regions. Most species require abundant moisture and shade, while some grow in open, dry situations. *Selaginellites*, a fossil genus, has been recognized in deposits as old as the Lower Carboniferous.

Sporophyte. In general, the sporophyte of *Selaginella* has the same habit as that of *Lycopodium*, but is nearly always smaller and more delicate. The stems are dichotomously branched and usually trailing, but are often erect or climbing. *Rhizophores*, which are special leafless branches of the main stem, are found in many species. They produce adventitious roots at their tips. The leaves are scale-like and numerous, generally occurring in four longitudinal rows. Each leaf bears a *ligule*, a minute flap-like outgrowth arising from the basal portion of the adaxial surface. The ligule is prominent only during the early development of the leaf.

In some species of *Selaginella* the leaves are all alike and symmetrically arranged around the stem, but in most species the leaves are spread out horizontally and usually of two kinds. These are regularly arranged with reference to each other, there being two rows of small dorsal leaves and two rows of large ventral ones (Fig. 189*A*). In contrast to *Lycopodium*, a definite apical cell is usually present at the tip of the root and stem, but some species appear to have an apical meristem (Fig. 187).

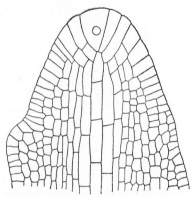

Fig. 187. Median longitudinal section through the stem tip of *Selaginella bigelovii*, showing the apical cell and its derivatives, × 500.

Vascular Anatomy. The leaves have an epidermis and a loose mesophyll, the stomata usually being confined to the lower surface. The chloroplasts are large and few in number, sometimes only one occurring in each cell. Each leaf has a single median vein. The adult stem generally consists of a single, dorsiventrally flattened protostele with two lateral protoxylem groups (Fig. 188). The metaxylem develops toward the center, and so the stem is exarch. In some species the stele is cylindrical and in some two, three, or more separate steles are present. One species has reached the siphonostelic condition. The conducting tissues show an amphicribral arrangement, the xylem being completely surrounded by the phloem. Outside the pericycle, which is generally one-layered, a broad air space occurs. This is traversed by elongated cells (trabeculae) consisting of endodermal cells united with one or more cells that have a common origin with the endodermis. As in *Lycopodium*, no cambium is present and so there is no secondary thickening. In some species the cortical cells are thick-walled.

Sporangia. In all species of *Selaginella* definite terminal strobili are present. Where the foliage leaves are all alike, the sporophylls and leaves are either similar or only slightly differentiated. Where the foliage leaves are of two kinds, the sporophylls are smaller than the large leaves (Fig. 189*A*). As in *Lycopodium*, the sporangia are solitary, adaxial, unilocular, and eusporangiate in development (Fig. 189*B*, *C*). Each is probably derived from a transverse row of initials. These generally appear on the

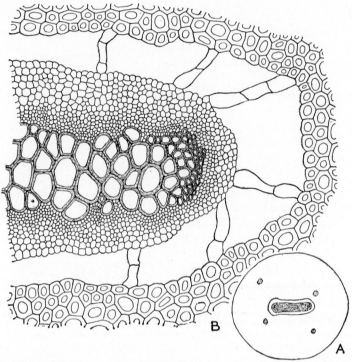

Fig. 188. Stem structure of *Selaginella flabellata*. *A*, diagram of cross section, showing central flattened protostele surrounded by cortex, ×10. *B*, enlarged view of portion of stele, showing exarch xylem surrounded by a wide zone of phloem and an air space traversed by trabeculae, ×200.

stem just above the place where the young sporophyll arises from it (Fig. 190*A*–*C*). Although cauline in origin, the young sporangium is soon carried out on the sporophyll and then looks as if it had originated there. The wall of the young sporangium consists of a single layer of cells but it soon becomes two-layered. In contrast to the other lycopods, the tapetum is not derived from the wall tissue but from the outermost layer of sporogenous tissue. As in *Lycopodium*, it does not break down until the spores are formed. The innermost wall layer also disorganizes at this time, and so the mature sporangium has only a single layer of wall cells. Each sporangium is borne on a short stalk. Dehiscence takes place by means of a vertical slit.

Selaginella is heterosporous, each strobilus usually bearing two kinds of sporangia—*microsporangia* and *megasporangia* (Fig. 189*B*, *C*). The microsporangia, which are often reddish, generally occur in the upper part of the strobilus, while the megasporangia, which are commonly yellowish, are borne below. The megasporangia are usually slightly larger than the microsporangia and are generally four-lobed.

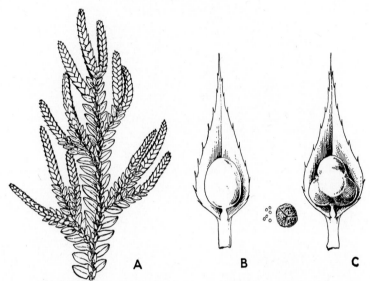

Fig. 189. *Selaginella willldenovii. A*, branch with leaves and strobili, twice natural size; *B*, a microsporophyll with a microsporangium containing numerous microspores, ×25; *C*, a megasporophyll with a megasporangium containing four megaspores, ×25; several microspores and a megaspore drawn to the same scale are also shown.

Both kinds of sporangia develop alike as far as the stage in which the sporogenous tissue is differentiated. In the microsporangium practically all the mother cells divide to produce tetrads, and consequently many small spores are formed (Fig. 192*A*). These are the *microspores*. In the megasporangium, on the other hand, all the mother cells degenerate but one, which greatly enlarges and forms a tetrad of thick-walled spores that eventually fill the sporangium (Figs. 191 and 192*B*). These are the *megaspores*. The sporophylls that produce the microsporangia are *microsporophylls*, while those bearing megasporangia are *megasporophylls*. Usually the sporophylls themselves, however, are of approximately the same size and form. Like the foliage leaves, each sporophyll bears a ligule. It is situated just beyond the sporangium (Figs. 190 and 192).

Upon germination, the microspores give rise to male gametophytes and the megaspores to female gametophytes. Thus heterospory involves not only a differentiation of spores but also a differentiation of gametophytes.

Gametophytes. The male gametophyte of *Selaginella* is developed entirely within the microspore. It is without chlorophyll and greatly reduced. Its development is initiated before the spore is shed from the sporangium and is completed later. A small *prothallial* or *vegetative* cell is

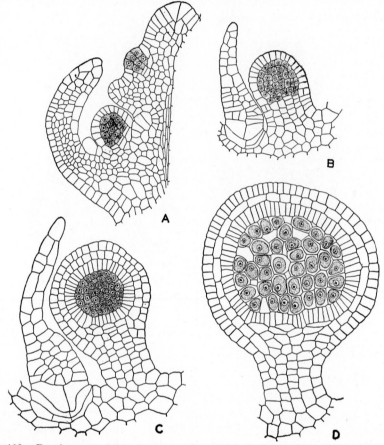

Fig. 190.   Development of the microsporangium of *Selaginella galeottii*, ×320.   *A*, median longitudinal section of portion of apex of strobilus, showing early stages; *B*, slightly later stage with ligule to the left; *C*, young sporangium with sporogenous tissue surrounded by tapetum and two wall layers; *D*, older sporangium, the sporogenous cells beginning to round up.

cut off, the large remaining cell forming a single antheridium (Fig. 193). At first this consists of four primary spermatogenous cells surrounded by a sterile jacket of eight cells, and usually the male gametophyte is shed from the microsporangium in this condition. Later the spermatogenous cells increase in number to 128 or 256, each finally giving rise to a sperm. Meanwhile the jacket cells disintegrate, leaving the mass of sperms free within the microspore wall. The sperms are small, curved, and biciliate.

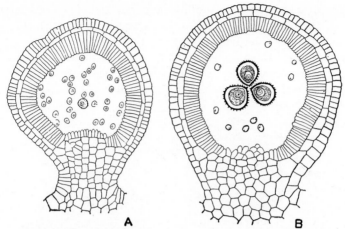

FIG. 191. Longitudinal sections of young megasporangia of *Selaginella*, ×200. *A*, megasporangium of *Selaginella emmeliana* with spore mother cells, the functional one enlarging; *B*, megasporangium of *Selaginella apoda*, showing three of the four megaspores.

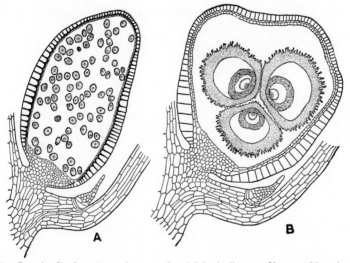

FIG. 192. Longitudinal sections of sporangia of *Selaginella emmeliana*, ×80. *A*, a microsporangium with numerous microspores; *B*, a megasporangium with three of the four developing megaspores.

The female gametophyte develops within the megaspore but is not so greatly reduced as the male gametophyte. The megaspore germinates while still within the megasporangium and long before it has reached its full size. The protoplast of the young megaspore is apically situated and consists of a vesicle with a small nucleus. It has a thick membrane that seems to grow more rapidly than itself, leaving a fluid-filled space between the protoplast and the membrane. The membrane soon differentiates into an outer and inner layer that also separate as a result of a more rapid growth of the outer layer, thus forming a second fluid-filled space (Figs. 191*B* and 192*B*). The female gametophyte begins to develop by free-nuclear division. Its protoplast enlarges until it comes in contact with the inner spore coat, which later comes in contact with the outer coat, thereby obliterating both cavities. The nuclei in the young gametophyte

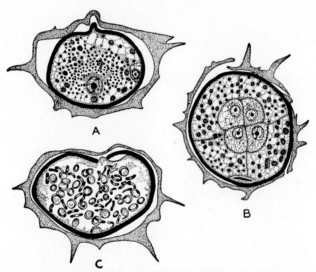

FIG. 193. Sections through the male gametophyte of *Selaginella kraussiana* in different stages of development. *A*, early stage, consisting of a small prothallial cell and an antheridial cell; *B*, later stage with prothallial cell and antheridium consisting of four primary spermatogenous cells surrounded by eight jacket cells; *C*, mature gametophyte with nearly ripe sperms lying free inside microspore wall. (*After Slagg.*)

lie in a peripheral layer of cytoplasm surrounding a large central vacuole (Fig. 194*A*).

After the female gametophyte has undergone a series of free-nuclear divisions, wall formation begins at the apical (pointed) end. At this place the spore wall ruptures and the gametophytic tissue protrudes slightly, developing archegonia and in some species rhizoids also, or rhizoids and chlorophyll. The main portion of the gametophyte, lying within the megaspore wall, acts as a large food reservoir. In many species there is a marked differentiation between the deeper nutritive region and the exposed portion, and often the former is not divided into cells (Fig. 194*B*). The development of the archegonium is similar to that of *Lycopodium* except that the neck is very short and no basal cell is formed. There is usually only one neck canal cell.

Although, in most species, the early development of the female gametophyte occurs while the megaspore is still within the megasporangium, archegonia generally do not appear until the megaspore is shed. In some species the megaspore is retained until fertilization has occurred, or even until the embryo has appeared. Here the male gametophytes are carried to the megasporophylls by wind or gravity and there they liberate their sperms. In such cases it is apparent that a condition closely approaching seed formation is reached.

Embryo. The embryo of *Selaginella* resembles that of *Lycopodium* in a general way, but shows certain important differences and some variation

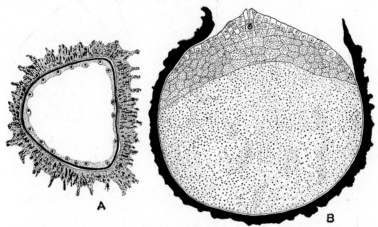

Fig. 194. Female gametophyte of *Selaginella apoda*. *A*, section of megaspore containing young gametophyte in free-nuclear stage; *B*, section of megaspore with mature gametophyte, consisting of a large nutritive cell and small-celled tissue in which an archegonium has developed. (*After Lyon.*)

among the different species (Fig. 195). Commonly the first division of the fertilized egg, which is transverse, separates an outer suspensor cell from an inner embryonal cell, but the suspensor usually becomes more highly developed than in *Lycopodium*. No quadrant stage is formed. Instead the embryonal cell produces three cells—a terminal one, which forms the stem, and two lateral ones, each of which gives rise to a leaf. One of the leaf segments produces the foot and later the primary root. In some species the foot and root, as well as the suspensor, are derived from the upper cell that arises from the first division of the fertilized egg.

Summary. The stem of *Selaginella* is elongated and branched, the leaves numerous and small. Each leaf bears a ligule. The vascular system of the stem is typically an exarch protostele with amphicribral organization; sometimes more than one stele is present. There is no secondary thickening. All species have a definite strobilus and are heterosporous. The microsporangia produce many microspores, the megasporangia four megaspores. Dehiscence takes place by means of a vertical slit. The male gametophyte, developed entirely inside the microspore, consists of only one prothallial cell and one antheridium, the latter producing many small biciliate sperms.   The female gametophyte, with relatively exten-sive vegetative tissue, develops largely within the megaspore, the protrud-ing portion forming several archegonia.   These are of an advanced type

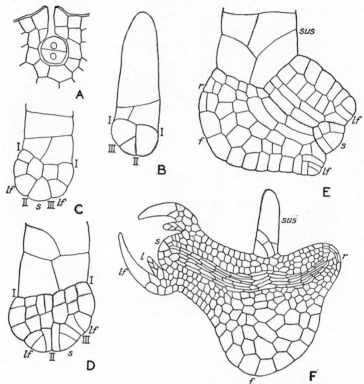

Fig. 195.   Development of the embryo of *Selaginella martensii*. *A*, first division of ferti-lized egg into suspensor and embryonal cells; *B*, embryonal cell divided into three cells; *C*, differentiation of stem and leaf primordia; *D*, later stage, the stem and leaf primordia developing by an apical cell; *E*, later stage, showing differentiation of foot and root; *F*, older embryo; *sus*, suspensor; *s*, stem tip, *lf*, leaf; *l*, ligule; *r*, root tip; *f*, foot. (*After Pfeffer*.)

with only one neck canal cell.   The embryo has a suspensor.   *Selaginella* is related to *Lycopodium*, differing from it chiefly in being heterosporous.

3. Lepidodendrales

The Lepidodendrales are a Paleozoic group of lycopods.   They ranged from the Devonian through the Permian but made their greatest display during the Upper Carboniferous, when they were one of the dominant plant groups.   They were chiefly tree-like and often reached a height of 30 m. or more.   The two most prominent genera were *Lepidodendron* and

Fig. 196. Portion of restoration of Carboniferous swamp forest in the Chicago Natural History Museum, showing trunks of *Sigillaria rugosa* (to left) and *Sigillaria saulli* (to right), and cones of *Lepidostrobus ovatifolius* (upper left); also two seed ferns: *Neuropteris decipiens* (right center) and *Neuropteris heterophylla* (below).

Sigillaria[1] (Fig. 196). Both bore numerous narrow simple leaves that, upon falling, left characteristic scars on the stem. The stems of *Lepidodendron* were dichotomously and freely branched and the leaves were frequently up to 15 or 20 cm. long. The stems of *Sigillaria* were slightly or not at all branched and the leaves, in some species, reached a length of 1 m. The leaves of all the Lepidodendrales had a single vascular bundle and in all of them a ligule, deeply sunken in a pit, was present. In both

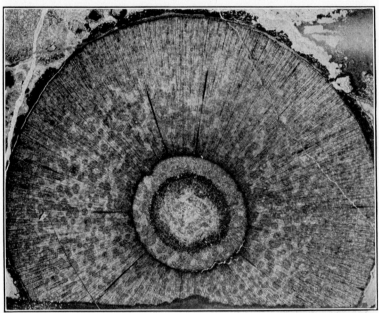

Fig. 197. Transverse section of stem of *Lepidodendron wünschianum*, an ectophloic siphonostele. The central pith is surrounded, in turn, by a narrow cylinder of primary wood, an extensive zone of secondary wood, and an outer layer of bark.

Lepidodendron and *Sigillaria* the base of the main stem was attached to four descending branches (rhizophores) that spread out horizontally and underwent repeated forking. They were covered with roots.

The stem was either a protostele or, more commonly, an ectophloic siphonostele (with the phloem outside the xylem). A primitive feature was the presence of exarch primary wood. The stem was characterized by marked secondary thickening (Fig. 197). The stem of *Sigillaria* sometimes reached a diameter of 2 m.

---

[1] Plant fossils usually occur as detached organs or fragments. Only rarely is one part of the plant found attached to another part. Until such connections are found, detached organs of the same kind are placed in a "form genus." For example, *Lepidodendron* was originally a stem genus. Its leaves were placed in the form genus *Lepidophyllum* and its cones in *Lepidostrobus*. Its root-bearing parts, indistinguishable from those of *Sigillaria*, are included in the form genus *Stigmaria*.

Definite strobili were present, in *Lepidodendron,* at the ends of the branches, in *Sigillaria,* in whorls along the stem. The sporophylls and foliage leaves were rather similar in form. As in all lycopods, the large sporangia were solitary, adaxial, and unilocular. The ligule was situated beyond the sporangium. The Lepidodendrales were heterosporous, the megasporangia generally containing 8 to 16 megaspores. In some cases trabeculae, consisting of sterile plates forming incomplete partitions, were present both in the microsporangia and megasporangia.

The gametophytes were developed inside the spores. The nature of the sperms is unknown. The archegonia were similar to those of *Selaginella.* The embryo is also unknown. In *Lepidocarpon,* a cone genus, the mature megasporangium had only one megaspore and, except for a narrow opening at the top, was invested by an integument that arose from below. This sporangium, although seed-like, was shed with the sporophyll before fertilization took place.

4. Isoetales

Isoetes is the only living genus belonging to the Isoetales. It has about 60 species widely distributed throughout temperate regions but rare in the tropics. It grows on muddy flats, in wet meadows, along stream and pond margins, or submerged in shallow water. A few species grow in drier habitats. Fossils resembling *Isoetes* are known from the Cretaceous and Tertiary periods.

Sporophyte. Superficially *Isoetes* is entirely different in appearance from any other living pteridophyte, resembling a

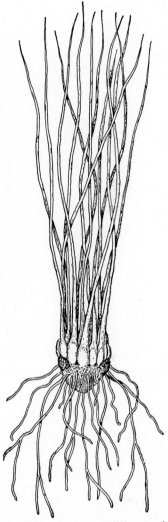

Fig. 198. *Isoetes nuttallii,* natural size.

small rush or tufted grass. Its common name is "quillwort." The stem is erect, tuberous, unbranched, and very short (Fig. 198). It gives rise to a crowded rosette of linear, spirally arranged leaves that are commonly about 5 to 15 cm., rarely 30 cm. or more, in length. The stem is either two-lobed or three-lobed, depending on the species. It is covered by overlapping leaf bases. Between its lobes arise numerous dichotomously branched roots. As in *Selaginella*, each leaf has a ligule, arising at its base on the adaxial side. The root and stem grow by means of a meristem (Fig. 199). The stem has both an apical and a basal meristem.

Vascular Anatomy. Each leaf has a single vascular bundle and four long air passages with numerous transverse partitions. Stomata are present only on leaves exposed to the air. The stem structure is rather complicated and difficult to interpret. Many botanists regard the upper part

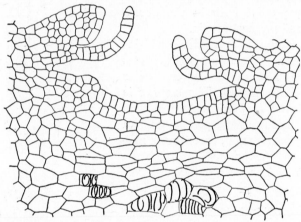

Fig. 199. Longitudinal section through the stem tip of *Isoetes howellii*, showing the apical meristem and developing sporophylls, each with a prominent ligule, ×300.

of the stem, which bears the leaves, as the stem proper and the lower portion, which bears the roots, as a rhizophore, although no such differentiation is evident externally.

The vascular cylinder, representing a greatly reduced protostele, is surrounded by an extensive cortex (Fig. 200). A notable feature of the stem of *Isoetes* is the occurrence of secondary thickening. The primary xylem, consisting of extremely short tracheids intermixed with considerable parenchyma, is surrounded by a narrow zone of primary phloem. This, in turn, is enclosed by a "prismatic layer," which represents the internal product of cambial activity. On the outside the cambium adds new tissue to the cortex. This tissue, which is parenchymatous, has the position of secondary phloem but not its structure. The tissues forming the prismatic layer are not uniform, but are differentiated into alternating zones of thin-walled and thick-walled cells. The thin-walled cells are ordinary parenchyma, while the thick-walled cells are lignified and have scalariform and reticulate markings. Thus the prismatic layer has the position of secondary xylem but not its typical structure. Whether the prismatic layer contains any secondary phloem, as has been claimed, is a matter of considerable uncertainty.

As cambial activity continues, the outer tissues of the stem are constantly sloughed off, the cortex finally being made up wholly of secondary tissue. Numerous leaf traces arise from the stele of the stem, one going to each leaf. In the lower part of the stem (rhizophore) root traces sim-

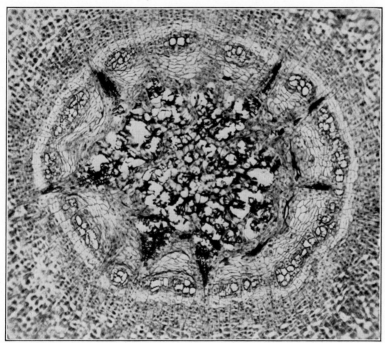

Fig. 200. Cross section of the central portion of the stem of *Isoetes howellii*, ×100. The primary xylem, in the center, is surrounded by a narrow zone of primary phloem enclosed by tissues derived from the cambium.

ilarly pass from the stele to the roots. The root traces contain much more xylem and phloem than the leaf traces.

Sporangia. *Isoetes*, like *Selaginella*, is heterosporous, but nearly all the leaves are sporophylls. As a rule, the outer leaves bear megasporangia and the inner ones microsporangia, while the few central leaves are sterile. The sporangia, mostly 4 to 7 mm., but up to 10 mm. in length, are larger than those of any other living pteridophyte. They are solitary and adaxial, each one being sunken in a cavity at the base of the sporophyll just below the ligule (Fig. 201*A*, *B*). Each sporangium is partially or completely overgrown by a membrane called the *velum*. The microsporangia may produce as many as 300,000 microspores, the megasporangia up to 300 megaspores. In each of the two kinds of sporangia sterile plates, called *trabeculae*, extend inward to form incomplete partitions.   The spores are freed by the gradual decay of the sporangium wall.

The sporangium arises from a transverse row of initials, three or four in number, and is eusporangiate in development (Fig. 201*C*).   In early stages the two kinds of sporangia are indistinguishable from each other.

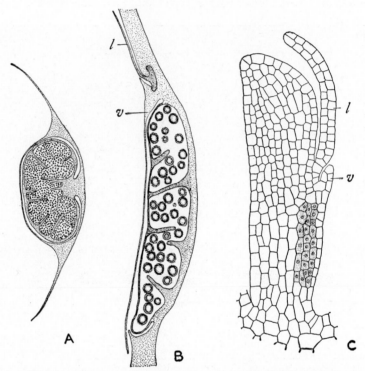

Fig. 201.   Sporangia of *Isoetes*.   *A*, cross section of microsporangium of *Isoetes nuttallii*, ×15; *B*, longitudinal section of megasporangium of *Isoetes nuttallii*, ×10; *C*, longitudinal section of young microsporophyll of *Isoetes howellii*, showing sporogenous tissue (shaded), ×250; *l*, ligule; *v*, velum.

After a large amount of potentially sporogenous tissue has been differentiated, some of it forms the sterile trabeculae.   The sporangium wall consists of four layers of cells, the inner layer forming a tapetum that also borders the trabeculae (Fig. 202).   The tapetum does not disorganize for a long while.   In the microsporangium all the cells not taking part in the formation of the wall, trabeculae, and tapetum become functional spore mother cells.   In the megasporangium the trabeculae are fewer and thicker, the tapetum comprises several layers, and most of the spore mother cells divide and contribute nourishment to a much smaller number that enlarge and form tetrads.   As in *Selaginella*, the megaspore wall is very thick.

Gametophytes. The male gametophyte, like that of *Selaginella*, is developed inside the microspore and similarly consists of a small prothallial cell and an antheridium (Fig. 203). The latter has a sterile jacket of four cells investing four spermatogenous cells, each of which gives rise to a

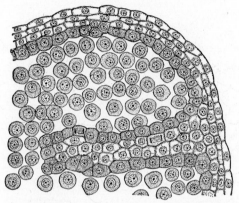

Fig. 202. Cross section of small portion of a microsporangium of *Isoetes nuttallii*, showing the wall, tapetum, a trabecula, and spore mother cells, ×400.

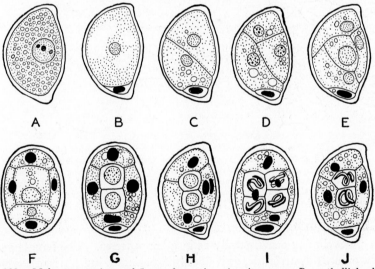

Fig. 203. Male gametophyte of *Isoetes lacustris*. *A*, microspore; *B*, prothallial cell cut off; *C* to *F*, formation of four jacket cells and primary spermatogenous cell; *G* and *H*, division of spermatogenous cell; *I* and *J*, formation of four sperms. *H* and *J* sectioned at right angles to *G* and *I*. (*After Liebig.*)

single sperm. It is noteworthy that only four sperms are produced, as this is the lowest number in pteridophytes. The sperms are large, coiled, and multiciliate, thus differing from those of the other Lycopodiinae (Fig. 204*E*).

The female gametophyte develops inside the megaspore and resembles in a general way that of *Selaginella* (Fig. 204*A*). The megaspore is uninucleate when shed. Free-nuclear division occurs, followed by wall formation in the apical region. Then walls fill in the entire megaspore

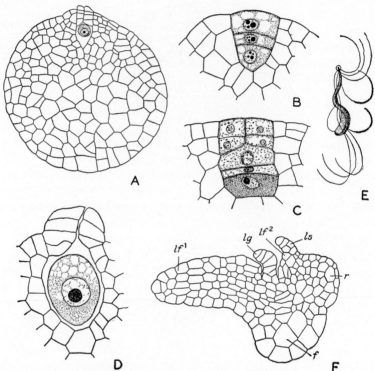

Fig. 204. Female gametophyte and archegonia of *Isoetes echinospora* (*A* to *D*), sperm of *Isoetes malinveriana* (*E*), and embryo of *Isoetes lacustris* (*F*). *A*, female gametophyte with a mature archegonium, the megaspore wall removed, ×140; *B*, young archegonium with primary neck cell, neck canal cell, and primary ventral cell, ×400; *C*, later stage, showing two tiers of neck cells, neck canal cell, ventral canal cell, and egg, ×400; *D*, archegonium with mature egg, ×430; *E*, sperm; *F*, embryo; *f*, foot; *r*, root; *lf¹*, first leaf; *lf²*, second leaf; *lg*, ligule; *ls*, sheath of first leaf. (*A to D, after Campbell; E, after Belajeff; F, after Liebig.*)

cavity, developing centripetally as in gymnosperms. The female gametophyte does not protrude, as it does in *Selaginella*, but a triradiate crack develops in the megaspore wall along which one or several archegonia and numerous rhizoids appear. In some species the rhizoids are few or wanting. The archegonium is completely embedded. It consists of four tiers of neck cells, a single binucleate neck canal cell, a ventral canal cell, and an egg (Fig. 204*B–D*). No basal cell is formed in development. The archegonium of *Isoetes*, like that of *Selaginella*, represents an advanced type.

Embryo. The embryo of *Isoetes* differs from that of other living Lyco-podiinae in lacking a suspensor. The fertilized egg undergoes a trans-verse division, but both segments take part in the formation of the embryo proper. A quadrant stage is organized. It seems probable that the two outer cells form the foot, one of the two inner cells the root, and the other inner cell the leaf. As the embryo develops, a greater growth on one side causes it to curve until it finally becomes inverted, the foot lying below and the root and leaf above (Fig. 204*F*). The stem makes its appearance later between the root and leaf. It may originate from either.

Summary. *Isoetes* has an unbranched tuberous stem bearing a rel-atively few large leaves, each of these having a ligule. The vascular sys-tem of the stem is a greatly reduced protostele, amphicribral in organ-ization, and with secondary thickening. A definite strobilus is not organized, unless the whole plant be considered as one. *Isoetes* is hetero-sporous, the megasporangia producing many megaspores, the micro-sporangia a much greater number of microspores. Trabeculae are formed in both kinds of sporangia. There is no regular dehiscence. The male gametophyte, formed inside the microspore, consists of a single prothallial cell and a single antheridium, the latter producing four large multiciliate sperms. The female gametophyte, developed inside the megaspore, has considerable vegetative tissue and one to several archegonia. These have only one neck canal cell. The embryo is without a suspensor. Although having a number of characters in common with the other living lycopods, *Isoetes* occupies an isolated position because of its general habit, leaves, multiciliate sperms, and absence of a suspensor.

3. EQUISETINAE[1]

The Equisetinae, like the Lycopodiinae, are a group of ancient origin and were much more abundant and diversified during the Paleozoic than they are today (Fig. 258). They are characterized by jointed, longi-tudinally fluted stems bearing mostly small, simple leaves arising in whorls and usually united to form a sheath around each node. This cyclic arrangement of leaves is in marked contrast to the spiral arrange-ment characteristic of other pteridophytes. The sporangia are mostly numerous and borne on the underside of stalk-like *sporangiophores* that are nearly always organized to form a compact strobilus. Of the four orders—the Hyeniales, Sphenophyllales, Equisetales, and Calamitales—only the third has living members.

1. Hyeniales

The Hyeniales are the oldest and most primitive order of Equisetinae, in some respects resembling the Psilophytales. They comprise two

[1] Also called Sphenopsida or Articulatae.

genera, *Hyenia* and *Calamophyton*, both of which lived during the middle Devonian. The aerial shoots were slender and dichotomously branched and, in one species of *Hyenia*, are known to have arisen from a stout horizontal rhizome. The stems were jointed in *Calamophyton* but not in *Hyenia* (Fig. 205). The leaves were small, narrow, and whorled. In *Hyenia* they were forked several times, in *Calamophyton* forked only once. Little is known of the vascular anatomy. The stem of *Calamophyton* was apparently siphonostelic and is thought to have undergone some secondary thickening.

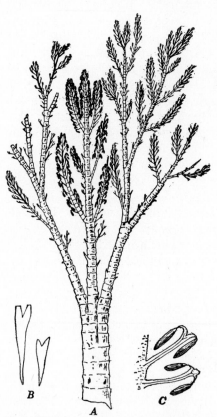

The sporangia of the Hyeniales were borne on sporangiophores that were grouped to form a loose strobilus in which no bracts were present. In both genera the sporangiophores were once forked, the tip of each division being recurved and bearing two or three pendent sporangia in *Hyenia*, but only one sporangium in *Calamophyton*. Presumably the Hyeniales were homosporous.

2. Sphenophyllales

Fig. 205. *Calamophyton primaevum. A*, reconstruction of aerial shoot; *B*, sterile leaves; *C*, sporangiophores. (*After Kräusel and Weyland.*)

This is an order of Paleozoic plants ranging from the Devonian to the Triassic. In many respects it is intermediate between the Lycopodiinae and Equisetinae; in fact, it is often considered as a separate class of pteridophytes. There are three important genera: *Sphenophyllum*, *Cheirostrobus*, and *Pseudobornia*.

The slender fluted stem bore whorls of leaves separated by elongated internodes, with branches arising at the nodes (Fig. 206). The leaves, usually six at a node, were mostly simple and wedged-shaped, but were often dichotomously divided into narrow lobes, while in *Pseudobornia* fern-like leaflets were present. The stem, in all cases, was a protostele with exarch xylem and a considerable amount of secondary thickening.

The strobili were terminal and composed of whorled sporophylls showing little or no resemblance to the foliage leaves. In *Sphenophyllum* the bases of the sporophylls were united to form a cup-like sheath, but the tips were free (Fig. 207). The sporangia were borne singly or in pairs on long sporangiophores that arose from the adaxial side of the sporophylls,

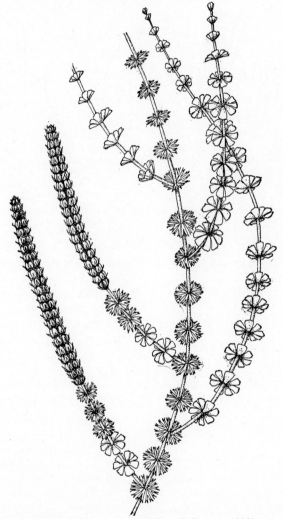

Fig. 206. Reconstruction of the shoot of *Sphenophyllum cuneifolium*, one-third natural size. (*From Gilbert M. Smith.*)

either singly or several together. The sporangia were pendent from the distal end of the sporangiophore, which was often expanded to form a terminal disk. The strobilus of *Cheirostrobus*, a form genus of Carboniferous age, was more complex than that of *Sphenophyllum*, each sporophyll consisting of three lower sterile segments arranged in one plane and three upper fertile ones. Each fertile segment was a sporangiophore bearing four sporangia. The strobilus of *Cheirostrobus* was the most complex one in all pteridophytes.

All the Sphenophyllales were homosporous. Nothing is known of the gametophyte generation.

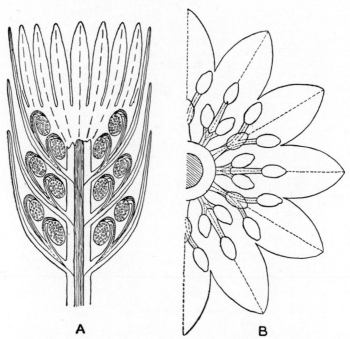

A   **B**

Fig. 207. *Sphenophyllum dawsoni.* *A*, diagram of longitudinal section of cone, showing three whorls of sporophylls and, above, whorl of sporophylls in surface view seen from the inside; *B*, diagram of one-half of a single whorl of sporophylls and sporangiophores. (*A*, after Scott; *B*, after Hirmer.*)

3. Equisetales

The Equisetales, often called horsetails, are herbaceous plants comprising a single surviving genus, *Equisetum*, with about 25 species cosmopolitan in distribution. Although related to Paleozoic forms, this order became prominent in the Mesozoic. *Equisetites*, one of the Triassic horsetails, had a stem 20 cm. in diameter and in general was built on a vastly grander scale than modern forms. The common horsetails of temperate regions grow in swamps, meadows, forests, and sandy wastes.

Sporophyte. The largest living species, *Equisetum giganteum*, of tropical America, reaches a height of 12 m. but has a weak stem only about 2 to 3 cm. in diameter at the base. Most of the other species are less than

1 m. tall. The sporophyte of *Equisetum* has a horizontal branching rhizome with whorled leaves at the nodes. It gives rise to erect green shoots that may be either simple or monopodially branched, the branches, like the leaves, arising in whorls (Fig. 208). In some species the shoots

FIG. 208. Erect shoots of *Equisetum hyemale*. The stems are green, unbranched, and bear whorls of scale-like leaves at the nodes.

branch repeatedly. The stems are longitudinally ridged and grooved, the ridges of one internode alternating with those of the internode immediately above and below. The stems are more or less impregnated with silica, giving them a rough, harsh feel. Roots occur on the rhizome and at the base of the erect stems. They arise in whorls at the nodes.

The nodes are solid but the internodes have a large central cavity. The aerial stems carry on practically all the work of photosynthesis. The leaves are scale-like, their tips being free but their bases united to form a sheath around the node. The number of leaves at a node corresponds to the number of ridges on the stem, each leaf standing directly above a ridge of the internode directly below it. The stem branches are not axillary but arise at the node alternately with the leaf primordia and at the same level, later breaking through the united leaf bases. Thus the number of branches at a node usually equals the number of leaves. Growth of the root and stem takes place by means of a tetrahedral apical cell that cuts off three rows of lateral segments with striking regularity (Fig. 209).

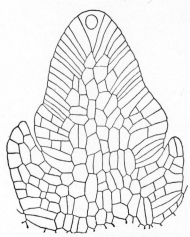

FIG. 209. Median longitudinal section through the stem tip of *Equisetum arvense*, showing apical cell and its derivatives, ×200.

Vascular Anatomy. The stem of *Equisetum* is characterized by a much-reduced vascular system. The greatest development of xylem occurs at the nodes, where it forms a transverse band. From here a leaf trace goes to each leaf, forming a single median vein. A cross section through an internode shows an extensive cortex bounded externally by an epidermis, a circle of small, isolated, vascular bundles separated from one another by broad bands of parenchyma, and a hollow pith (Fig. 210A). The cortex is peculiar in having a ring of large air spaces, called *vallecular canals*, one of which lies beneath each furrow present on the outer surface of the stem.

The epidermis has thick, strongly silicified cell walls. Underlying it is a band of sclerenchyma projecting inward beneath the ridges and sometimes not continuous across the grooves. Green tissue occupies most of the cortical region, occurring largely or entirely beneath the furrows. Stomata, communicating with the green tissue, are situated in the grooves. Their guard cells are peculiar in that each lies inside and next to a subsidiary cell, so that they seem to be double.

Internal to the vallecular canals and alternating with them, and so lying beneath the ridges, are the smaller *carinal canals*, one of which belongs to each vascular bundle. The carinal canals mark the position of the protoxylem, the disorganization of which results in their formation. The metaxylem, which is greatly reduced in amount, lies along the sides of and external to the carinal canals (Fig. 210B). It develops centrifugally, a condition designated as endarch. A small group of phloem elements, consisting of sieve tubes and parenchyma, are present. The phloem has a collateral relation to the xylem. No secondary tissues are

formed. Generally a continuous endodermis surrounds the ring of vascular bundles, but often an endodermis occurs both inside and outside the
bundles. Sometimes each bundle is enclosed by its own endodermis.
Although the vascular bundles are small and widely separated, because of

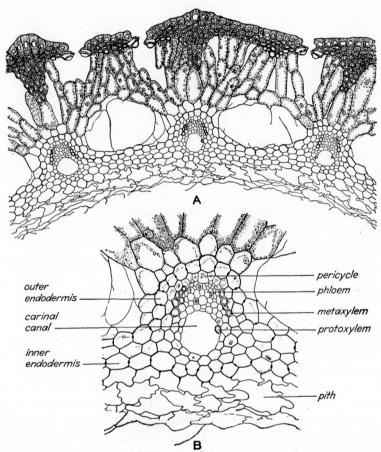

A

outer
endodermis

carinal
canal

inner
endodermis

pericycle

phloem

metaxylem

protoxylem

pith

B

FIG. 210. Stem structure of *Equisetum hyemale* var. *intermedium*. *A*, portion of cross
section of an internode, showing thick-walled epidermis with three stomata, sclerenchyma,
green tissue, two vallecular canals, and three vascular bundles, ×100; *B*, a single vascular
bundle, ×250.

their arrangement and the position of the xylem and phloem, the stem of
Equisetum is an ectophloic siphonostele.

Sporangium. The strobili of *Equisetum* are solitary and terminal on
the main stem or sometimes on its branches. Generally they are borne on
ordinary green shoots, but in some species they occur on special shoots.
In *Equisetum arvense*, for example, there are two kinds of aerial shoots.
They arise from the same rhizome but at different times of the year.

The first shoots to appear above ground in the spring are fertile but are unbranched, yellowish brown, and lacking in chlorophyll. They wither soon after the spores are shed. Green, branching, sterile shoots then appear and persist throughout the summer.

The strobilus of *Equisetum* consists of a central axis bearing numerous whorled sporangiophores (Fig. 211*A*). The development of sporophylls is entirely suppressed. Each sporangiophore is peltate and bears 5 to 10 pendent, sac-like sporangia attached to the margin of a six-sided disk. This is supported by a short stalk that arises directly from the axis of the strobilus and is perpendicular to it (Fig. 211*B*, *C*).

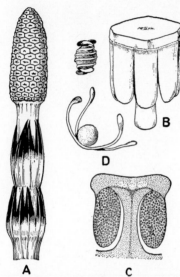

The sporangium, which is eusporangiate in development, arises from a single superficial initial and not, as in the Lycopodiinae, from a row of initials (Fig. 212). However, the sporogenous tissue is derived not only from the inner segment that results from the first periclinal division of the initial but also, in part, from the outer segment (Fig. 212*D*). The tapetum is derived from the wall, which becomes several layers thick but, when the sporangium is mature, consists of a single layer of cells, the inner layers breaking down. In contrast to that of the lycopods, the tapetum becomes two- or three-layered and soon disorganizes, forming a *plasmodium* around the spore mother cells. Following the formation of tetrads, the tapetal plasmodium is absorbed by the developing spores. *Equisetum* is homosporous. The spores are unique in containing numerous chloroplasts when ripe and in having, on the outside, two slender bands derived from the outer layer of the spore wall (Fig. 211*D*). These are hygroscopic and assist in spore dispersal. Each band is attached to the spore at its middle, the tips being spatulate. The bands uncoil when dry and wrap around the spore when moist. When the spores are ripe, the axis of the cone elongates slightly, separating the sporangiophores. The sporangia dehisce by means of a longitudinal slit that appears on their inner side.

Fig. 211. Spore-bearing structures of *Equisetum arvense*. *A*, terminal portion of fertile shoot with strobilus, natural size. *B*, a single sporangiophore, ×15; *C*, longitudinal section of same, ×15; *D*, two ripe spores, ×150.

Gametophyte. The spores of *Equisetum* are short-lived and germinate at once. The gametophyte is usually less than 10 mm. in diameter. It

consists of a rounded, cushion-like base of colorless tissue that gives rise to
numerous upright lobes of green tissue (Fig. 213*A*).   These are irregular,
thin, and plate-like.   Rhizoids are abundantly produced on the lower
surface.   The base has a marginal meristem.   Both kinds of sex organs

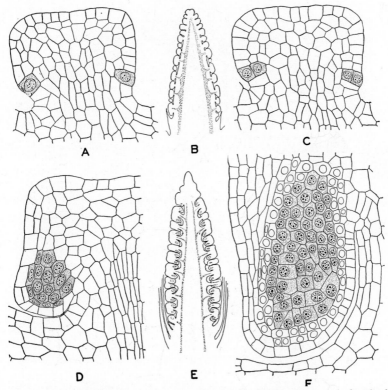

FIG. 212.   Early development of the sporangium of *Equisetum arvense. A*, longitudinal
section of young sporangiophore with two sporangium initials, ×200; *B*, longitudinal
section of young strobilus, ×12; *C*, a sporangiophore of same, showing first division of
initials, ×200; *D*, longitudinal section of one-half of sporangiophore, showing early differentiation of sporogenous tissue, ×200; *E*, longitudinal section of slightly older strobilus
than shown above, ×8; *F*, a sporangium of same, showing further development of sporogenous tissue and differentiation of tapetum, ×200.

are borne on the basal portion of the same prothallium but are seldom
present at the same time.   The archegonia usually appear before the
antheridia.   When closely crowded, the prothallia are small and bear
only antheridia.   For this reason, they were once erroneously regarded
as dioecious.   The development of the antheridium resembles that of the
lycopods (Fig. 213*B–E*).   The superficial initial divides by a transverse
wall, the outer segment producing the sterile jacket and the inner one the
spermatogenous tissue.   The sperms are large, coiled, and multiciliate.

The archegonium develops as in other pteridophytes, but no basal cell is formed (Fig. 213*F–H*).   It has either one neck canal cell or two of them separated by a vertical wall.

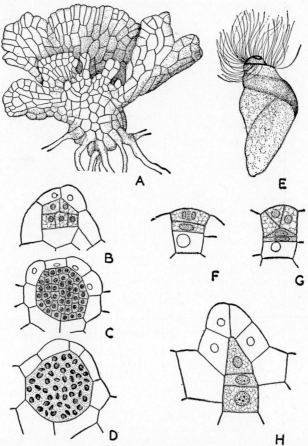

Fig. 213.   *Equisetum telmateia.   A*, gametophyte with archegonia occurring beneath the upright lobes, ×38; *B*, young antheridium, showing sterile jacket and spermatogenous tissue; *C*, slightly older antheridium; *D*, mature antheridium with nearly ripe sperms; *E*, sperm of *Equisetum arvense; F*, young archegonium with primary neck cell and central cell; *G*, slightly older archegonium, showing neck cells, primary neck canal cell, and primary ventral cell; *H*, nearly mature archegonium with neck canal cell, ventral canal cell, and egg; *B, C, D*, ×210; *F, G, H*, ×325.   (*A, after Walker; E, after Sharp; B, C, D and F, G, H, after Gilbert M. Smith.*)

Embryo.   The embryo does not have a suspensor.   The fertilized egg divides transversely, then into quadrants, the inner segments forming the foot and root, the outer ones the stem and leaf.   The stem and root segments soon form an apical cell.

Summary.   The elongated, jointed, longitudinally fluted stem bears numerous small, simple, whorled leaves united to form a sheath around

Fig. 214. Portion of restoration of Carboniferous swamp forest in the Chicago Natural History Museum, showing *Calamites* (tree in center) and a fallen trunk of *Sigillaria*. The small plants in the foreground are *Sphenophyllum emarginatum*.

each node. Branches, where present, are also whorled and arise alternately with the leaves. The vascular system of the stem is a much-reduced ectophloic siphonostele with widely separated, endarch, collateral bundles. There is no secondary thickening. All species are homosporous and have a definite strobilus composed of whorled, peltate sporangiophores, each bearing 5 to 10 pendent sporangia with longitudinal dehiscence.   Sporophylls are absent.   The prothallium is aerial and cushion-like, with erect, green, ribbon-like lobes.   The sperms are numerous, large, and multiciliate.   The archegonia have one or two neck canal cells. The embryo lacks a suspensor.   The Equisetales are a distinct order, superficially unlike any other group of living pteridophytes.

4. Calamitales

This is a Paleozoic order closely related to the Equisetales and often combined with it.   It ranged from the Devonian to the Triassic.   The

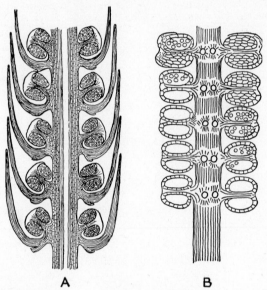

A   **B**

FIG. 215. Longitudinal sections of cones of Calamitales. *A, Palaeostachya,* showing peltate sporangiophores in axils of bracts, diagrammatic; *B, Archaeocalamites,* showing axis bearing sporangiophores only. (*A, after Scott; B, after Renault.*)

principal genus is *Calamites* (Fig. 214).   The Calamitales were tree-like forms, some reaching a height of 20 or 30 m. and a diameter of 1 m.   The hollow stems bore whorled leaves and branches, the leaves being either free or united at the base.   Although mostly small and narrow, the leaves were larger than in modern horsetails, while in *Archaeocalamites* they were large, dichotomously divided into narrow segments, and somewhat fern-like in appearance.

The vascular anatomy was of an advanced type.   The stem was an ectophloic siphonostele, the primary xylem occurring in isolated, collateral vascular bundles arranged in a circle around a hollow pith.   The bundles were prevailingly endarch but were mesarch in *Protocalamites*.   The young stem of the Calamitales was essentially similar to an adult stem of *Equisetum* but became different as a result of secondary thickening, a feature of the group.   Generally the primary tissues were surrounded by a continuous cylinder of secondary wood.

The strobili were made up of whorled, peltate sporangiophores resembling those of *Equisetum*, except that each bore only four pendent sporangia.   In *Archaeocalamites* the cone consisted entirely of sporangiophores, but in most of the other genera bracts were also present, a whorl of bracts alternating with a whorl of sporangiophores (Fig. 215).   These bracts have been interpreted by some botanists as sporophylls.   In *Calamostachys* the alternating whorls of bracts and sporangiophores were equidistant, but in *Palaeostachya* the sporangiophores were situated just above each whorl of bracts, *i.e.*, in their axils.

The Calamitales were either homosporous or heterosporous, depending on the species.   Many megaspores were produced in each megasporangium.   The difference between the two kinds of spores was not so pronounced as in the heterosporous lycopods and ferns.   The gametophyte generation is unknown.

CHAPTER VII

PTERIDOPHYTA (CONTINUED)

4. FILICINAE[1]

The ferns constitute the largest and most representative group of pteridophytes of the present day, numbering about 7,800 species. They are widely distributed over the earth, nearly all growing in moist, shady places. Although making their best display in the tropics, both in number of species and in luxuriance of growth, they are also well represented in temperate regions. The branched or unbranched stem usually bears a few large, spirally arranged leaves that are sometimes simple but are generally divided into leaflets. There are no strobili, the sporangia being very numerous on the margin or abaxial side of the leaves, or borne in special structures called sporocarps. The sporangia may be solitary but more commonly are borne in groups.

Like other vascular plants, the Filicinae possess branch, leaf, and root traces that arise from the stele of the stem and pass outward through the cortex. In all the Filicinae, except those with protostelic stems, the departure of a leaf trace causes an interruption in the continuity of the stele, forming a *leaf gap* (Fig. 221). Leaf gaps are present in ferns and seed plants but not in the lower pteridophytes. Branch gaps are present, however, in all vascular plants having siphonostelic stems (except in *Equisetum*).

The Filicinae were well represented in the Paleozoic, but did not hold as dominant a place in the flora as was once thought (Fig. 258). Most of the fossil fern leaves found in Carboniferous deposits belong to the Cycadofilicales, an order of primitive gymnosperms. Some of the Paleozoic ferns may be referred to two orders with living representatives (Marattiales and Filicales), but most of them belong to the Coenopteridales, an extinct order whose relationships to the others are not clear. Living ferns belong to four orders: Ophioglossales, Marattiales, Filicales, and Hydropteridales.

1. Coenopteridales

The Coenopteridales range from the Devonian to the Permian. They are regarded as the most primitive group of Filicinae, in some respects resembling the Psilophytales. These ferns were all of small or medium size. The stems were erect or horizontal and always protostelic. The

---

[1] Sometimes combined with the Spermatophyta under the name of Pteropsida.

stele was either circular in outline (Botryopteridaceae) or more or less lobed (Zygopteridaceae).   In the most primitive members division of the frond was not limited to one plane and the leaf stalk bore a series of bifurcating branches (Fig. 216).   In some cases the differentiation between stem and leaf was imperfect in that no blade was formed.

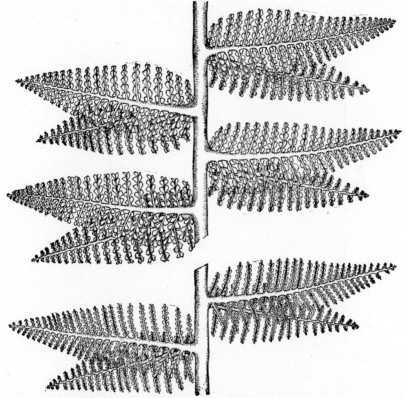

FIG. 216.   Reconstruction of the leaf of *Etapteris lacattei;* fertile portion above and sterile portion below; one-quarter natural size.   (*After Hirmer.*)

The Coenopteridales were eusporangiate and homosporous.   The sporangia were large and either terminal or marginal on the ultimate divisions of the frond.   Sometimes the sporangia were united to form a synangium-like structure.   The output of spores was large.   The sporangium wall was more than one layer of cells thick.   Dehiscence took place by a terminal pore or a longitudinal slit; in the latter case a rudimentary annulus was present.

2. Ophioglossales

The Ophioglossales comprise 3 genera and about 80 species.   *Ophioglossum* and *Botrychium*, each with about the same number of species, are widely distributed, while *Helminthostachys*, with a single species, is confined to Polynesia and tropical Asia. The Ophioglossales are unknown as fossils but constitute the most primitive order of living ferns.

Sporophyte. Most of the Ophioglossales are erect terrestrial plants. The stem is a short, upright, unbranched rhizome producing a few large

Fig. 217. *Ophioglossum californicum,* about one and one-half times natural size.

leaves and numerous rather fleshy roots. Usually only one leaf is formed each year. The smallest species of *Ophioglossum* and *Botrychium* are less than 8 cm. tall, but several species of *Botrychium* may reach a height of 60 cm. *Ophioglossum pendulum*, an epiphyte of the Oriental tropics, has a creeping stem and pendent leaves that are frequently 1.5 m. long. The leaf of *Helminthostachys* is about 30 cm. in length.

As a rule, the leaf blade of *Ophioglossum* is simple, while that of *Botrychium* is pinnately divided (Figs. 217 and 218). The leaf blade of *Helmin-*

thostachys is palmately divided.   Except in *Botrychium virginianum*, the leaves are fleshy.   The blade has many veins that in *Ophioglossum* are reticulate but in the two other genera branch dichotomously and end freely.   At the apex of the rhizome is a large bud containing the primordia of leaves that expand during the next four or five seasons.   In all genera

Fig. 218.   *Botrychium dissectum*, about one-half natural size.   (*From Chamberlain.*)

the stem tip and each successive leaf are ensheathed by the base of the next older leaf.   The vernation of the Ophioglossales is not circinate, as in the higher ferns, but erect.   Both the root and stem increase in length by means of a tetrahedral apical cell.

Vascular Anatomy.   The leaf blade is simple in structure, with an epidermis enclosing uniform mesophyll.   Stomata may occur on both

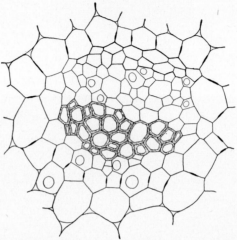

FIG. 219.   Cross section of the stelar portion of the root of *Ophioglossum californicum,* showing the thick-walled xylem in contact with the thin-walled phloem, both surrounded by the pericycle and endodermis, ×250.

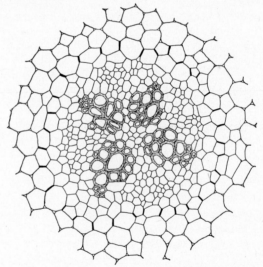

FIG. 220.   Cross section of the stelar portion of the root of *Botrychium virginianum,* showing four xylem groups, ×150.

sides of the blade or only on the lower side.   In *Ophioglossum* the root is very simple in structure, generally having but one xylem group and either one or two phloem groups (Fig. 219).   In *Botrychium* the root has two to four xylem groups (Fig. 220), in *Helminthostachys* four to seven.   The roots of all genera are exarch and without secondary thickening.

The vascular anatomy of the stem is of an advanced type.   In *Botrych-*

ium and *Helminthostachys* the stem is an ectophloic siphonostele, while in *Ophioglossum*, because of the presence of very large, overlapping leaf gaps, the bundles are widely separated and a dictyostele is formed. In all genera the relation of the xylem to the phloem is collateral. The development of the xylem is mesarch in *Helminthostachys* and endarch in the two other genera. A notable feature of *Botrychium* is the presence of a stelar cambium and of marked secondary thickening (Fig. 221).

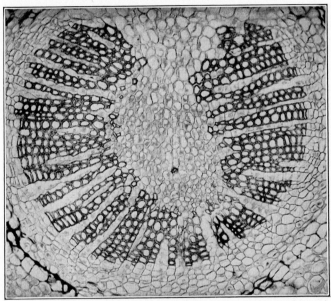

FIG. 221. Cross section of the central portion of the rhizome of *Botrychium virginianum*, an ectophloic siphonostele, ×72. Most of the xylem is of secondary origin.

Although a considerable amount of secondary xylem is formed, there is little or no secondary phloem. The vascular rays are one layer of cells in width. An advanced feature is the occurrence, in *Botrychium* and *Helminthostachys*, of large tracheids with bordered pits instead of the scalariform markings found in other ferns. In *Ophioglossum* the tracheids are reticulate.

Sporangium. All the Ophioglossales are homosporous and eusporangiate. The most distinctive feature of the group is the presence of a "fertile spike," a sporangium-bearing stalk that arises from the basal portion of the leaf as a specialized leaf segment. In *Ophioglossum* the fertile segment is relatively simple, being cylindrical and unbranched, and bearing two lateral rows of sunken sporangia (Fig. 217). Each sporangium does not seem to arise from a single initial cell but from a small group of initials.

In *Botrychium* the fertile segment is more complex than in *Ophioglossum*. In nearly all species it is pinnately branched, the narrow divisions bearing two rows of spherical sporangia that are not embedded but project on a very short stalk (Fig. 218). In development, the sporangia arise separately, each from a single initial. In *Helminthostachys* the fertile segment is spike-like and bears two rows of crowded, oval, stalked sporangia, a number of which may be borne on a single stalk. The vascular anatomy of the leaf and the occurrence of occasional reversions indicate that

Fig. 222. Cross section of the petiole of *Botrychium virginianum*, ×10.

the fertile segment of *Ophioglossum* and *Botrychium* represents two united basal leaflets, while in *Helminthostachys* it represents a single leaflet.

In almost all the Ophioglossales each leaf trace arises from the stele of the stem as a single strand, but branches before or as it enters the leaf. A cross section of the petiole of *Ophioglossum* shows a single row of vascular bundles arranged in a circle, those on the adaxial side passing into the "fertile spike" and the others going into the sterile blade. The petiole of *Botrychium*, just below the fertile segment, usually displays two pairs of vascular bundles arranged symmetrically on each side (Fig. 222). From the two larger ones, which are crescent-shaped, a pair of smaller bundles branch off and pass into the fertile segment, while at higher levels two small bundles similarly depart to each pair of sterile leaflets.

The sporangium wall, in the Ophioglossales, is about five layers of cells thick. No annulus is formed. The tapetum is probably derived from the innermost layer of wall tissue and may consist of one layer or several layers of cells. In all three genera the tapetum is peculiar in that the protoplasts are liberated from their cells before the spores are in the tetrad stage (Fig. 223). These protoplasts fuse to form a multinucleate plasmodium that surrounds groups of spore mother cells and contributes nourishment to them. These groups break up just prior to the formation of tetrads. The plasmodium disappears as the spores mature. Each sporangium produces a large number of spores. Dehiscence occurs by

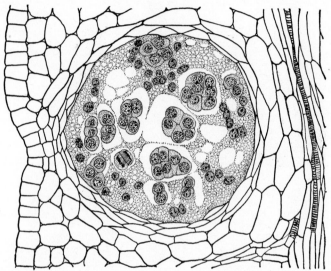

FIG. 223. Longitudinal section through portion of young fertile spike of *Ophioglossum californicum*, showing groups of spore mother cells surrounded by multinucleate plasmodium derived from the tapetum, ×130.

means of a longitudinal slit in *Helminthostachys* and by a transverse slit in the two other genera.

Gametophyte. In all the Ophioglossales the prothallium is subterranean, saprophytic, and without chlorophyll. An endophytic fungus is always present. The prothallium of *Ophioglossum* is cylindrical and either simple or branched (Fig. 224C, D). It may reach a length, in *Ophioglossum vulgatum*, of 6 cm. Rhizoids are wanting. The antheridia and archegonia are scattered and intermixed. The gametophyte of *Botrychium* is tuberous, dorsiventral, and flattened (Fig. 224A). It reaches a length, in some species, of 18 mm., in others, of only 3 mm. The surface may be smooth or covered with rhizoids, according to the species. The antheridia are borne on a median dorsal ridge, while the archegonia, appearing later, form a row on each side of the ridge (Fig. 224B). In *Helminthostachys* the prothallium is somewhat similar to that of *Botrychium*, but is more irregular and has a lobed basal portion that gives rise to an upright cylindrical branch bearing sex organs.   As in *Botrychium*, the antheridia appear before the archegonia.

The antheridium of the Ophioglossales is large and sunken (Fig. 225*A*, *B*).   It develops as in the lower pteridophytes, the spermatogenous tissue

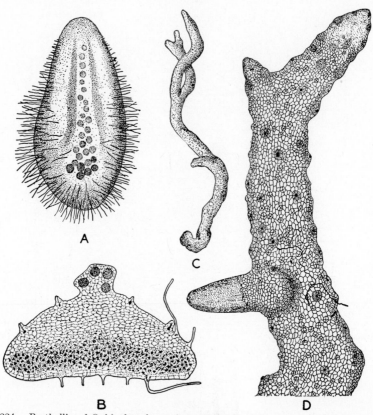

FIG. 224.   Prothallia of Ophioglossales.   *A*, prothallium of *Botrychium virginianum* with dorsal ridge bearing antheridia, ×16; *B*, cross section of same, showing antheridia on ridge, archegonia on the sides, and fungal zone below, ×17; *C* and *D*, *Ophioglossum vulgatum;* *C*, entire prothallium, about ×2; *D*, one-half of a prothallium with antheridia and archegonia on surface and, to left, a young sporophyte with first root, ×30.   (*A* and *B*, after Jeffrey; *C* and *D*, after Bruchmann.)

arising from the inner segment resulting from a periclinal division of the superficial initial.   In *Ophioglossum* the wall remains one-layered, but in the two other genera it becomes two-layered.   The sperms are numerous, large, coiled, and multiciliate (Fig. 225*C*).   The archegonium initial is also superficial and divides periclinally, the outer cell forming the neck and the inner one giving rise to the central cell and basal cell (Fig. 225*D–G*).   A basal cell is not present, however, in some species of *Botrychium*.   The axial row, derived from the central cell, consists of a single binucleate neck canal cell, a very inconspicuous ventral canal cell, and an egg.

Embryo. The embryo of *Botrychium dissectum* and that of *Helmintho-stachys* are unique in that a suspensor is developed, but in all the other

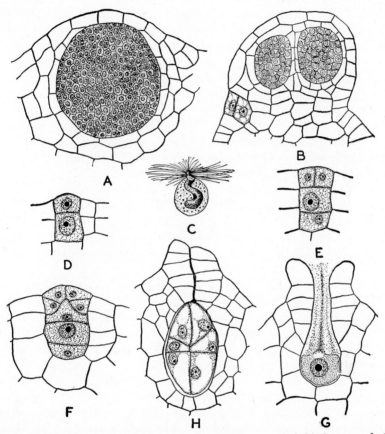

FIG. 225. Sex organs of Ophioglossales. *A*, antheridium of *Ophioglossum vulgatum*, ×150; *B*, antheridia of *Botrychium virginianum*, ×200; *C*, sperm of *Ophioglossum; D* to *G*, development of archegonium of *Ophioglossum vulgatum*, ×225; *D*, first division of initial; *E*, young archegonium with two neck cells, central cell, and basal cell; *F*, later stage, showing division of central cell; *G*, mature archegonium; *H*, young embryo of *Botrychium virginianum*, ×250. (*B and H, after Jeffrey; others after Bruchmann.*)

Ophioglossales none is present. The first wall in the fertilized egg is transverse and usually a quadrant stage is formed, but the subsequent divisions are irregular and rather indefinite (Fig. 225*H*). The embryonic organs are differentiated rather late, and so it is not possible to assign them to definite quadrants. The entire inner portion of the embryo forms the foot, while the outer portion gives rise to the root, stem, and leaf. Generally the root arises first and grows considerably before the other organs are differentiated. The leaf is the last member to appear.

Summary. The Ophioglossales are homosporous and eusporangiate. The sporangia are borne on a characteristic "fertile spike," which probably represents a single leaflet in *Helminthostachys* and two united basal leaflets in *Ophioglossum* and *Botrychium*. The sporangium wall is several layers of cells thick and is without an annulus. The leaves are erect in vernation, not circinate. The gametophyte is subterranean, saprophytic, and without chlorophyll. It contains an endophytic fungus. The antheridium develops as in the other eusporangiate pteridophytes. The inner portion of the embryo forms the foot, the outer portion the root, stem, and leaf. The Ophioglossales have a number of distinctive features. The vegetative structure of the sporophyte is advanced, but the spore-producing structures and the gametophyte are primitive. The order may have been derived from the Coenopteridales, but does not seem to have given rise to any other modern group.

3. Marattiales

The Marattiales are an ancient order of ferns extending back into the Paleozoic. In certain respects they are intermediate between the Ophioglossales and Filicales. Although once widespread and abundant, they are represented today by only 7 genera and about 55 species almost exclusively tropical in distribution. The largest genus is *Angiopteris*, with 25 species. It is found only in the Eastern Hemisphere. Two other important genera, each with about 13 species, are *Marattia*, occurring in tropical regions throughout the world, and *Danaea*, confined to tropical America. The four other genera, each with a single species, are confined to southern Asia.

Sporophyte. The Marattiales are mostly large ferns with thick fleshy leaves (Fig. 226). In most species of *Danaea* the stem is creeping and occasionally branched, but in nearly all other members of the order it is short, stout, erect, and unbranched. The stem is always covered with persistent leaf bases. The roots are thick and fleshy and the leaves, which in *Angiopteris* may exceed 5 m. in length, are in nearly all cases pinnately divided. A peculiarity of the group is the occurrence of a pair of fleshy stipules at the base of each leaf. The venation is dichotomous and open except in one genus (*Christensenia*), where it is reticulate. The vernation is circinate throughout the order. Elongation of the root and stem takes place by means of a meristem, an apical cell being present only in young plants. In possessing an apical meristem, the Marattiales differ from all other ferns.

Vascular Anatomy. A cross section through a leaf reveals an epidermis on both surfaces, with stomata present only below. Palisade tissue is

FIG. 226. *Angiopteris evecta.* (*From Wettstein.*)

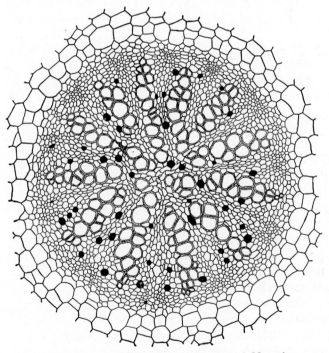

FIG. 227. Cross section of the stelar portion of the root of *Marattia*, an exarch radial protostele with many protoxylem points, ×75.

developed beneath the upper epidermis, the rest of the mesophyll consisting of spongy tissue. The roots of the Marattiales are characterized by a large number of protoxylem points (Fig. 227). The xylem is usually lignified to the center.

The vascular anatomy of the stem is very complex. The cortex consists of parenchyma containing mucilage canals, but no sclerenchyma is present. The vascular cylinder is a dictyostele with large overlapping leaf gaps and widely separated bundles. The latter, in all genera, are

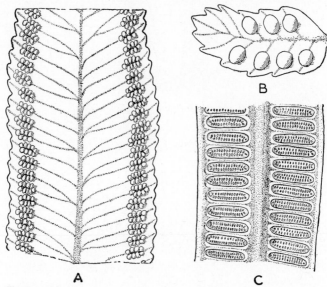

Fig. 228. Portion of leaflet of *Angiopteris* (*A*) with sori, leaflet of *Marattia* (*B*) with oval synangia, and portion of leaflet of *Danaea* (*C*) with elongated sunken synangia, ×3.

amphicribral (phloem surrounding the xylem) and either mesarch or endarch in development. In *Danaea* the vascular bundles are seen, in a cross-sectional view of the stem, to be arranged in a single circle surrounding the pith. In *Marattia* the stem is more complex in that two concentric circles of bundles are present, while in *Angiopteris*, where the stem reaches its greatest degree of complexity, there is a series of four or five circles of vascular bundles. In all the Marattiales the stem bundles undergo more or less branching and fusion, and commissural strands, connecting certain parts of the vascular system with one another, arise inside the dictyostele. Secondary thickening does not occur. As in the higher ferns, the tracheids are scalariform.

Sporangium. The Marattiales resemble the Ophioglossales in being homosporous and eusporangiate, in having a sporangium wall consisting of several layers of cells, and in lacking an annulus. The sporangia, however, are not borne in a "fertile spike" but on the abaxial side of the leaves. Generally the fertile and sterile leaves are alike in form, but in *Danaea* they are different. The sporangia are sessile and borne in distinct sori, these being generally in two rows. In *Angiopteris* the sporangia are free (Fig. 228*A*), but in *Marattia* and *Danaea* they are united to form *synangia*. The synangia of *Marattia* are superficial, oval, or rounded, and borne near the ends of the veins (Fig. 228*B*). The synangia of *Danaea* are sunken, linear, and borne along the veins; they cover almost completely the backs of the fertile leaflets (Fig. 228*C*).

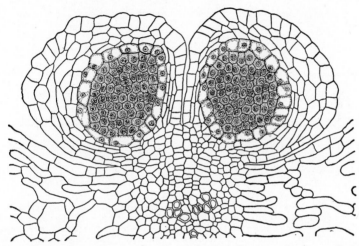

FIG. 229. Section through two sporangia of *Angiopteris evecta*, showing wall, tapetum, and sporogenous tissue, ×200.

All the sporangia in a sorus originate at the same time, each arising from a single initial cell. The sporogenous tissue is differentiated early and, from the cells immediately surrounding it, the tapetum, consisting of one or two layers, is derived (Fig. 229). The tapetum breaks down when the spore tetrads are formed, its substance being absorbed by the developing spores. It does not form a plasmodium. The sporangium of the Marattiales is a relatively large structure, producing a great many spores (1,500 to 7,000). A rudimentary annulus is present in *Angiopteris*, but there is none in *Marattia* and *Danaea*. Dehiscence takes place by means of a median slit or, in *Danaea*, by a terminal pore.

Gametophyte. The Marattiales have a comparatively large gametophyte, sometimes reaching a length of 3 cm., and consisting of a flat, dark green thallus that may be heart-shaped, orbicular, or irregularly lobed. It resembles the gametophyte of the Filicales except that it is relatively thick, long-lived, and, as in the Ophioglossales, provided with an endophytic fungus. The median portion of the prothallium forms a thick cushion. Rhizoids arise from the ventral surface; in *Angiopteris* and *Marattia* they are unicellular, but in *Danaea* they are septate. The antheridia occur on both the upper and lower surfaces of the prothallium, but the archegonia are confined to the lower side, where they are borne on the thickened median portion. Both antheridia and archegonia are sunken. They develop as in the Ophioglossales (Figs. 230 and 231). In the archegonium a basal cell is usually formed in *Marattia* but not in

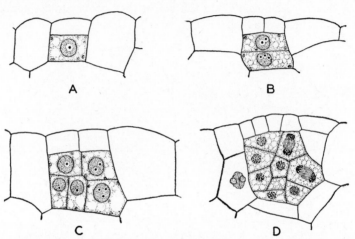

Fig. 230. Early stages in the development of the antheridium of *Angiopteris evecta*, ×350. *A*, division of antheridial initial into primary wall cell and primary spermatogenous cell; *B*, anticlinal division of primary wall cell and periclinal division of primary spermatogenous cell; *C*, further divisions of spermatogenous cells; *D*, slightly later stage, showing completion of antheridial wall by cutting off of a layer of cells from adjacent cells of the prothallium. (*After Haupt.*)

Angiopteris and *Danaea*. There may be either two neck canal cells or a single binucleate one. As in all ferns, the sperms are coiled and multiciliate.

Embryo. The development of the embryo is unlike either that of the Ophioglossales or of the higher ferns. The first division of the fertilized egg is transverse and a quadrant stage is organized. The two outer segments (those next to the neck of the archegonium) give rise to the foot, the two inner ones to the stem and leaf, the leaf arising from the segment nearer the apical region of the prothallium. The root appears later from the inner portion of the embryo. A suspensor has been observed in some species of *Danaea* and exceptionally in *Angiopteris*.

Summary. Like the Ophioglossales, the Marattiales are homosporous and eusporangiate, but the sporangia are borne on the abaxial side of the leaves, usually in synangia. The sporangium wall consists of several layers of cells and is without a definite annulus. The vernation is circinate. The leaves have a pair of fleshy stipules. The gametophyte is

flat, green, and aerial.   It is relatively thick and contains an endophytic
fungus.   The development of the antheridium is like that of the Ophioglossales.   The inner portion of the embryo forms the stem, leaf, and root,

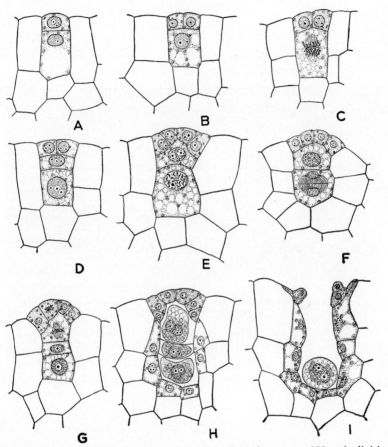

Fig. 231.   Development of the archegonium of *Angiopteris evecta*, ×350.   *A*, division of
archegonium initial into primary neck cell and central cell; *B*, anticlinal division of primary
neck cell; *C* and *D*, periclinal division of central cell to form neck canal cell and ventral
cell; *E*, formation of two tiers of neck cells; *F*, division of ventral cell to form ventral canal
cell and egg; *G* and *H*, formation of a single binucleate neck canal cell, of three tiers of neck
cells, and of the sterile jacket; *I*, mature archegonium with egg ready for fertilization.
(*After Haupt.*)

the outer portion the foot.   The Marattiales have characters in common
both with the Ophioglossales and the Filicales and, in their degree of complexity, occupy a position between them.   These three orders do not form
a phylogenetic series.   Instead, they seem to have been derived independently from a common ancestry.

4. Filicales

The Filicales constitute by far the largest order of modern ferns, including 12 families, about 170 genera, and approximately 7,600 species. They make their greatest display in the tropics, but are also well represented in temperate regions. The fossil record of the two most primitive families (Osmundaceae and Schizaeaceae), and possibly of a third one (Gleicheniaceae), extends back into the Paleozoic, but that of the other families does not reach beyond the Mesozoic.

Fig. 232. *Gleichenia costaricensis*, photographed near the summit of the Poás volcano in Costa Rica.

Families. The Filicales comprise 7 principal families and 5 small ones of minor importance. All of them have living representatives. The chief families are as follows:

1. *Osmundaceae.* This is the most primitive family. It comprises 3 genera and about 20 species and occurs in both temperate and tropical regions. *Osmunda* is the principal genus, including over one-half the species. It is widely distributed, three species being found in temperate parts of North America.

2. *Schizaeaceae.* This primitive family, including 4 genera and about 160 species, is chiefly tropical. *Schizaea* and *Lygodium* are widely distributed. *Anemia*, the largest genus, is found in tropical America, while *Mohria* is confined to eastern Africa. The family is represented in the Eastern and Southeastern United States by two species of *Schizaea*, one of *Lygodium*, and two of *Anemia*, all of which are rare.

3. *Gleicheniaceae.* This small family of about 130 species includes 3 genera, of which *Gleichenia*, with all the species but two, is of greatest importance (Fig. 232). It is confined to the tropics and subtropics of both the Eastern and Western Hemispheres.

Fig. 233. *Dicksonia antarctica*, a tree fern cultivated in the Huntington Botanical Gardens at San Marino, California.

4. *Hymenophyllaceae.* These are the "filmy ferns," small delicate forms chiefly tropical in distribution. There are about 400 species, nearly equally divided between *Hymenophyllum* and *Trichomanes*. Two species of *Trichomanes* are found in the Eastern United States.

5. *Dicksoniaceae.* To this group belong 9 genera and about 125 species mainly tropical in distribution. The chief genera are *Dicksonia*, *Cibotium*, and *Dennstaedtia*.[1] The first two are arborescent (Fig. 233). One species of *Dennstaedtia* is found in the Eastern United States.

6. *Cyatheaceae.* This is a family of tree ferns, including 3 genera and about 700 species. Here belong *Cyathea*, *Alsophila*, and *Hemitelia*, all large genera widely distributed throughout the tropics.

[1] The position of this genus is uncertain. It is often placed in the Polypodiaceae.

7. *Polypodiaceae.* The Polypodiaceae constitute the highest and largest family of true ferns. Although chiefly tropical, it includes nearly all the ferns of temperate regions. About 150 genera and 6,000 species are known. The following list includes most of the large genera: *Pteris, Adiantum, Athyrium, Cheilanthes, Dryopteris, Polystichum, Asplenium, Blechnum, Elaphoglossum,* and *Polypodium.*

Sporophyte. The sporophyte of the Filicales displays great variation in size, ranging from small delicate herbs to trees 18 m. or more in height. Most members of the group are terrestrial, but some are climbing, some epiphytic, and a few aquatic. The stem may be subterranean or aerial, erect or horizontal, and branched or unbranched. In most true ferns, and in all the common species of temperate regions, the stem is a creeping rhizome without aerial branches. The leaves of tropical species are evergreen. Those of temperate species, with few exceptions, die at the end of the growing season, new ones appearing each spring. The tree ferns of tropical regions have an erect, woody, unbranched stem bearing a terminal cluster of large leaves (Fig. 233).

Some true ferns have simple leaves but most of them have large, characteristic, pinnately divided leaves often called *fronds.* Their leaflets, termed *pinnae,* are usually again divided, the smaller segments being known as *pinnules.* The leaves are generally firm and leathery but are often thin and membranaceous, being very delicate in the "filmy ferns" (Hymenophyllaceae). Stipular wings are present at the base of the petiole in the Osmundaceae but not in the other families. In unfolding from the bud, the leaves uncoil from the base toward the apex and continue to grow at the tip until they have reached their full size. This familiar behavior, known as *circinate vernation,* is very characteristic. The leaves have an elaborate system of branching veins, the branching being nearly always dichotomous and open, but sometimes reticulate (Fig. 240). Branching of the rhizome is usually monopodial but occasionally dichotomous; that of the roots is always monopodial.

In nearly all the Filicales the root tip displays a large tetrahedral apical cell that undergoes very regular segmentation, cutting off cells from the three sides and also from the forward face to form the root cap (Fig. 234). The stem tip likewise grows by means of a large apical cell that nearly always is tetrahedral, cutting off segments in regular succession, but only from the three lateral faces. In the bracken (*Pteridium aquilinum*) a modified form of dolabrate apical cell is present, forming segments right and left.

Vascular Anatomy. The anatomy of the roots and leaves is essentially similar to that of the spermatophytes. The leaves have an upper and a lower epidermis with stomata usually confined to the lower surface, mesophyll, and vascular bundles. As a rule, the mesophyll is uniform. In nearly all the Filicales the root has a stele with two protoxylem groups.

The stems of the Filicales display four different stelar types, being either a protostele, an amphiphloic siphonostele, an ectophloic siphonostele, or a dictyostele. The dictyostele is the most common as well as the

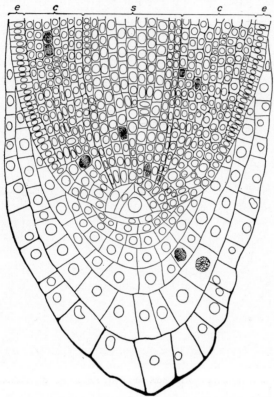

Fig. 234. Median longitudinal section through the root tip of *Pteris gigantea*, showing tetrahedral apical cell from which all the other cells have been derived; *e*, epidermis; *c*, cortex; *s*, stele. (*After Hof.*)

most advanced type, but the amphiphloic siphonostele is also of rather frequent occurrence. The other two types are uncommon.

The protoxylem consists of spiral tracheids—elongated cells with spiral thickenings on their walls. The metaxylem is made up almost entirely of scalariform tracheids. These are elongated cells, pointed at each end, with transverse bands of thickening resembling the rungs of a ladder. In nearly all the Filicales the development of the wood is mesarch, the protoxylem being surrounded on all sides by the metaxylem (Fig. 239). Generally the phloem surrounds the xylem, the vascular tissues thus showing an amphicribral arrangement. Sclerenchyma is usually prominently developed. There is no secondary thickening, even in the tree ferns.

Except in protostelic stems, prominent leaf gaps are formed in connection with the departure of leaf traces, as in all the orders of Filicinae. In addition to leaf gaps, perforations not related to the departure of leaf

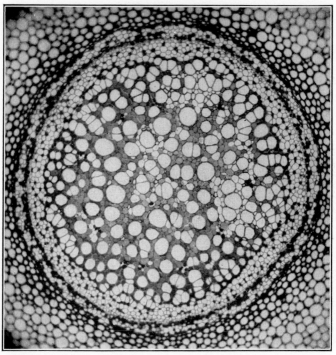

Fig. 235.   Cross section of the central portion of the rhizome of *Gleichenia costaricensis*, a protostele, ×50.

traces are sometimes developed in the vascular cylinder, especially in ferns with elongated rhizomes. In many forms accessory vascular strands are present, usually inside the vascular cylinder. In the common bracken (*Pteridium aquilinum*) we have a well-known example of the occurrence of medullary strands combined with a considerable amount of perforation of the vascular cylinder (Fig. 238). Accessory vascular strands are present also in many tree ferns.

Protostele. The protostele, representing the most primitive vascular type, is found only in a few genera, such as *Lygodium*, *Gleichenia*, *Hymenophyllum*, and *Trichomanes*; but it occurs as the earliest developmental stage in most other true ferns.

Gleichenia displays a typical protostele (Fig. 235). No pith is present, the xylem occupying the center of the stem. A cross section of the rhizome shows a more or less sclerenchymatous cortex, a continuous and distinct endodermis, a several-layered pericycle, and a narrow but continuous band of phloem. The xylem forms a solid central mass consisting of groups of large scalariform tracheids intermixed with parenchyma. Numerous mesarch protoxylem groups are scattered throughout the meta-

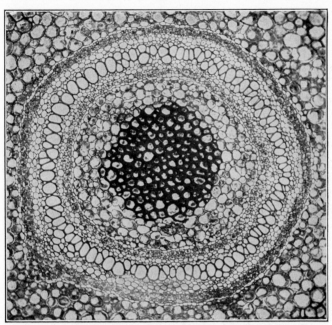

FIG. 236. Cross section of the central portion of the rhizome of *Dennstaedtia punctilobula*, an amphiphloic siphonostele, ×80. In the center of the pith is a group of thick-walled sclerenchyma fibers.

xylem. Leaf traces are connected directly with the stele, forming no gaps.

Amphiphloic Siphonostele. This stelar type may be seen in such well-known ferns as *Adiantum* and *Dennstaedtia*, as well as in a number of others. Here the vascular tissues form a cylinder enclosing a pith, the xylem being surrounded both externally and internally by a complete zone of phloem (Fig. 236).

A transverse section of the rhizome of *Dennstaedtia punctilobula*, the hay-scented fern of the Eastern United States, shows a thick outer cortical region composed of dark-colored sclerenchyma and a thin inner parenchymatous region. An outer endodermis delimits the cortex from the outer pericycle, which consists of two or three layers. Next come the outer phloem, the xylem, the inner phloem, the inner pericycle, the inner endodermis, and the pith. Both the outer and inner phloem are made up almost entirely of sieve tubes but are separated from the xylem by a small amount of parenchyma.   The xylem forms a narrow cylinder composed of scalariform tracheids.   Apparently no protoxylem is present. The inner pericycle usually comprises only one or two layers.   The outer portion of the pith consists of parenchyma, the central part of scleren-chyma.   The continuity of the vascular cylinder is interrupted by the

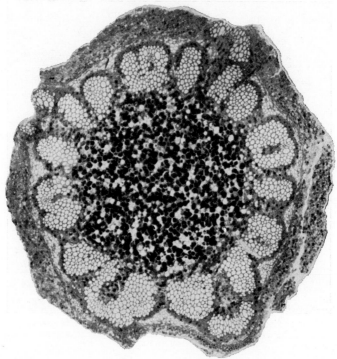

Fig. 237.   Cross section of the central portion of the rhizome of *Osmunda cinnamomea*, an ectophloic siphonostele, ×19.

departure of leaf traces and the gap formed by each is closed above before the next trace is given off.   The endodermis is continuous around the margins of the leaf gaps.   Because the internodes are shorter in the rhi-zome of *Adiantum*, the leaf gaps are more numerous.   Furthermore, the woody cylinder is wider and consists of both tracheids and parenchyma.

   Ectophloic Siphonostele.   The ectophloic siphonostele differs from the amphiphloic in lacking internal phloem.   Although found in *Schizaea*, it can be seen to better advantage in *Osmunda*.   Here the rhizome is covered with persistent overlapping leaf bases.   The outer cortex is extensive and consists mainly of dark-colored sclerenchyma, while the inner cortex is narrow and parenchymatous.   The endodermis is distinct and continuous, even where the stele is interrupted by the outward pas-

sage of leaf traces. The pericycle consists of one to four layers of parenchyma forming a complete sheath. As seen in cross section, the vascular
cylinder of *Osmunda* consists of a ring of mesarch xylem strands separated by parenchymatous "rays" that pass outward from the large pith
(Fig. 237). In some species the pith may contain sclerenchyma. Surrounding the xylem is a continuous layer of phloem made up chiefly of
sieve tubes, while between the xylem and phloem are several layers of
elongated parenchymatous cells continuous with the "rays." The xylem

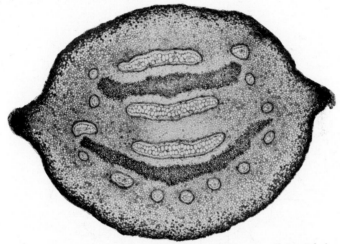

Fig. 238. Cross section of the rhizome of *Pteridium aquilinum*, a dictyostele in which the
vascular cylinder encloses two or more medullary bundles and two bands of dark, heavy-
walled sclerenchyma fibers, ×8.

really consists of a cylindrical network forming a hollow cylinder, the
meshes or "rays" being leaf gaps.

Dictyostele. Among the lower families of Filicales, a dictyostele is present in *Mohria* and most species of *Anemia*, both members of the Schizaeaceae. Dictyostelic stems are also found in some of the Dicksoniaceae,
but the greatest number occur among the Cyatheaceae and Polypodiaceae. The dictyostelic condition has been derived from the siphonostelic
by the overlapping of leaf gaps, so that several or many separate vascular
strands are seen in a cross section of the stem. In complex dictyosteles
the vascular cylinder consists of a tubular network.

A transverse section of the rhizome of *Polypodium* shows a number
of small, widely separated vascular strands arranged in a circle. The
rhizome of *Pteridium*, which is dorsiventral, consists of two series of
strands—a circle of small peripheral ones enclosing two large central
strands, or sometimes more than two as a result of branching (Fig. 238).
The dorsal bundle is band-like and larger than the other peripheral ones.

The bundles are amphicribral with mesarch xylem (Fig. 239). Each is surrounded by an endodermis that encloses a continuous pericycle usually comprising only a single layer of cells. The ground tissue of the rhizome consists of parenchyma surrounded by an outer zone of thick-walled cells. In the central region are two transverse bands of sclerenchyma, one occurring above and one below the medullary strands. The lower band is larger than the upper one and slightly curved.

Sorus. In most of the Filicales the sporangia are borne on the abaxial surface of ordinary foliage leaves. In the Schizaeaceae the sporangia are

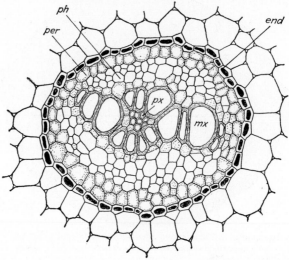

Fig. 239. Cross section of a vascular bundle from the rhizome of *Pteridium aquilinum*, ×200; *end*, endodermis; *per*, pericycle; *ph*, phloem; *px*, protoxylem; *mx*, metaxylem.

solitary, but in the other families they occur in groups called *sori*. Generally the sori are arranged on either side of the midrib, but in many genera they are marginal or nearly so (Fig. 240). Ordinarily the leaf segments that bear the sporangia are unmodified. Often, however, a marked differentiation exists between sterile and fertile leaflets, the latter being conspicuously contracted. This condition prevails in *Osmunda*, the Schizaeaceae, *Onoclea, Blechnum*, etc. The same leaf may produce both sterile and fertile leaflets, or the entire leaf may be made up of either one kind or the other.

Some ferns have naked sori, but usually each sorus is covered by a flaplike membrane called the *indusium* (Fig. 240). Although absent in the Osmundaceae and Gleicheniaceae, an indusium is present in the Schizaeaceae, Hymenophyllaceae, Dicksoniaceae, Cyatheaceae (except *Alsophila*), and in most of the Polypodiaceae (*Polypodium* being a notable exception). Generally the indusium represents a special outgrowth of the leaf, but it may be formed by the inrolled leaf margin. Such a "false indusium" is present in the Schizaeaceae, Hymenophyllaceae, Dicksoniaceae, and in such well-known genera of Polypodiaceae as *Pteris*, *Pteridium*, *Adiantum*, *Pellaea*, *Cheilanthes*, and *Notholaena* (Fig. 240*B*, *D*). This condition

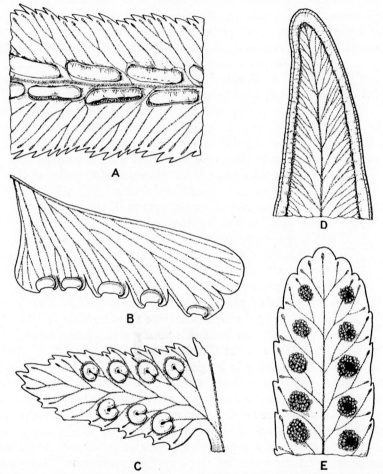

Fig. 240. Portion of the leaflets of five common ferns, illustrating differences in sori and indusia, ×4. *A*, *Woodwardia*; *B*, *Adiantum*; *C*, *Dryopteris*; *D*, *Pteridium*; *E*, *Polypodium*. In *B* and *D* a false indusium is seen, while in *E* there is no indusium.

may be regarded as primitive. In a number of true ferns the sori lose their individuality by a spreading of the sporangia over the leaf surface or along the leaf margin. Such "confluent sori" are seen in *Pityrogramma*, *Elaphoglossum*, *Pteris*, and *Pteridium*.

With respect to the order of appearance of the sporangia within the sorus, three conditions are recognized, as follows: (1) The *simple sorus*, where all the sporangia arise at the same time and therefore are all of the same age, is found among the most primitive families, *viz.*, Osmundaceae, Schizaeaceae, and Gleicheniaceae. (2) The *gradate sorus*, in which the sporangia arise in basipetal succession on an elongating receptacle, occurs in the Hymenophyllaceae, Dicksoniaceae, and Cyatheaceae. (3) The *mixed sorus*, where sporangia of different ages are intermingled in the same sorus and show no developmental sequence, is the most advanced type. It is characteristic of all the Polypodiaceae except *Woodsia* and *Onoclea*, which are gradate.

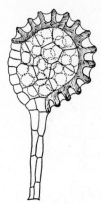

Fig. 241. Mature sporangium of one of the Polypodiaceae, showing the incomplete vertical annulus, ×150.

Sporangium. The sporangium in the Polypodiaceae is slightly flattened and has a long, slender stalk (Fig. 241). It also has a rather long stalk in the Dicksoniaceae and Cyatheaceae, but in the lower families it has a short, stout stalk or none. In all the Filicales the sporangium wall consists of a single layer of cells. A special feature is the presence of an *annulus*, a group or, more commonly, a ring of specialized cells that brings about the dehiscence of the sporangium. Its cells have all but their outer walls thickened. Drying causes a contraction of the thickened band, resulting in a state of tension that finally ruptures the sporangium wall. As the annulus bends backward, the spore mass is exposed. Then, suddenly, the annulus springs to its original position, hurling the spores into the air.

The Osmundaceae have a rudimentary annulus (Fig. 242). In both this family and the Schizaeaceae the annulus is apical, while in the Gleicheniaceae it is equatorial. Dehiscence in all three families is longitudinal. In the Hymenophyllaceae, Dicksoniaceae, and Cyatheaceae the annulus is oblique and the dehiscence is obliquely lateral. In the Polypodiaceae the annulus is vertical, extending only about two-thirds of the way around the sporangium (Fig. 241). Dehiscence is transverse.

The Filicales resemble the Ophioglossales and Marattiales in being homosporous, but differ in that they are *leptosporangiate*. This means that the sporogenous tissue is developed from the outer segment arising from the first periclinal division of the initial, rather than from the inner segment, as among eusporangiate pteridophytes. The sporangium initial consists of a single superficial or marginal cell that becomes papillate. A periclinal division separates an inner cell from an outer cell, and then three oblique walls appear in the latter in such a way that a tetrahedral apical cell is formed. This cuts off a variable number of segments that form a short stalk (Fig. 243*A*). The sporangium now enlarges above and, by means of a periclinal division, an outer *cap cell* is separated from an inner *primary sporogenous cell* (Fig. 243*B*). The sporangium wall is developed by subsequent anticlinal divisions from the cap cell and the three uppermost stalk cells (Fig. 243*C*). In all the Filicales the sporangium wall remains one layer of cells thick.

A unique feature is introduced by the formation of the tapetum from the primary sporogenous cell rather than from the wall tissue. The tapetum arises from four cells, one of which is cut off each of the four faces of the primary sporogenous cell (Fig. 243*D, E*). The tapetum may remain

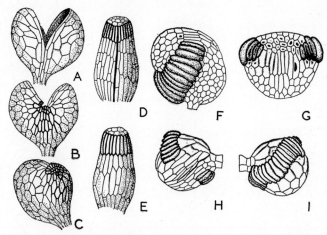

Fig. 242. Sporangia of some leptosporangiate ferns. *A, B, C, Osmunda regalis,* with rudimentary annulus; *D* and *E, Anemia phyllitidis,* with apical annulus; *F* and *G, Gleichenia circinata,* with equatorial annulus; *H* and *I, Hymenophyllum dilatum,* with oblique annulus. (*After Wettstein.*)

single-layered, but in nearly all the Filicales its cells divide periclinally to form two layers (Fig. 243*F, G*). The innermost cell of the sporangium meanwhile undergoes division to form the spore mother cells (Fig. 243*F–H*). When these round off, the tapetum disorganizes and forms a plasmodium that later surrounds them. The number of spores formed in each sporangium exhibits considerable variation, but is relatively high (up to 512) in the lower families and relatively low (commonly 64 or less) in the advanced families. This tendency to reduce the spore output is a significant feature of Filicinean evolution.

Gametophyte. The typical gametophyte of the Filicales is entirely aerial and consists of a flat, green, heart-shaped thallus usually about 6 mm. in diameter (Fig. 244). Numerous unicellular rhizoids grow from its ventral surface into the soil. There is no endophytic fungus, except in the Gleicheniaceae and sometimes in the Schizaeaceae and Hymenophyllaceae. In *Hymenophyllum* the gametophyte is an irregularly branched ribbon, while in *Trichomanes* and *Schizaea* it is filamentous and branched, resembling a moss protonema.

The germinating spore gives rise to a short green filament and a rhizoid. Soon an apical cell with two cutting faces arises and a flat thallus develops. Then an apical cell with three cutting faces is formed and the median portion of the prothallium becomes slightly thickened, the wings remaining

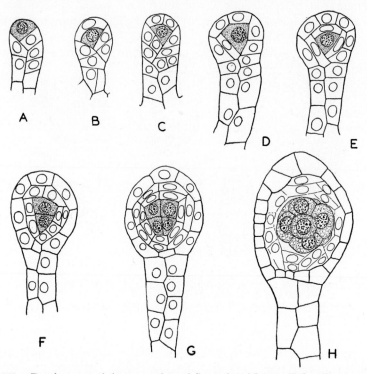

Fig. 243.   Development of the sporangium of *Cyrtomium falcatum* (Polypodiaceae), ×400. *A*, young stage, showing tetrahedral apical cell cutting off segments to form a stalk; *B*, formation of cap cell and primary sporogenous cell; *C*, anticlinal division of cap cell; *D*, formation of first tapetal cell from primary sporogenous cell; *E*, completion of tapetum; *F* and *G*, later stages, the tapetum becoming two-layered; *H*, breaking down of tapetum and rounding off of spore mother cells.

one-layered.   Eventually a group of initials is formed in the apical notch, replacing the apical cell.

In most of the Filicales the prothallium is monoecious, the sex organs arising from the ventral surface.   The antheridia appear at a very early stage, often when the prothallium is still filamentous, and continue to be produced for a long time.   The first antheridia are often marginal as well as ventral in position.   Later they become irregularly scattered over the entire ventral surface.   The antheridia are not embedded in the prothallium but project beyond its surface.

The antheridia of the Filicales differ greatly in development from those of the lower pteridophytes (Fig. 245). The initial is superficial and papillate. The first wall is transverse, the antheridium developing from the outer cell. This then undergoes a second transverse division, cutting off a *basal ring cell*. Due to increasing turgidity of the upper cell, the wall formed, called the *funnel wall*, becomes concave and approaches the first

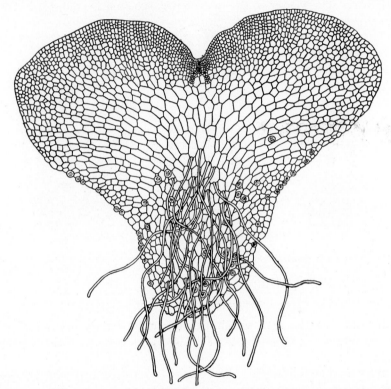

FIG. 244. Ventral view of a fern prothallium (Polypodiaceae), showing rhizoids and numerous antheridia in the older portion and three archegonia near the growing notch, ×35.

wall, finally touching it (Fig. 245A). Next a *dome wall* appears, delimiting an outer cell from a central cell (Fig. 245B). The dome wall is hemispherical and nearly concentric with the outer surface of the antheridium. The appearance of a second funnel wall in the outer cell results in the formation of another ring cell and a cap cell, thus completing the sterile jacket (Fig. 245C–E). The output of sperms in the higher families is commonly 32. As in the other ferns, the sperms are large, coiled, and multiciliate (Fig. 245F).

The archegonia appear late in the development of the gametophyte, thus occurring in the median portion near the growing notch (Fig. 244).

The initial is superficial but remains embedded. It divides transversely, the outer segment being the *primary neck cell* and the inner one dividing again to form the *central cell* and *basal cell* (Fig. 246*A*, *B*). The central cell gives rise to the axial row, which consists of a single binucleate *neck canal cell*, a small *ventral canal cell*, and the *egg* (Fig. 246*C–E*). In the Osmundaceae and Gleicheniaceae the neck canal nuclei may be separated by a wall. The venter of the mature archegonium is embedded in the

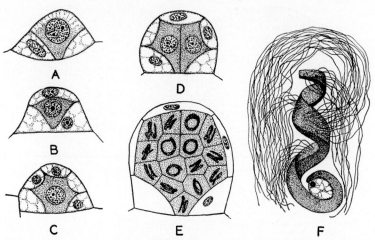

Fig. 245. Stages in development of the antheridium of *Nephrolepis* (*A to E*), ×700, and a sperm of *Dryopteris* (*F*), more highly magnified. *A*, cutting off a basal ring cell by funnel wall; *B*, appearance of dome wall, delimiting of outer cell from central cell; *C*, formation of second funnel wall; *D*, first division of central cell; *E*, mature antheridium with sperms forming in spermatogenous cells. (*A to E, after Gilbert M. Smith; F, after Yamanouchi.*)

prothallium, but the neck, which usually curves slightly backward, projects beyond the surface (Fig. 246*F*). The neck consists of four vertical rows of cells.

Embryo. The Filicales are characterized by a striking regularity in the early divisions of the embryo. The first division of the fertilized egg is not transverse but vertical, *i.e.*, parallel with the long axis of the archegonium (Fig. 247*A*). By a division of each daughter cell at right angles to the plane of the first division, quadrants are formed (Fig. 247*B*). Of the two inner cells, the anterior one gives rise to the stem and the posterior one to the foot. Of the two outer cells (those nearer the neck of the archegonium), the anterior one forms the first leaf and the posterior one the primary root. Thus the arrangement of the quadrants differs conspicuously from that found among the eusporangiate ferns. The subsequent divisions are at first regular, resulting in a globular embryo in which the four primary organs may be easily distinguished (Fig. 247*C*). Later growth, however, is irregular, the leaf and root developing more rapidly and soon breaking through the calyptra (Fig. 247*D*).

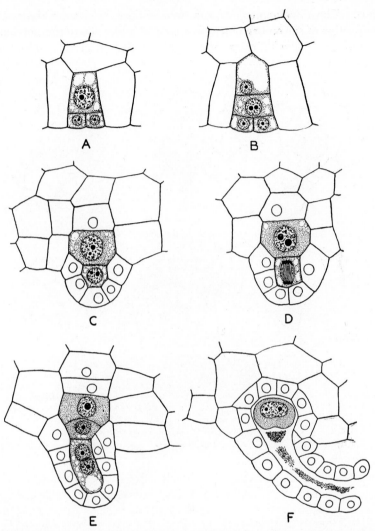

FIG. 246. Development of the archegonium of *Dryopteris*, ×350. *A*, division of archegonium initial into an inner and outer cell, the latter having again divided anticlinally to
form two neck cells; *B*, formation of central cell and basal cell; *C*, division of central cell
into ventral cell and neck canal cell; *D*, division of neck canal cell nucleus; *E*, nearly mature
archegonium with egg, ventral canal cell, and binucleate neck canal cell; *F*, archegonium
with egg ready for fertilization.

Summary. The Filicales are homosporous and leptosporangiate.
The sporangia are borne on the abaxial side of the leaves and are not in
synangia. The sporangium wall, one layer of cells thick, has an annulus.
The vernation is circinate. The gametophyte is flat, green, and thin
(sometimes filamentous); with few exceptions it is without an endophytic

fungus. The development of the antheridium is characteristic. The inner portion of the embryo forms the stem and foot, the outer portion the leaf and root. The Filicales are a highly organized group. Their prin-

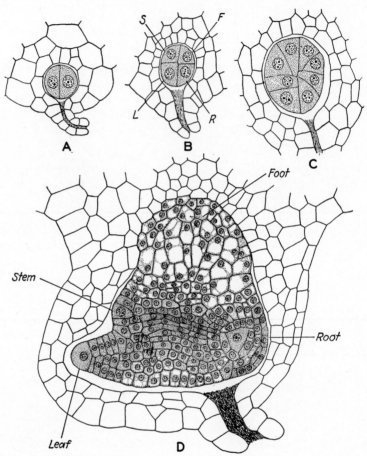

FIG 247. Stages in development of the embryo of a polypodiaceous fern, ×225. *A*, two-celled stage; *B*, four-celled stage; *C*, slightly later stage; *D*, embryo showing differentiation of organs.

cipal advance over the eusporangiate ferns lies in the development of their spore-producing structures.

5. Hydropteridales

The Hydropteridales include 2 families, 5 genera, and nearly 90 species. The two families are probably of separate origin and their inclusion in the same order is largely a matter of convenience. Both are more advanced than any of the families of Filicales, however, and in the same ways. All these plants live in water or in wet places and are appropriately called "water ferns." They constitute the most highly developed group of modern pteridophytes.

1. MARSILEACEAE

To the Marsileaceae belong 3 genera. *Marsilea*, with 65 species, and *Pilularia*, with 6 species, are widely distributed, while *Regnellidium*, with

FIG. 248. *Marsilea vestita.* View of plants growing in swampy ground.

a single species, is confined to southern Brazil. They live on muddy flats or submerged in water, rooting in the mud.

Sporophyte. In all three genera the stem is a slender, creeping, branched rhizome that produces erect leaves but no upright shoots. The leaves are arranged alternately in two rows along the upper side of the rhizome, while along the lower side roots are borne at the nodes. Each leaf of *Marsilea* has a long petiole and four terminal leaflets (Fig. 248). *Regnellidium* has two leaflets, while in *Pilularia* leaflets are wanting, the whole leaf consisting merely of a petiole. As in the Filicales, the leaves exhibit circinate vernation and dichotomous venation. The stem develops from a tetrahedral apical cell that cuts off three longitudinal rows of segments. The leaves arise from the two dorsal rows, the roots from the ventral row. The rhizome of *Marsilea* is an amphiphloic siphonostele without secondary thickening (Fig. 249). The rhizome of *Pilularia* is similar except that the vascular tissues are reduced.

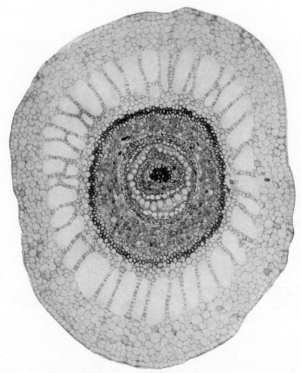

Fig. 249. Cross section of the rhizome of *Marsilea quadrifolia*, an amphiphloic sipho-nostele, ×50.

Sporocarp. The sporangia of the Marsileaceae are borne in special structures, called *sporocarps*, which occur on long or short stalks arising adaxially from the petiole of the leaf. They are usually borne singly, but in some species of *Marsilea* several or even many may be borne together. The sporocarp is a specialized leaf segment enclosing a group of sori. In *Marsilea* it is an ovoid or bean-shaped structure with a hard outer covering (Fig. 251). It contains 14 to 20 sori. In *Pilularia* the sporocarp is spherical and contains 2 to 4 sori. In both genera the sori are arranged in two rows. Each is surrounded by an indusium and contains both microsporangia and megasporangia. The sporangium wall is only one layer of cells in thickness, as in the Filicales, but is without an annulus. The sporangia are leptosporangiate in development. Four cavities appear in the young sporocarp of *Marsilea* and from the layer of cells lining them the sporangia arise, each sorus coming from a single marginal cell (Fig. 250*A*). The sporangia appear in basipetal succession on an elongating receptacle, the sorus thus being gradate, as in certain families

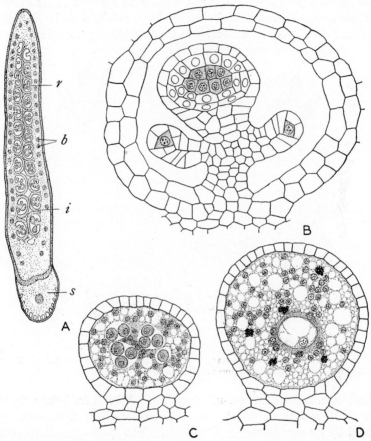

Fig. 250. Sporangia of *Marsilea quadrifolia*. *A*, horizontal section through a young sporocarp, showing early development of two rows of sori, ×25; *B*, longitudinal section through a young sorus and investing indusium, showing a developing megasporangium with sporogenous tissue and tapetum, and two younger microsporangia below, each with a primary sporogenous cell, ×400; *C*, megasporangium with young megaspores and tapetal plasmodium, ×300; *D*, megasporangium with enlarging functional megaspore, abortive megaspores, and tapetal plasmodium, ×300; *r*, receptacle; *b*, vascular bundles; *i*, indusium; *s*, stalk of sporocarp.

of the Filicales (see page 286). The tapetum, cut off from the sporogenous tissue, becomes two-layered (Fig. 250*B*). In both kinds of sporangia 32 or 64 young spores are formed. In the microsporangia all of these mature, but in the megasporangium only one spore matures, the others degenerating (Fig. 250*C*, *D*). The functional megaspore greatly enlarges and develops a very thick cell wall, as in the other heterosporous pterido-phytes.   In both kinds of sporangia the tapetum breaks down to form a multinucleate plasmodium that surrounds and nourishes the young spores.

The sporocarp of *Marsilea* is remarkable on account of its longevity, some specimens having been known to have retained their viability for 50 years.   If placed in water after the hard outer covering has been

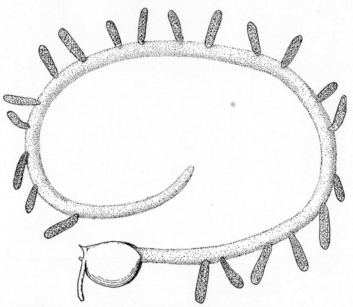

Fig. 251.   Germination of the sporocarp of *Marsilea vestita*, twice natural size.   Extrusion of mucilaginous ring to which the sori are attached.

cracked, germination is unusually prompt.   Within an hour a mucilag-inous ring appears to which the sori are attached, each sorus being enclosed by its own indusium (Fig. 251).   The spores germinate at once and the gametophytes develop with startling rapidity.

Gametophytes.   The male gametophyte of *Marsilea* reaches maturity within 10 to 20 hours after the microspore germinates.   It does not emerge from the spore, but develops inside, as in *Selaginella* and *Isoetes*. After a prothallial cell is cut off, the rest of the spore divides in half, each half becoming an antheridium (Fig. 252A–C).   Additional divisions result in the formation of two primary spermatogenous cells surrounded by a sterile jacket (Fig. 252D–F).   Each of the primary spermatogenous cells gives rise to a group of 16 sperms (Fig. 252G–I).   The sperms of *Marsilea* are corkscrew-like and multiciliate (Fig. 252J).

The female gametophyte of *Marsilea* is peculiar in that no internal tissue is developed and only one archegonium is formed. At the apex of the megaspore, where the wall is relatively thin, there is a papilla filled with dense cytoplasm in which the nucleus lies (Fig. 253*A*). When the spore germinates, the nucleus divides and a small cell is cut off by a transverse wall (Fig. 253*B*). The rest of the gametophyte acts as a

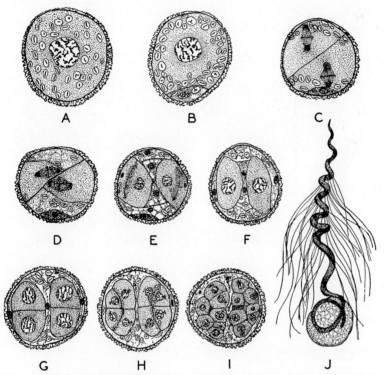

FIG. 252. Male gametophyte of *Marsilea quadrifolia*. *A*, microspore with starch grains in cytoplasm; *B*, prothallial cell cut off; *C*, microspore divided into two antheridium initials, in each of which a jacket cell is being formed; *D* and *E*, additional jacket cells being cut off; *F*, two primary spermatogenous cells enlarging; *G*, *H*, *I*, stages showing increase in spermatogenous cells to sixteen in each of the two antheridia; *J*, mature sperm, ×1,200; other stages, ×350. (*After Sharp.*)

food reservoir. The small cell is the archegonium initial, the larger one the nutritive cell. As development proceeds, the archegonium breaks through the megaspore wall. The mature archegonium consists of a large egg, a small ventral canal cell, a small neck canal cell, and a sterile jacket (Fig. 253*D*). The neck is short, consisting of only two tiers of four cells each. Mucilage above the archegonium forms a deep funnel into which the sperms collect.

Embryo. In the development of the embryo, the first wall is vertical, as in the Filicales, and then a quadrant stage appears (Fig. 253*E*). The

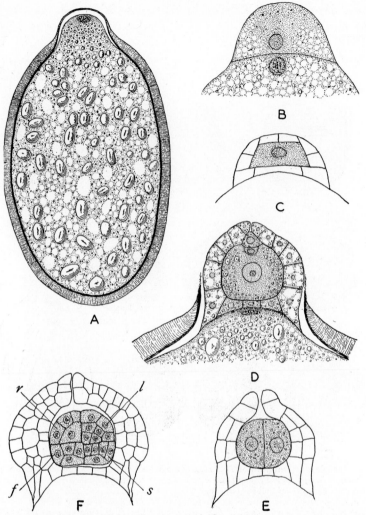

Fig. 253. Female gametophyte of *Marsilea quadrifolia*. *A*, longitudinal section of megaspore; *B*, archegonium initial cut off at apex of spore; *C*, young archegonium with central cell surrounded by neck cells and sterile jacket; *D*, mature archegonium, showing large egg, small ventral canal cell, and neck canal cell; *E*, two-celled embryo; *F*, embryo, enclosed by calyptra, showing differentiation into foot (*f*), root (*r*), leaf (*l*), and stem (*s*); *A*, ×100; *B* to *F*, ×250.

arrangement of the segments is such that the two outer segments (those nearer the neck of the archegonium) give rise to the leaf and root, the two inner ones to the stem and foot, the leaf and stem developing from segments on the same side (Fig. 253*F*).   With respect to the arrangement of the primary organs, the embryo of the Marsileaceae is similar to that of the Filicales.

2. Salviniaceae

To the Salviniaceae belong 2 genera of widespread occurrence, *Salvinia*, with 11 species, and *Azolla*, with 4 species. Both are small plants that float on the surface of quiet water. Their fossil history does not extend beyond the Tertiary.

Fig. 254. Floating plants of *Salvinia rotundifolia* (*A*), natural size, and of *Azolla filiculoides* (*B*), twice natural size.

Sporophyte. *Salvinia* has a slender, slightly branched stem bearing two kinds of leaves. The dorsal leaves are in four rows (Fig. 254*A*). They are 12 to 18 mm. long, entire, oval or oblong, flat, and overlapping. The ventral leaves, which occur in two rows, hang down into the water and look like roots, being much dissected into filiform divisions. The ventral leaves are probably absorptive in function, true roots being wanting. *Azolla* has pinnately branched stems covered with minute, crowded, overlapping leaves alternately arranged in two dorsal rows (Fig. 254*B*). Each leaf has two lobes, the upper lobe floating and the lower one submerged. The upper lobe contains cavities in which colonies of *Anabaena* live. Long, slender rootlets arise from the lower side of the stem.

In both genera the leaves are folded in the bud, not circinate as in the Marsileaceae and Filicales. Each leaf has a single vascular bundle. The stem develops by means of an apical cell with two cutting faces. The vascular tissues are greatly reduced. The stem of *Salvinia* appears to be an ectophloic siphonostele, that of *Azolla* an amphicribral protostele.

Sporocarps. The sporocarps of the Salviniaceae are globular and thin-walled, two or three occurring on a common stalk. In *Salvinia* they are borne in groups at the base of the ventral leaves, arising as outgrowths from them. In *Azolla* they are borne on lateral branches, chiefly in pairs, on the lower lobes of the first leaves to appear. In both genera the sporocarps consist of an indusium enclosing a single sorus. The indusium becomes hard at maturity, forming a nut-like structure.

The sporocarps are of two kinds, both occurring on the same plant. One contains only microsporangia and the other only megasporangia. In *Salvinia* the two kinds of sporocarps are of the same size and contain many sporangia, but in *Azolla* the megasporocarps are much smaller than the microsporocarps and contain only one megasporangium. At first each sporocarp of *Azolla* contains a young megasporangium with several younger microsporangia at its base. Only one kind of sporangium continues its development, however, the other kind aborting (Fig. 255). In both genera the microsporangia are borne on long, slender stalks arising from a basal receptacle, while the megasporangia are short-stalked or nearly sessile (Figs. 255 and 256*A*). As in the Marsileaceae, the sorus is gradate. The sporangium wall is only one layer of cells thick and no annulus is formed.

As in the Marsileaceae and Filicales, the development of the sporangia is leptosporangiate (Figs. 255*A* and 256*B*). In the microsporangium of both *Salvinia* and *Azolla* 16 spore mother cells are formed and all of these give rise to tetrads, resulting in the formation of 64 microspores. In the megasporangium of both genera, however, only 8 spore mother cells are formed. These give rise to 32 megaspores, but only one of these matures, the rest degenerating (Fig. 256*D*). The functional megaspore enlarges until it finally completely fills the sporangium. It becomes very thick-walled. In both genera the tapetum, which is cut off from the sporogenous tissue and consists of a single layer of cells, breaks down before the spores are ripe, forming a plasmodial matrix around them (Figs. 255*B* and 256*C*, *D*).　　Eventually this hardens.

　　In the microsporangium of *Azolla* four to eight masses, called *massulae*, are organized from the tapetal plasmodium and within these the microspores are embedded.　　The massulae of some species of *Azolla* produce hair-like appendages (*glochidia*) with sagittate tips (Fig. 257*A*).　　They

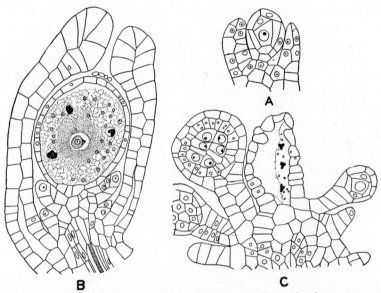

Fig. 255.　Sporangia of *Azolla caroliniana*.　*A*, young sporocarp, showing a young megasporangium and the developing indusium; *B*, megasporocarp, showing the terminal megasporangium with one functional and three abortive megaspores, and undeveloped microsporangia below; *C*, microsporocarp with developing microsporangia and an abortive megasporangium.　(*After Pfeiffer.*)

escape from the microsporangia and are carried to the megaspores, to which they become fastened by means of the glochidia.　　The microspores germinate within the massulae.　　In *Salvinia* they germinate while still within the microsporangia.　　The megaspores remain inside the megasporangia, which break away and, in *Salvinia*, float on the surface of the water.

　　Gametophytes.　　The male gametophyte of the Salviniaceae is peculiar in that the microspore produces a papillate outgrowth that forms one or two external antheridia, the internal portion functioning as a large nutritive cell (Fig. 257*B*).　　In both genera a small prothallial cell is cut off from the nutritive cell.　　In *Salvinia*, where there are two antheridia, each is enclosed by a sterile jacket and each produces four sperms.　　In *Azolla* there is only one antheridium and it produces eight sperms (Fig. 257C). The sperms are coiled and multiciliate.

In the formation of the female gametophyte, the nucleus of the megaspore divides near the apical end and a small lenticular cell is cut off. The larger cell later undergoes free-nuclear division, but no walls are formed and the cell becomes a food reservoir. The smaller cell gives rise to a tissue that breaks through the heavy megaspore wall and produces

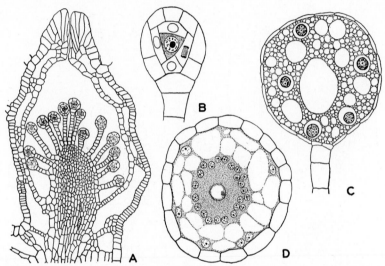

Fig. 256. Sporangia of *Salvinia rotundifolia*. *A*, longitudinal section through a young microsporocarp, ×100; *B*, young microsporangium, showing primary sporogenous cell surrounded by tapetum, ×600; *C*, older microsporangium, showing spores embedded in hardened tapetal plasmodium, ×160; *D*, developing megasporangium, showing young functional megaspore surrounded by tapetal nuclei, the nonfunctional megaspores near the wall, ×280.

several archegonia (Fig. 257D). This tissue turns green and becomes rather extensive in *Salvinia*, but in *Azolla* is smaller and has little or no chlorophyll. The archegonia resemble those of *Marsilea*, except that the single neck canal cell is usually binucleate.

Embryo. In both genera the fertilized egg, by means of two divisions at right angles to each other, gives rise to quadrants, but the first wall is longitudinal in *Salvinia* and transverse in *Azolla*. The relation of the four primary organs to one another is the same as in the other leptosporangiate ferns.

Summary. The Hydropteridales are heterosporous and leptosporangiate. The sporangia are borne in sporocarps representing either a modified leaf segment (Marsileaceae) or a modified indusium (Salviniaceae). Both microsporangia and megasporangia occur in the same sporocarp (Marsileaceae) or in separate sporocarps (Salviniaceae). The sporangium wall is only one layer of cells thick and is without an annulus. The vernation is circinate (Marsileaceae) or folded (Salviniaceae). The gametophytes are greatly reduced, developing largely within the spore wall. The development of the embryo is essentially the same as in the Filicales. The Hydropteridales are a specialized aquatic group, the two families apparently having been derived independently from the Filicales.

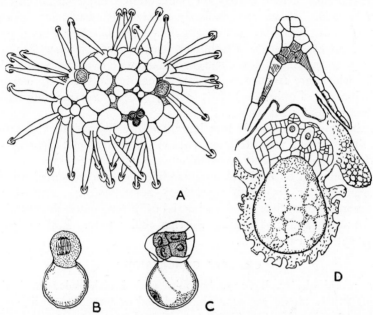

FIG. 257. *Azolla filiculoides.* *A*, massula with glochidia and enclosed microspores, ×250; *B*, germinating microspore, the antheridium initial dividing, ×560; *C*, male gametophyte with small prothallial cell, large nutritive cell, and external antheridium, ×560; *D*, female gametophyte, showing the large nutritive cell and the extruded tissue bearing archegonia, ×65. (*After Campbell.*)

COMPARISON OF THE CLASSES OF PTERIDOPHYTES

The most important distinguishing characters of the four classes of pteridophytes are as follows:

Psilophytinae. Leaves small, simple, spiral, generally without veins, often wanting. Roots absent. Stem mostly an exarch protostele. Leaf gaps absent. Definite strobili not organized. Sporangia solitary, terminal; on elongated branches and unilocular or (in Psilotales) on greatly reduced branches and bilocular or trilocular; tapetum wanting. Homosporous. Prothallia (in Psilotales) tuberous, subterranean, not green. Sperms multiciliate. Embryo without a suspensor.

Lycopodiinae. Leaves simple, usually small and numerous, generally spiral, with a single vein. Stem mostly an exarch protostele. Leaf gaps

absent. Definite strobili usually present. Sporangia borne on sporophylls, solitary, adaxial, unilocular; trabeculae sometimes present.
Homosporous (in Lycopodiales) or heterosporous. Prothallia in homosporous forms tuberous, wholly or in part subterranean, and with chlorophyll only in the aerial portion. Sperms biciliate or (in Isoetales) multiciliate. Embryo with or (in Isoetales) without a suspensor.

Equisetinae. Leaves mostly small and simple, numerous, cyclic, with
a single vein. Stems conspicuously jointed, longitudinally grooved.
Stem an endarch siphonostele or (in Sphenophyllales) an exarch protostele. Leaf gaps absent. Strobili present. Sporangia generally borne
in groups on sporangiophores, usually adaxial with reference to the sporophylls, which are frequently absent. Homosporous or heterosporous.
Prothallia (in Equisetales) flat, aerial, green. Sperms multiciliate.
Embryo without a suspensor.

Filicinae. Leaves mostly few, large, and divided, spiral, with numerous veins. Stem a protostele, siphonostele, or dictyostele; typically mesarch. Leaf gaps present. Strobili absent. Sporangia numerous and
generally abaxial on modified or unmodified leaflets, commonly in sori.
Homosporous or (in Hydropteridales) heterosporous. Prothallia in
homosporous forms flat, green, and aerial or (in Ophioglossales) tuberous,
subterranean, and not green. Sperms multiciliate. Embryo nearly
always without a suspensor.

GENERAL CONCLUSIONS

All pteridophytes have archegonia and multicellular antheridia,
although these organs are somewhat reduced as compared with those of
bryophytes. Fertilization is still conditioned by the presence of water.
All pteridophytes display a distinct alternation of generations, but
advance far beyond the bryophytes in the possession of an independent
sporophyte with a leafy stem, true roots, and a well-developed vascular
system. The sporophyte is nourished by the gametophyte only during
the early stages of its development.

Independent Sporophyte. In the evolution of the plant kingdom the
first land plants to have established an independent sporophyte must
necessarily have developed one with (1) a means of anchorage and of
absorbing water directly from the soil and (2) a means of displaying green
tissue to the light and air. In practically all existing pteridophytes the
sporophyte carries on water absorption by roots and photosynthesis by
leaves borne on a stem. Food manufacture has become primarily a function of the sporophyte, leaving fertilization as the main function of the
gametophyte. This arrangement permits the sporophyte to grow upward
into the air. A large plant displaying leaves to the light and air requires
a constant supply of water as well as a means of mechanical support.

These demands are met, in the pteridophytes, mainly by the vascular system. Thus the sporophyte, in achieving independence, has developed roots, stems, and leaves, with a system of conducting and supporting tissues extending throughout the plant body.

Among existing pteridophytes the Psilotales are unique in having a sporophyte that shows little organization into vegetative organs. Their poorly developed leaves (without veins in *Psilotum*) and lack of roots, although probably related to a partially saprophytic existence, are to be regarded as primitive features, since they are shared with the extinct Psilophytales, a group which the Psilotales resemble in other respects as well.

The size of the leaves must be considered in relation to the size of the stem. From this standpoint, small simple leaves, without a petiole, are found in nearly all members of the three lower classes, while large leaves, with a petiole and with a blade that is almost always divided into leaflets, are characteristic of the ferns. Moreover, ferns are the only pterido- phytes having leaf gaps, a feature setting them off in marked contrast to the lower classes and indicating a relationship to the seed plants, where leaf gaps are universally present. Except in the Equisetinae, where they are cyclic, the leaves of pteridophytes are fundamentally spiral in arrangement.

The leaves of the Psilophytinae, except those of *Tmesipteris*, are vein- less, while those of the Lycopodiinae have a single unbranched vein. These groups are said to be *microphyllous* (small-leaved), for even the leaves of the Lepidodendrales and Isoetales, though larger than those of other lycopods, are narrow and have only one vein. The leaves of microphyllous pteridophytes probably represent emergences, or simple outgrowths from the stem. The Filicinae are *megaphyllous* (large-leaved) and their leaves have many branching veins. Such leaves apparently have evolved from a lateral branch system that has become flattened and limited in growth. Thus the leaves of lycopods and those of ferns have probably had a different origin and so are not homologous. Most of the Equisetinae have small simple leaves with a single vein, but some of the fossil members have larger leaves with leaflets and branching veins. This indicates that the group was originally megaphyllous, the small leaves having been derived from larger ones by reduction.

The Strobilus. A second contribution of the pteridophytes to the evolu- tion of the plant kingdom has been the organization of a strobilus. Orig- inally no distinction may have existed between sporophylls and foliage leaves, a condition found in the simpler species of *Lycopodium*. But gradually, as a result of "division of labor," sporophylls became less leaf- like and were organized to form a compact strobilus. Although not pres- ent in modern ferns, a strobilus is characteristic of nearly all the other groups of living pteridophytes, as well as of a number of extinct forms. Its appearance is important because it is a feature carried on into the spermatophytes.

In the Lycopodiinae and Filicinae the sporangia are borne in connection with some or all of the leaves. In the Lycopodiinae they are solitary and adaxial, in the Filicinae numerous and mainly abaxial. In the Psilophytinae the sporangia are terminal, either on the main stem (Psilophytales) or on a very short lateral branch (Psilotales). In the Equisetinae the sporangia are borne on sporangiophores. The sporangium of the pteridophytes is always epidermal in origin and may arise from a single cell or a small group of cells. In its development, all pteridophytes are eusporangiate except two orders of ferns, the Filicales and Hydropteridales, which are leptosporangiate. With the exception of the Psilotales, a tapetum is present in all living pteridophytes. In the Lycopodiinae the tapetum is persistent, but in the Equisetinae and Filicinae it soon breaks down.

Heterospory. The appearance of heterospory represents a third great forward step in evolution introduced by the pteridophytes. Among modern representatives it occurs only in *Selaginella*, *Isoetes*, and the five genera of the Marsileaceae and Salviniaceae. Heterospory was developed, however, in many extinct forms. It introduces into the life history two kinds of spores, two kinds of gametophytes, and a great reduction in the gametophyte generation. Heterospory, introduced by the pteridophytes, is an established feature of the spermatophytes. In fact, it makes seed formation possible.

The gametophytes of homosporous pteridophytes may be tuberous and subterranean, as in the Psilotales, Lycopodiales, and Ophioglossales, where the absence of chlorophyll is associated with a saprophytic mode of nutrition; or they may be flat, green, and aerial, as in the Equisetales, Marattiales, and Filicales. In practically all homosporous pteridophytes both kinds of sex organs are borne in comparatively large numbers on the same gametophyte. In the heterosporous forms, however, the gametophytes are always dioecious and reduced, both kinds developing largely or entirely within the spore wall. The male gametophyte produces only one or two prothallial cells and one or two antheridia. The female gametophyte usually has more vegetative tissue, but generally only one to several archegonia.

The gametophyte of the homosporous pteridophytes, with much vegetative tissue, must not only make its own food, but also enough for the embryo sporophyte that is dependent upon it. The development of such a gametophyte requires a considerable period of favorable external conditions. This handicap is largely avoided by the heterosporous pteridophytes. Their gametophytes are formed inside the spores that produce them and do not emerge except, in some cases, to a very slight extent. Each lives on food stored within the spore. The advantage of heterospory lies in the fact that, since the gametophytes derive their nourishment from food made by the sporophyte, they are independent of such external conditions as might interfere with the growth of a free-living gametophyte.

Except in the Anthocerotales, the sex organs of bryophytes are superficial structures, but in the pteridophytes they are embedded, either wholly or in part. Moreover, as compared with the sex organs of bryophytes, both the antheridia and archegonia of pteridophytes are reduced. The greatest reduction of spermatogenous tissue occurs in the heterosporous forms, reaching an extreme in *Isoetes*, where each antheridium produces only four sperms. The most primitive archegonia, those with the greatest number of neck canal cells, are found in *Lycopodium*. In nearly all the other homosporous pteridophytes there are either two neck canal cells or, more commonly, only one, this being usually binucleate. In the heterosporous forms there is a single neck canal cell that may be either binucleate or uninucleate, according to the genus. Nearly all pteridophytes have multiciliate sperms. Biciliate sperms, resembling those of bryophytes, are confined to *Lycopodium, Phylloglossum,* and *Selaginella.*

Interrelationships. The Psilophytales are the oldest known and most primitive group of vascular plants. Whether they were derived from ancestors resembling bryophytes or directly from alga-like forms is a matter of difference of opinion. It is rather generally agreed, however, that the Psilophytales gave rise to the other pteridophytes, since transitional forms have been found. The Lycopodiinae, Equisetinae, and Filicinae separated early from the Psilophytales and each has subsequently pursued an independent course of evolution. The Psilophytales also gave rise to the Psilotales, a group that has made relatively little progress and one that stands apart from the other existing groups.

The Lycopodiinae are a relatively primitive group in spite of the fact that some members have advanced to the condition of heterospory. They reached their climax in the Paleozoic and are now relatively unimportant members of the flora. There is no evidence that they have given rise to any of the higher groups. The Equisetinae, more advanced than the Lycopodiinae, also made their greatest display during the Paleozoic. They are a peculiar group with many features not seen in any other vascular plants. They also represent a line of evolution that ends blindly.

The Filicinae are the most highly developed of all pteridophytes and show much progress among themselves. It is generally believed, on the basis of much morphological and paleobotanical evidence, that the ferns have given rise to the seed plants. The leptosporangiate ferns are essentially modern, while the eusporangiate ferns are more ancient and more primitive. The Paleozoic ancestors of the spermatophytes must have developed heterospory, but the only known heterosporous ferns are the two families of Hydropteridales, both of which are modern and highly specialized. Yet, aside from heterospory, there are many resemblances between the eusporangiate ferns and the Cycadofilicales of the Paleozoic, which are the most primitive group of gymnosperms.

CHAPTER VIII

SPERMATOPHYTA

The spermatophytes constitute the highest and largest division of the plant kingdom, numbering approximately 196,000 species. They comprise the two classes Gymnospermae and Angiospermae, the former being not only the older and more primitive group, but by far the smaller one today. Spermatophytes are found in all parts of the world and in the most diverse habitats. Although the angiosperms dominate the land vegetation, they include members that have become aquatic, epiphytic, and, through partial or complete loss of chlorophyll, saprophytic or parasitic.

All spermatophytes are characterized by the production of seeds, a feature that at once distinguishes them from the lower groups. Like the pteridophytes, they are vascular plants with an independent sporophyte; but in spermatophytes the sporophyte attains its greatest complexity, while the gametophyte is obscure and so reduced that it is entirely dependent upon the sporophyte for its nutrition.

Spermatophytes range in size from the minute floating duckweeds, some no larger than the head of a pin, to the giant redwoods of California and certain eucalypts of Australia, both of which may reach a height of 100 m. All modern gymnosperms are woody plants, while the angiosperms include both woody and herbaceous types. The stem undergoes lateral branching, the branches nearly always arising in the leaf axils. Most commonly the branching is monopodial. Elongation of the root and stem is accomplished by a terminal meristem, never by an apical cell. All seed plants are heterosporous. The microsporangia and megasporangia are borne by members that are essentially foliar in nature but, although homologous with the sporophylls of pteridophytes, are nearly always more highly modified. Among spermatophytes it is customary to designate the microsporophyll as a *stamen*, the megasporophyll as a *carpel*, and the megasporangium as an *ovule*.[1] The megasporangium produces a single functional megaspore. Because the megaspore is not shed, the female gametophyte develops inside the megasporangium. This feature makes seed formation possible.

In practically all gymnosperms the female gametophyte produces archegonia, but in angiosperms archegonia are eliminated. The male

---

[1] Really the megasporangium is only part of the ovule, *e.g.*, the nucellus.

gametophyte does not form antheridia, but gives rise directly to two sperms or their equivalent. Swimming sperms, universal throughout the bryophytes and pteridophytes, occur only in two orders of living gymnosperms, being replaced in all other spermatophytes by nonmotile male cells. In all seed plants the sperms or male cells, as the case may be, reach the egg through the agency of pollen tubes, within which they develop. Following fertilization, the embryo develops inside the ovule, which becomes a seed.

1. GYMNOSPERMAE

The gymnosperms, numbering only about 700 living species, are an ancient group with a long geologic history. All the evidence points to

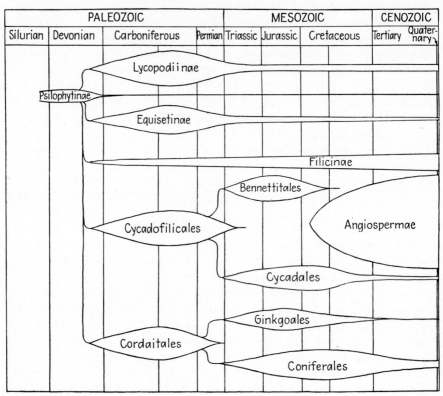

Fig. 258. Diagram showing the geologic distribution and the relationships of the major groups of vascular plants.

their origin from the ferns. They were abundant during the Paleozoic, while during the greater part of the Mesozoic they became the dominant group of land plants (Fig. 258). All existing gymnosperms are woody plants and most of them are trees. Gymnosperm means "naked seed," the seeds being borne not in a closed vessel, as they are in angiosperms, but freely exposed. The class includes seven orders: the Cycadofilicales, Bennettitales, Cycadales, Cordaitales, Ginkgoales, Coniferales, and Gnetales. Of these, the first, second, and fourth are entirely extinct.

1. Cycadofilicales

The Cycadofilicales[1] are the oldest and most primitive group of seed plants. Although some fossil remains have come from late Devonian deposits, the group did not become abundant and widespread until the Upper Carboniferous (Fig. 258). It declined greatly during the Permian, but persisted into the Triassic, when it soon became extinct. The Cycadofilicales are of great interest because, as their name implies, they are transitional between the ferns and the cycads.

Sporophyte. The general aspect of the Cycadofilicales was distinctly fern-like (Fig. 259). Some forms resembled modern tree ferns, but most of them were smaller. Some appear to have been climbers. The leaves, when found as impressions in the rocks, are so fern-like that they cannot be distinguished from the leaves of true ferns except when found in association with stems, sporangia, or seeds. The stem anatomy is fern-like also, but the development of secondary wood is characteristic. This wood consisted of pitted rather than scalariform tracheids. Three stelar types were represented among the Cycadofilicales, each constituting a "stem genus." *Heterangium* was a protostele, *Medullosa* a polystele (with three separate steles), and *Lyginopteris* an ectophloic siphonostele (Fig. 260). In each case the primary xylem was mesarch, a fern character. The leaf traces were double and direct; they were mesarch throughout.

Microsporangium. The microsporangia of the Cycadofilicales were at one time regarded as the sporangia of ferns. The microsporophyll (stamen) resembled an ordinary fern frond having fertile and sterile pinnae. In the "stamen genus" *Crossotheca* each fertile pinnule was more or less peltate and bore six to eight bilocular microsporangia on its lower side. This is designated as the "epaulet" type of stamen (Fig. 261*A*, *B*). Another, characteristic of the stamen genus *Calymmatotheca*, is known as the "cupule" type because the microsporangia were borne within a cup-like structure formed at the end of a naked branch (Fig. 261*C*). In some of the Cycadofilicales the microsporangia occurred as synangia on the abaxial surface of fern-like leaves.

Megasporangium. In none of the Cycadofilicales was a strobilus organized. Commonly the fern-like leaves were dimorphic, some being fertile and others sterile. The fertile leaves bore terminal ovules on their ultimate divisions (Figs. 196 and 259). The seeds were usually enclosed in a cupule (Fig. 262). As in other seed plants, the ovule consisted of a

[1] Often called Pteridospermae.

FIG. 259. Portion of restoration of Carboniferous swamp forest in the Chicago Natural History Museum. Plants belonging to the Cycadofilicales include *Lyginopteris oldhamia*, a climber leaning against the large tree near the center, *Neuropteris decipiens*, in left center, and *Neuropteris heterophylla*, in lower left center.

central portion, the *nucellus*, surrounded by an *integument* except at its apex, where a narrow passageway, the *micropyle*, was formed. In the Cycadofilicales the integument commonly was free from the nucellus only in the upper portion of the ovule, but in some cases was wholly free. The nucellus was prominently beaked and contained a deep pollen chamber in

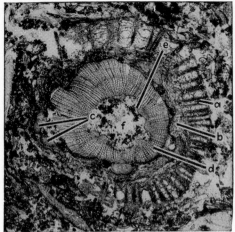

FIG. 260. Cross section of small stem of *Lyginopteris oldhamia*, ×5; *a*, sclerenchyma bands in outer cortex; *b*, inner cortex and phloem; *c*, double leaf trace; *d*, secondary xylem; *e*, primary xylem; *f*, pith. (*From Arnold.*)

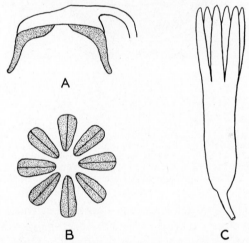

FIG. 261. Microsporangia of Cycadofilicales. *A*, diagrammatic longitudinal section of a fertile pinnule of *Crossotheca*, showing epaulet type with peltate limb and pendent sporangia, ×3; *B*, cross section of same, showing bilocular sporangia; *C*, cupule type, *Codonotheca*, with sporangia on the inner surface of the valves, natural size. (*A and B, after Kidston; C, after Sellards.*)

which the microspores accumulated. The Cycadofilicales must have had swimming sperms.

Gametophytes. Pollen grains, found in pollen chambers, contain a tissue of numerous cells, all of which were probably spermatogenous. The sperms seem to agree in form with those of existing cycads. No evidence of pollen tubes has ever been found and it is probable that they were not produced.   Remains of the female gametophyte are fragmentary, but it is certain that archegonia were developed in the micropylar region of the nucellus, the microspores apparently coming directly in contact with them.   No embryos have ever been found in the seeds, perhaps because they did not develop until after the seeds had been shed.

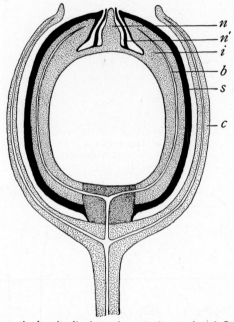

Fig. 262. Diagrammatic longitudinal section of the ovule of *Lyginopteris oldhamia* (*Lagenostoma lomaxii*) with its investing cupule; *n*, central portion of nucellus; *n'*, outer hardened portion with the pollen chamber between; *i*, inner fleshy layer of integument; *b*, vascular bundle; *s*, outer stony layer of integument; *c*, cupule.   (*After Oliver.*)

Summary.   The Cycadofilicales are a group that was dominant in the Paleozoic.   It is closely related to the Filicinae, the general habit, leaves, and microsporangiate structures being distinctly fern-like.   The vascular anatomy is also fern-like, but with the addition of secondary wood. Three stelar types are represented.   A primitive feature is the occurrence of mesarch xylem throughout the plant, an advanced feature, the presence of pitted tracheids.   There is no strobilus and the sporophylls are leaf-like and not highly differentiated from foliage leaves.   The microsporangia resemble fern sporangia in being numerous on the sporophylls, but the megasporangia, in forming seeds, show a great advance.   The Cycadofilicales are transitional between the ferns and cycads.   They were probably ancestral to both the Bennettitales and Cycadales.

2. Bennettitales

The Bennettitales were a Mesozoic order, world-wide in distribution. They ranged from the Triassic to the Upper Cretaceous but reached their greatest display during the Jurassic (Fig. 258). The four principal genera are *Cycadeoidea, Williamsonia, Williamsoniella,* and *Wielandiella.* In

Fig. 263. Upper part of a large stem of *Cycadeoidea.* Some of the strobili are projecting and some have fallen out, leaving cavities. The specimen is about 60 cm. high.

spite of their many distinctive features, the Bennettitales were probably direct descendants of the Paleozoic Cycadofilicales.

Sporophyte. The Bennettitales were more diversified in habit than modern cycads. Few forms exceeded 2 m. in height and most of them were under 1 m. The stems of *Cycadeoidea* were mostly short, stout, and unbranched (Fig. 263), while those of *Williamsonia* were tall and columnar, often with a few lateral branches. They bore a crown of large fern-like leaves at the summit. The stems were covered with an armor of persistent leaf bases and a mass of woolly scales, forming a ramentum, as in many tree ferns. The stems of *Williamsoniella* and *Wielandiella* were slender, dichotomously branched, and smooth, with a cluster of leaves at the points of forking. Except in *Williamsoniella*, the leaves of the Bennettitales were pinnately divided into many leaflets.

Fig. 264. *Cycadeoidea ingens.* Photograph of a model of the strobilus in the Chicago Natural History Museum.

The stem was an ectophloic siphonostele, a cross section showing a large pith, a thin vascular cylinder, and a thick cortex. The vascular bundles were collateral and endarch. Secondary wood, although scanty in amount, was always present. Most of the tracheids were scalariform, but in some cases were pitted. The leaf traces were single and direct, becoming mesarch after entering the leaves.

Strobilus. In *Cycadeoidea* numerous strobili were borne on short stalks occurring among the leaf bases, each strobilus being axillary (Fig. 263). In *Williamsonia* the cones were long-stalked and borne in the apical crown of leaves. In the two other genera the strobili were borne singly in an upright position where the stem underwent forking. The order is characterized by bisporangiate strobili (mostly monosporangiate in *William-*

sonia), the two kinds of sporophylls having the same relation to each other as have the stamens and carpels in a flower of the magnolia. Each cone consisted of four sets of members: an outer sheath of sterile bracts, a whorl of microsporophylls, stalked ovules, and interseminal scales (Fig. 264).

In *Cycadeoidea*, the microsporangiate structures had advanced but little beyond the fern condition. The microsporophylls (stamens), 10 to

Fig. 265.   Diagram of a longitudinal section of the strobilus of *Cycadeoidea*, showing hairy bracts below, two pinnate microsporophylls, and the central ovule-bearing axis.   (*After Wieland.*)

20 in number, were large, leaf-like, and pinnately divided, each division bearing two lateral rows of abaxial sporangia borne in synangia like those of the Marattiales (Fig. 265).   The megasporophylls and interseminal scales were closely crowded together at the summit of the strobilus axis, forming a compact ovoid body.   Each ovule was borne at the end of a stalk that probably represents a reduced sporophyll (Fig. 266*A*).   The stalks were more or less vertical, the middle one being the longest.   The interseminal scales probably represent sterile sporophylls.   The ovule had a basal cupule and a three-layered integument consisting of an outer fleshy, a middle stony, and an inner fleshy layer.   The micropyle was

long, and a prominent nucellar beak and pollen chamber were developed (Fig. 266*B*). Thus it seems certain that the Bennettitales had swimming sperms. Nothing is known of the gametophytes. The embryo was dicotyledonous and completely filled the seed, no endosperm having been present at maturity.

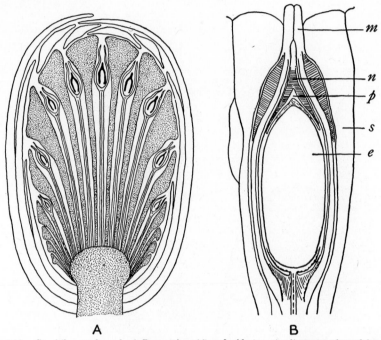

A   **B**

Fig. 266. Strobilus and seed of *Bennettites* (*Cycadeoidea*). *A*, diagram of seed-bearing strobilus, showing sheathing bracts, long-stalked seeds, and interseminal scales; *B*, longitudinal section of seed; *m*, micropylar tube; *n*, nucellar beak; *p*, pollen chamber; *s*, interseminal scale; *e*, embryo space. (*A, after Scott and others; B, after Wieland and Lignier.*)

Summary. The Bennettitales are a group dominant in the Mesozoic and intermediate in some respects between the Cycadofilicales and the Cycadales. Characters common to the Cycadofilicales include branching of the stem, a ramentum, direct leaf traces, leaf-like microsporophylls with synangia, and the ovule structure. An advance is seen in the organization of a strobilus. Characters common to the Cycadales are the general habit of some of the genera, the leaves, and the vascular anatomy, the stem being an endarch siphonostele with relatively little secondary wood. Distinctive features of the group are the bisporangiate strobili and the occurrence of both fertile and sterile megasporophylls, the latter bearing solitary terminal ovules. The Bennettitales are considered too specialized in their spore-bearing structures to have given rise to the Cycadales. Both groups seem to have had an independent origin from the Cycadofilicales. The resemblance between the bisporangiate cycadeoid cone and the flower of the magnolia and its allies has suggested that the angiosperms may have been derived from the Bennettitales, but there is little evidence to support this view (see page 411).

3. Cycadales

This order includes 9 living genera and about 100 species, all of which are tropical or subtropical in distribution. Four of the genera belong to the Western Hemisphere and five to the Eastern Hemisphere. *Zamia*, the

FIG. 267. *Dioon edule* with a large female cone 28 cm. in diameter. The leaves are up to 1.5 m. long.

largest genus, has about 30 species; it ranges from Florida to Chili. *Microcycas* is confined to western Cuba, *Dioon* and *Ceratozamia* to southern Mexico. *Cycas*, with 20 species, ranges from Japan to Australia and Madagascar. *Bowenia* and *Macrozamia* are found only in Australia, *Stangeria* and *Encephalartos* only in Africa. The Cycadales are closely related to the Bennettitales and like them were probably derived directly from the Cycadofilicales. They flourished throughout the Mesozoic and reached their greatest display in the Lower Cretaceous, when they were much more widespread than they are today (Fig. 258).

Sporophyte. The stems of cycads are either subterranean and tuberous or aerial and columnar. They bear a crown of large fern-like leaves (Fig. 267). The stems of the columnar forms are covered with an armor of persistent leaf bases. The stem is rarely branched and is commonly less than 3 m. high. The tallest species (*Macrozamia hopei*) sometimes reaches a height of 18 m. The leaves are pinnate (bipinnate in *Bowenia*)

and are borne in close spiral arrangement at the apex of the stem.   They
are rather tough and leathery and vary in length from 5 cm. to 3 m.,
depending on the species.   The venation, often described as parallel, is
really dichotomous, as in most ferns (Fig. 268A).   In *Cycas*, however, the
leaflets have no veins except a prominent midrib.   The vernation is

Fig. 268.   Leaves of cycads.   *A*, two leaflets of *Zamia skinneri*, showing dichotomous
venation, one-half natural size; *B*, young leaves of *Cycas circinalis*, showing circinate
vernation, one-fifth natural size.

circinate in *Cycas* and either erect or somewhat circinate in the other
genera (Fig. 268B).

   The stem of the Cycadales is like that of the Bennettitales in being an
ectophloic siphonostele with a large pith, a thin vascular cylinder, and a
thick cortex (Fig. 269).   The vascular bundles of the stem are collateral
and endarch, but the leaf traces, leaf veins, and bundles of the strobilus
axis are mesarch and frequently amphicribral as well.   Secondary wood
is developed but is commonly small in amount.   It consists of tracheids
with bordered pits, except in *Zamia* and *Stangeria*, where the tracheids
are scalariform, like those of ferns.   The leaf traces of cycads are peculiar
in being double and indirect.   This means that, in passing from the stele

to the leaf, two leaf traces girdle the cortex in opposite directions, each passing about halfway around the stem in going from their point of origin to the leaf.

The cones of the Bennettitales, each occurring in the axil of a leaf, are borne laterally along the stem. In *Macrozamia* and *Encephalartos* the cones are also lateral and axillary, although arising close to the stem tip.

Fig. 269. Cross section of the stem of *Zamia floridana*, showing large pith, thin vascular cylinder, and thick cortex with portions of the girdling leaf traces, ×4.

In the other genera the original apical meristem is used up in the formation of a cone, and a new meristem appears at its base. This produces a branch that soon becomes erect and gives rise to a new crown of leaves. Thus the first cone produced by a plant is terminal, but all the rest are morphologically lateral, although borne at the summit of the stem. All cycads are monosporangiate and dioecious.

Staminate Strobilus. The staminate strobili are usually borne singly, but in *Zamia*, *Macrozamia*, and *Encephalartos* several or many may occur together (Fig. 270*B*). They are composed of an axis bearing many spirally arranged microsporophylls (stamens) that are always compactly organized. The microsporophylls are not at all leaf-like, but are narrow below and broadened above into a sterile tip (Fig. 271). The microsporangia are abaxial and borne in sori of two to five, but not in synangia. They range in number from over a thousand on each sporophyll in *Cycas* to a comparatively few in *Zamia*. Their development is eusporangiate, the initials being hypodermal in origin rather than epidermal as in the

FIG. 270.   Cones of cycads.   *A*, female cone of *Cycas revoluta*, consisting of a loose rosette of megasporophylls; *B*, male cones of *Zamia skinneri*; *C*, female cone of *Zamia skinneri* with nearly ripe seeds.

pteridophytes.   There may be only one initial or a row or plate of several initials.   The initials divide transversely, the outer segments being the primary wall cells and the inner ones the primary sporogenous cells.   A wall several layers in thickness is developed (Fig. 272).   The tapetum is cut off rather late, and so it is uncertain whether it is derived from the wall or from the sporogenous tissue.   The number of spores produced by each sporangium is high, ranging from 500 in *Zamia* to 30,000 in *Dioon*. Dehiscence occurs by means of a longitudinal slit.   In general, the microsporangium of the cycads shows a striking resemblance to the sporangium of the Marattiales, particularly to that of *Angiopteris* (Fig. 229).

Ovulate Strobilus.   In most genera the ovulate cones are borne singly, but in *Macrozamia* and *Encephalartos* they may occur in groups of two, three, or more.   They are com- posed of many spirally arranged, fleshy megasporophylls (carpels). In *Cycas* the megasporophylls are very loosely arranged to form a rosette that surrounds the stem tip, which later continues its growth upward through the rosette (Fig. 270*A*).   In *Dioon* the megasporo- phylls form a loose cone, but in all the other genera they are compactly organized (Figs. 267 and 270*C*). The megasporophylls of cycads exhibit a striking reduction series, ranging from pinnate types with six or eight ovules, in most species of *Cycas*, to peltate types with only two ovules, in the other genera (Fig. 273).   Throughout this series the megasporophylls become less

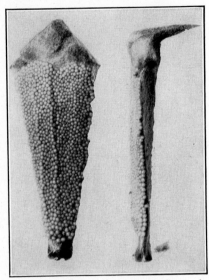

Fig. 271.   Microsporophylls of *Cycas cir- cinalis*, showing back (abaxial) and side views, one and one-half times natural size.

and less leaf-like and the strobilus increasingly more compact.

The main body of the ovule is the *nucellus* or megasporangium proper. It is surrounded by a single massive *integument* free from the nucellus only at its upper end and forming a narrow passageway, the *micropyle* (Fig. 274).   A prominent nucellar beak is developed, in the center of which a pollen chamber later arises.   The integument consists of an outer fleshy, a middle stony, and an inner fleshy layer.   Vascular strands are found in both fleshy layers.   They are composed of mesarch xylem.   Deep within the nucellar tissue a megaspore mother cell becomes differentiated.   It gives rise to a linear tetrad of megaspores.   Of these, only the innermost megaspore functions, the other three degenerating.

Female Gametophyte.   As in all seed plants, the megaspore germi- nates *in situ*, producing the female gametophyte.   Its formation involves several stages.   First, the megaspore enlarges and free-nuclear division occurs.   Then, by further enlargement, a central vacuole is formed, resulting in a parietal placing of the nuclei.   As nuclear division proceeds, walls come in, forming a tissue. This tissue develops centripetally until it reaches the center of the gametophyte. Two regions are now differentiated—a region of smaller cells that develops archegonia, situated near the micropylar end, and a deeper region of larger, nutritive cells.

As a rule, 3 to 5 archegonia are formed, but there may be as many as 10. In *Microcycas*, which is unique in this respect, as many as 200 archegonia

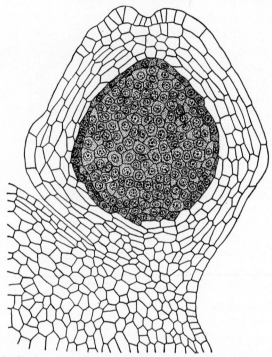

Fig. 272. Longitudinal section of microsporangium of *Zamia floridana*, showing sporogenous tissue surrounded by the tapetum (both shaded) and a wall five or six layers thick, ×150.

may appear. The archegonium initial is superficial and, by a periclinal division, an outer *primary neck cell* is differentiated from a *central cell* (Fig. 275*A, B*). The former undergoes a vertical division, thus forming two *neck cells*, a constant feature throughout the Cycadales (Fig. 275*C, D*). There are no neck canal cells. The central cell undergoes a marked enlargement. Its nucleus divides to form a *ventral canal nucleus* and an *egg nucleus*, but no wall is laid down between them. The ventral canal nucleus soon disorganizes and the egg is now ready for fertilization. An *archegonial chamber* is not present when the archegonia are young, but arises later. It is a depression formed by upgrowth of the adjacent tissue of the female gametophyte.

Male Gametophyte. The first division of the microspore nucleus results in the formation of a small persistent prothallial cell that is cut off close to the microspore wall. The larger cell divides again to form the *generative* and *tube cells,* and in this condition the pollen grain is shed (Fig. 276*A, B*). The pollen is transported by wind to the ovulate cone, whose sporophylls separate slightly at the time of pollination. A group

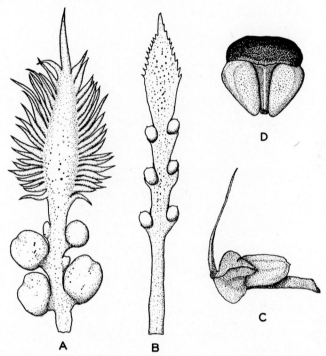

Fig. 273. Megasporophylls of cycads. *A, Cycas revoluta,* showing pinnate blade with conspicuous leaflets; *B, Cycas circinalis,* the leaflets reduced to teeth; *C, Macrozamia denisonii,* side view of sporophyll, the blade reduced to a spine; *D, Zamia floridana,* with peltate sporophyll; *A, B, C,* two-fifths natural size; *D,* four-fifths natural size.

of cells at the apex of the nucellus break down and form a droplet of liquid that exudes through the micropyle and to which some of the pollen grains adhere. As the droplet dries, the grains are drawn down into the pollen chamber formed by the disintegration of the cells that produced the drop-let. Then a pollen tube develops from each pollen grain, growing lat-erally into the nucellus. Its basal end advances downward, carrying the prothallial and generative cells with it. In the cycads the pollen tube is an absorbing organ, obtaining nourishment from the nucellar tissue, which is thereby destroyed. Soon after the pollen tube has begun to develop, the generative cell forms the *stalk* and *body cells,* the latter finally giving rise to two *sperm mother cells* (Figs. 276*C–E*). From each of these a motile sperm is organized. The sperms of cycads are large and multiciliate, the cilia arising from a blepharoplast (Figs. 277 and 278). In *Microcycas* 16 to 22 sperms are formed in each pollen tube.

After the pollen tube has penetrated the nucellar tissue and entered the archegonial chamber, it ruptures and frees the sperms, which then make their way toward the archegonia (Fig. 278). An entire sperm enters an

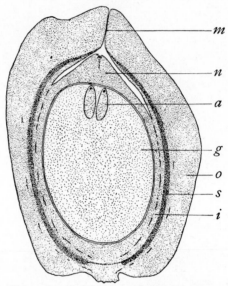

FIG. 274. *Zamia floridana.* Longitudinal section of the ovule shortly after pollination, ×4; *m*, micropyle; *n*, nucellus; *a*, archegonium; *g*, female gametophyte; *o*, outer fleshy layer of integument; *s*, middle stony layer; *i*, inner fleshy layer.

egg, but its nucleus soon separates from the cytoplasm and band of cilia, moving toward the egg nucleus and fusing with it.

Embryo. The nucleus of the fertilized egg undergoes 8 to 10 simultaneous divisions (only 6 in *Bowenia*) without the formation of cell walls (Fig. 279*A*). As a result, as many as over a thousand free nuclei may be produced. This free-nuclear stage is common to all cycads, but differences now appear. In the *Cycas* type of embryogeny persistent cell walls are formed throughout the fertilized egg. In the *Dioon* type cell walls appear throughout the egg but soon disappear except at its base. In *Zamia* wall formation is confined to the basal portion, not even evanescent walls appearing in the main body of the egg (Fig. 279*B*).

The cells at the base of the egg constitute the *proembryo.* Even where persistent cell walls appear above, the upper portion functions as a large food reservoir, contributing no cells to the formation of the new plant.

The proembryo soon becomes differentiated into three regions: an upper haustorial portion in contact with the nutritive material above, a middle zone of elongating cells forming the suspensor, and a terminal group of cells constituting the embryo itself (Fig. 279C). The suspensor becomes enormously elongated and highly coiled, pushing the embryo deep within

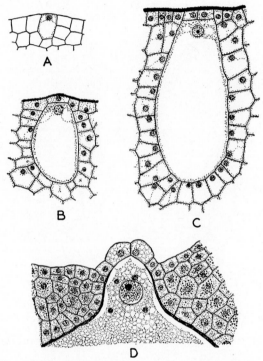

FIG. 275. Development of the archegonium of *Dioon edule*, ×85. *A*, archegonium initial; *B*, formation of primary neck cell and central cell; *C*, later stage with two neck cells; *D*, upper portion of archegonium with two neck cells and central cell nucleus. (*After Chamberlain.*)

the tissue of the female gametophyte. When mature, the embryo has a short axis, the *hypocotyl*, terminating at the end next to the suspensor in a root tip, or *radicle*. This is enclosed in a hard covering, the *coleorhiza*. At the opposite end of the hypocotyl is a minute stem tip, the *plumule*, lying between a pair of seed leaves, or *cotyledons*. The presence of two cotyledons is a constant feature of the Cycadales. As the embryo develops, food is stored in the vegetative tissue of the female gametophyte, forming "endosperm." This is a feature of all gymnosperms. The stored food is later absorbed by the embryo when the seed germinates. The ripe seed is usually white, cream-colored, orange, or red.

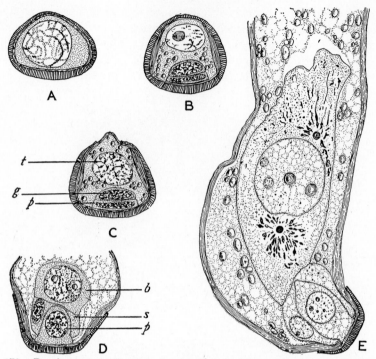

FIG. 276. Development of the male gametophyte of *Dioon edule*. *A*, microspore with nucleus in early prophase of first mitosis; *B*, shedding condition of pollen grain; *C*, beginning of pollen tube formation, showing prothallial cell (*p*), generative cell (*g*), and tube nucleus (*t*); *D*, formation of stalk cell (*s*) and body cell (*b*) from generative cell; *E*, later stage, the body cell much elongated and with two blepharoplasts showing conspicuous radiations; *A*, *B*, *C*, ×1,235; *D*, ×980; *E*, ×618. (*After Chamberlain.*)

The cycads are unique in that the seed germinates promptly, without going into a resting stage.   The stony coat is broken by the coleorhiza

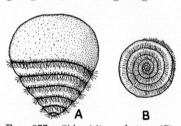

FIG. 277. Side (*A*) and top (*B*) views of a sperm of *Zamia floridana*, showing numerous cilia on a spiral band, ×100. (*After Webber.*)

enclosing the elongating root tip.   The coleorhiza is soon destroyed by the root tip, which then rapidly grows downward into the soil.   The stem remains inconspicuous, but a leaf soon develops. The cotyledons remain inside the seed coat, absorbing food from the "endosperm" and transferring it to the developing seedling.

Summary. The cycads resemble the ferns in their general habit, vascular anatomy, form and venation of the leaves, occurrence on the microsporophylls of abaxial sporangia in sori, structure of the microsporangia, and multiciliate sperms.   All these characters, as well as the ovule structure,

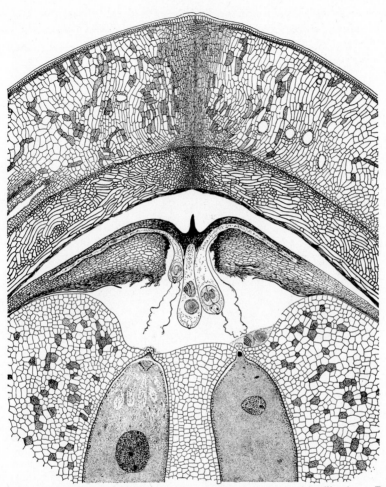

FIG. 278. Reconstruction of the ovule of *Dioon edule* at the time of fertilization. Pollen tube on the left shows undivided body cell; the one in the middle shows two sperms and remains of prothallial and stalk cells; the one on the right shows two sperm mother cells. Two pollen tubes have discharged their sperms. A sperm has entered the egg on the left; the one on the right still shows the ventral canal nucleus. Two sperms, in the thick liquid discharged from the pollen tube just above them, are ready to enter the egg. The dark line below the nucellus is the megaspore membrane. (*From Chamberlain.*)

are common to the Cycadofilicales, Bennettitales, and Cycadales. These three orders, considered together, are called cycadophytes. They represent a distinct line of evolution reaching far back into the Paleozoic. The stem of the Cycadales, like that of the Bennettitales, is an endarch siphonostele with a narrow zone of wood, the xylem in other aerial parts of the plant being mesarch. The dicotyledonous embryo is also suggestive of that of the Bennettitales. As compared with the other cycadophytes, the

Cycadales display the following distinctive features: infrequent branching of the stem, indirect and double leaf traces, monosporangiate and apparently terminal strobili, reduced microsporophylls, and, except in *Cycas*, reduced peltate megasporophylls with only two ovules.

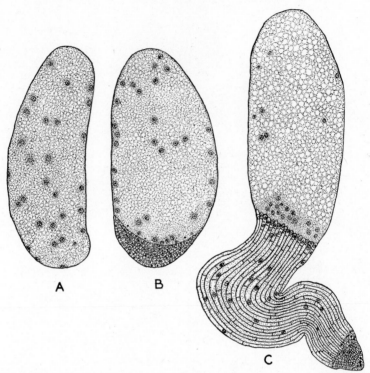

Fig. 279.   Early stages in embryogeny of *Zamia floridana*, ×25.   *A*, proembryo with free nuclei; *B*, wall formation at base of proembryo; *C*, differentiation into suspensor and embryo.

4. Cordaitales

The Cordaitales comprise an extinct group of Paleozoic gymnosperms, contemporaneous with the Cycadofilicales, but plants of a very different aspect. They appeared late in the Devonian, made their greatest display during the Upper Carboniferous, and almost disappeared before the end of the Permian (Fig. 258). Although the Cordaitales differ in many ways from the Cycadofilicales, their resemblances are such as to indicate that both groups may have had a common origin.

Sporophyte. The Cordaitales were tall trees with slender, branched stems often reaching a height of 30 m. (Fig. 280). The branches were covered with simple leaves that were generally long and narrow and borne in spiral arrangement. A cross section of the stem, which was an ectophloic siphonostele, shows a large pith, a thick or thin vascular cylinder, and a small cortex. In contrast to the mesarch collateral bundles of the Cycadofilicales, those of the Cordaitales were endarch and collateral. Secondary wood was well developed, its tracheids having bordered pits in

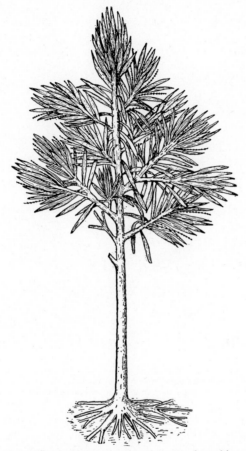

Fig. 280. Restoration of *Dorycordaites*, showing the roots, branching stem, simple leaves, and clusters of strobili borne on lateral branches. The stem was actually much longer than shown here. (*After Grand'Eury.*)

several rows, as in the modern coniferous genus, *Araucaria*. The leaf traces were double, collateral, and endarch, becoming mesarch in the leaves. In most cases the venation of the leaves was dichotomous.

Strobili. A feature of the Cordaitales was the presence of small strobili of two kinds, both occurring on the same plant and borne in clusters on lateral branches (Fig. 281). The strobili, about a centimeter in length, were completely ensheathed by sterile bracts. The staminate strobili were composed of spirally arranged microsporophylls and bracts, the lat-

ter representing sterile microsporophylls (Fig. 282*A*).   The microsporophylls (stamens) were long-stalked and bore two to five erect microsporangia at the tip.

The ovulate strobili were composed of bracts and ovules, the latter
borne on secondary axes in the axils of the bracts (Fig. 282*B*).   Thus the
strobilus was compound.   The integument of the ovule had an outer

Fig. 281.   *Cordaites laevis.*   Restoration of foliage-bearing branch with numerous strobili;
a large bud is shown at the right.   (*From Arnold, after Grand'Eury.*)

fleshy and a middle stony layer, but no inner fleshy layer.   The nucellus
was entirely free from the integument, its peripheral region being traversed by one set of vascular strands, another set occurring in the outer
fleshy layer of the integument.   A prominent nucellar beak and pollen
chamber were developed, indicating that the sperms were swimming.

Gametophytes.   As in the Cycadofilicales, a group of cells has been
found within the pollen grain, but it is uncertain whether they represent
vegetative or spermatogenous tissue.   The female gametophyte was similar to that of modern gymnosperms.   There were two archegonia, separated by a beak-like upgrowth of gametophyte tissue.   This is also a
feature of the modern genus *Ginkgo*.   The seeds were very similar to those
of the Cycadofilicales.   In neither group have seeds with embryos been
found.

Summary. The Cordaitales, a dominant Paleozoic group, seem not to have been derived from the Cycadofilicales, although both groups may have had a common origin. The stem is an endarch siphonostele. The primitive features of the group, which they share with the Cycadofilicales and the other cycadophytes, include a large pith, mesarch leaf bundles,

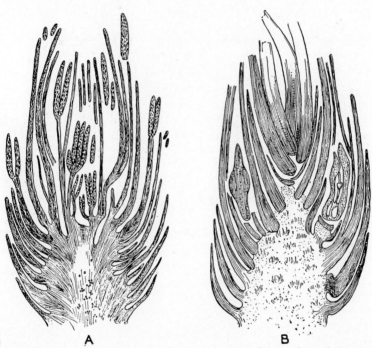

Fig. 282. Strobili of *Cordaianthus*, ×8. *A*, longitudinal section of staminate strobilus, showing sterile bracts and microsporophylls bearing terminal sporangia; *B*, longitudinal section of ovulate strobilus, showing sterile bracts and two stalked axillary ovules. (*After Renault.*)

the ovule structure, and swimming sperms. The advanced features are the branching habit, thick vascular cylinder, form of the leaves, and compound ovulate strobili. The Cordaitales seem to have given rise to both the Ginkgoales and Coniferales.

5. Ginkgoales

The Ginkgoales are represented by only one living species, *Ginkgo biloba*, a native of western China. It is widely cultivated but virtually unknown in the wild state. The order, probably derived from the Cordaitales during the Carboniferous, has been recognized as far back as the Permian. Its members were most abundant during the Mesozoic, particularly in the Jurassic, when the order had almost a world-wide dis-

Fig. 283.   A large tree of *Ginkgo biloba* on the grounds of the White House, Washington, D.C.

tribution (Fig. 258).   The most important Mesozoic genera were *Baiera* and *Ginkgo* itself, both represented by many species.

Sporophyte.   *Ginkgo* is a tree with the general habit of a conifer (Fig. 283).   It is excurrent when young, becoming round-topped in old age. Under favorable conditions, it may reach a height of 30 m.   There are two kinds of branches: long branches of unlimited growth bearing scattered leaves, and short branches of limited growth bearing a few leaves in a cluster. The leaves are deciduous. They have a long petiole and a broadly wedge-shaped blade (Fig. 284). The blade is typically bilobed but may be entire or each lobe may be partially divided into several nar-

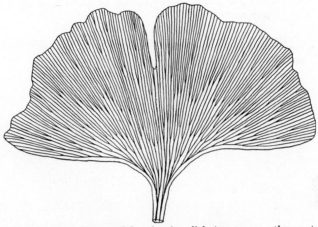

FIG. 284. Leaf blade of *Ginkgo biloba*, showing dichotomous venation, natural size.

FIG. 285. Cross section of long stem of *Ginkgo biloba*, showing small pith, thick vascular cylinder, and thin cortex, ×15.

row segments. The leaves are highly variable, even on the same tree. They exhibit dichotomous venation.

The stem of *Ginkgo* is an ectophloic siphonostele. The long stems have a small pith, a thick vascular cylinder, and a thin cortex, as in the Coniferales (Fig. 285).　The dwarf branches, on the other hand, have a large pith, a thin vascular cylinder, and a thick cortex, as in the Cycadales. The leaf traces are double and pass directly into the petiole.　Mesarch bundles occur only in the cotyledons, those in all other parts of the plant being collateral and endarch.　The tracheids of the secondary xylem have bordered pits in one or two rows.

Fig. 286.　Staminate strobili of *Ginkgo biloba*.　*A*, clusters of strobili borne on dwarf shoots, two-thirds natural size; *B*, enlarged view of a dwarf shoot with young leaves and four strobili.

The strobili of *Ginkgo* are monosporangiate and dioecious, as in the Cycadales.　They are borne at the end of the dwarf shoots, each in the axil of a leaf.

Staminate Strobilus.　The staminate strobili are composed of a central axis bearing many spirally arranged microsporophylls (stamens) forming a loose, catkin-like cluster (Fig. 286).　There are no sterile bracts among the sporophylls.　The microsporophyll consists of a long stalk ending in a knob that bears two, or occasionally three or four pendent microsporangia.　The knob is a reduced blade.　*Ginkgo* has continued the "epaulet" type of stamen found among the Cycadofilicales.　The microsporangium is eusporangiate in development, the initial being single and hypodermal. The wall consists of four to seven layers of cells, the tapetum being derived from the outermost layer of sporogenous tissue.　Dehiscence occurs by means of a longitudinal slit.

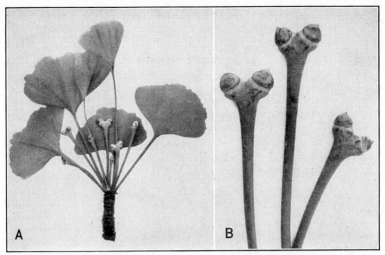

Fig. 287. Ovulate strobili of *Ginkgo biloba*. *A*, dwarf shoot bearing cluster of young leaves and ovulate strobili, two-fifths natural size; *B*, enlarged view of three strobili, each bearing two ovules.

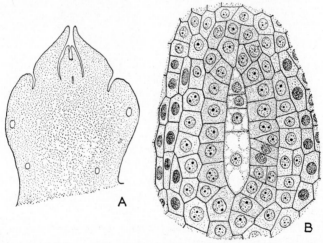

Fig. 288. *Ginkgo biloba*. *A*, longitudinal section of young ovule, showing "collar," integument, nucellus, and spore tetrad, ×15; *B*, enlarged view of tetrad of megaspores surrounded by nutritive tissue, ×400.

Ovulate Strobilus. The ovulate strobili are greatly reduced. Each consists of a long stalk that bears mostly two terminal ovules, only one of which ordinarily matures as a seed (Fig. 287). At the base of each ovule is a peculiar "collar." This probably represents a vestigial megasporophyll, since in rare instances it may become leaf-like. Sometimes three or four ovules may be borne on the same stalk. The ovule is characterized by a single massive integument. As in the Cycadales, this is three-layered, consisting of an outer fleshy, a middle stony, and an inner fleshy layer. A prominent nucellar beak and pollen chamber are present (Fig. 288*A*). Vascular strands are present in the outer fleshy layer, the inner set being suppressed. The megaspore mother cell is deep-seated but may be easily recognized, as it becomes invested with a glandular digestive

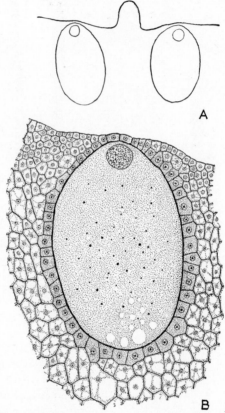

Fig. 289. Archegonium of *Ginkgo biloba*. *A*, micropylar end of female gametophyte, showing two archegonia, ×40; *B*, median longitudinal section of archegonium surrounded by tissue of the female gametophyte, showing central cell and two neck cells, ×100.

tissue. A linear tetrad is formed and only the innermost megaspore is functional (Fig. 288*B*).

Female Gametophyte. As in the Cycadales, the development of the female gametophyte is initiated by free-nuclear division, but the nuclei are parietally placed from the beginning. Wall formation is centripetal. A remarkable condition is seen in that the vegetative tissue of the female gametophyte develops chlorophyll and becomes bright green. As it develops, it encroaches upon the nucellar tissue and destroys nearly all of it. As a rule, only two archegonia appear, developing as in the cycads, except that a small ephemeral ventral canal cell is formed. A prominent beak arises between the archegonia, a feature also of the Cordaitales (Fig. 289).

Male Gametophyte. The development of the male gametophyte begins with the cutting off of two prothallial cells, of which the first is ephemeral, the second persistent. The remaining large cell divides unequally to form the generative and tube cells. This is the shedding

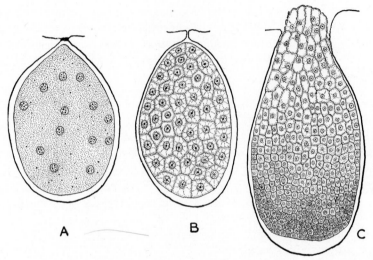

Fig. 290. Early embryogeny of *Ginkgo biloba*, ×75. *A*, free-nuclear stage; *B*, cellular stage; *C*, later stage with meristematic tissue at lower end.

condition of the pollen. The further development of the male gameto-phyte takes place as in the Cycadales. The pollen tubes are extensively branched and function as haustoria. The generative nucleus gives rise to the stalk and body nuclei, but these are not separated by a cell wall. A body cell is organized and divides to form two sperm mother cells, within each of which a large swimming sperm is formed. The sperm has a band of cilia like that of the cycads.

Embryo. In the development of the proembryo of *Ginkgo*, the first stage is one of free-nuclear division, 256 nuclei being formed (Fig. 290*A*). This is followed by a stage of wall formation, the entire egg becoming filled with tissue (Fig. 290*B*). The lower third of the proembryo now becomes meristematic, while the upper two-thirds remains dormant (Fig. 290*C*). The growing region gives rise to a short massive suspensor and a terminal embryo, the latter developing two cotyledons. On the whole, the embryo of *Ginkgo* is primitive. The ripe seed of *Ginkgo* is brownish yellow and about 2.5 cm. in diameter.

Summary. *Ginkgo biloba* is the sole survivor of an order that was widespread and abundant during the Mesozoic. It has retained the primitive reproductive features of its ancestors, its advance being wholly in vegetative characters. The stem is an endarch siphonostele, almost all traces of mesarch structure having disappeared. The pith is not large. Characters that the Ginkgoales have in common with the Cordaitales include the branching habit, thick vascular cylinder, venation of the leaves, structure of the stamens, ovule structure, and swimming sperms. The distinctive features of the Ginkgoales include the form of the leaves and the structure of the strobili. The ovulate strobili and megasporophylls are greatly reduced, the microsporophylls less so. The Ginkgoales may have been derived from the Cordaitales, but are themselves a blindly ending line.

6. Coniferales

The Coniferales constitute the largest order of living gymnosperms, including 6 families, 40 genera, and over 500 species. They are distributed throughout the North and South Temperate Zones, with only a few representatives in the tropics, where they occur at high altitudes. Conifers have been found as fossils as far back as the Permian, having probably been derived from the Cordaitales (Fig. 258). During the Mesozoic they became numerous and diversified into as many families as are represented today. As a group, the Coniferales reached their climax during the Lower Cretaceous.

Families. In the following outline, all the genera occurring in North America are named, together with several others of particular interest.

1. *Abietaceae.* This is a family almost entirely confined to the Northern Hemisphere. It comprises 9 genera and about 230 species. The largest genus is *Pinus*, with 90 species. Other important genera are *Cedrus, Larix, Picea, Tsuga, Pseudotsuga,* and *Abies.* Of the foregoing, all but *Cedrus* are represented in North America.

2. *Taxodiaceae.* Here belong 9 genera and 16 species, nearly all growing in the Northern Hemisphere. Only *Sequoia* and *Taxodium* are found in North America. *Metasequoia,* formerly known only in the fossil state, has recently been discovered growing in western China.

3. *Cupressaceae.* This family includes 10 genera and approximately 120 species. It is represented in both hemispheres. The following genera are found in North America: *Libocedrus, Thuja, Cupressus, Chamaecyparis,* and *Juniperus.* The largest genus, *Juniperus,* has 60 species.

4. *Araucariaceae.* This family has only 2 genera. Both *Agathis,* with 20 species, and *Araucaria,* with 12 species, are of wide distribution in the Southern Hemisphere.

5. *Podocarpaceae.* This family belongs almost exclusively to the

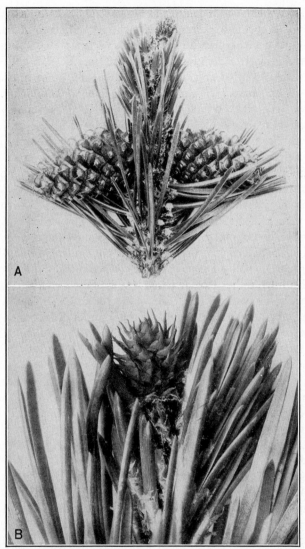

FIG. 291. Ovulate strobili of *Pinus contorta*. *A*, portion of leafy shoot with young cone and two one-year-old cones, three-fourths natural size; *B*, young cone at time of pollination, twice natural size.

Southern Hemisphere. It includes 6 genera and approximately 100 species. The largest genera are *Podocarpus*, with 70 species, and *Dacrydium*, with 20.

6. *Taxaceae*. Here belong 4 genera and 14 species, mainly occurring in the Northern Hemisphere. There are only two genera in North America, *Taxus* and *Torreya*.

Sporophyte.   Almost all conifers are trees, but a few are shrubs.   Typically they display the excurrent habit, with a tall straight trunk giving rise to numerous wide-spreading branches.   Nearly all conifers are evergreen, retaining their leaves for from 3 to 10 years.   The only deciduous forms in North America are *Larix* and *Taxodium.*   The largest conifers are the two species of *Sequoia,* both native to California.   *Sequoia sempervirens,* the redwood of the coastal region, sometimes reaches a height slightly in excess of 100 m., a diameter of 6 m.,[1] and an age of 1,300 years.   *Sequoia gigantea,* the big tree of the Sierra Nevada, attains a maximum height of somewhat less than 100 m., a diameter of 8 m.,[1] and an age of about 3,500 years.   This species is regarded by some botanists as distinct enough to constitute a separate genus, *Sequoiadendron.*

In almost all genera only stems of unlimited growth and with scattered leaves are present.   In *Pinus, Cedrus,* and *Larix,* however, both long and dwarf (spur) shoots occur.   In *Pinus* the long shoots bear scale-like leaves and in the axil of each arises a spur shoot bearing needle-like foliage leaves (Fig. 291).   Only *Pinus monophylla* produces one leaf on a spur; most species have either two or three leaves; *Pinus quadrifolia* has four; and some species have five.   In *Cedrus* and *Larix* foliage leaves are borne both on the long and dwarf shoots and the number of leaves on the latter is much larger than in *Pinus,* being usually 30 to 50.   In *Pinus* the entire spur falls away with the leaves, but in *Cedrus* and *Larix* only the leaves drop off, new ones appearing on the old spur, as in *Ginkgo.*

The leaves of conifers are small and always simple.   Their arrangement is spiral, except in the Cupressaceae, where it is cyclic.   The needle-like type of leaf, as seen in *Pinus* and the other Abietaceae, is the dominant one throughout the order (Fig. 291), but other types are also found.   Broad, flat leaves occur in *Agathis* and in many species of *Podocarpus* and *Araucaria.*   Scale-like leaves are characteristic of nearly all the Cupressaceae (Fig. 292).   Where the adult foliage is scale-like, often the juvenile leaves, appearing on seedlings, are needle-like.   The flat leaves of conifers have several or many parallel veins, while the needle-like and scale-like leaves have but a single vein.

A pine leaf is adapted to endure severe environmental conditions (Fig. 293).   On the outside is a single-layered epidermis with heavily cutinized cell walls and deeply sunken stomata.   Beneath the epidermis are one or more hypodermal layers also with thick walls.   The mesophyll is compact and peculiar in that the cells have infolded walls.   It generally contains a number of resin ducts.   The central tissue of the leaf, enclosed by an endodermis, contains one or two vascular bundles, the number depending on the species.   The xylem and phloem, nearly equal in amount and

---

[1] These diameters are measured at a height of about 3 m. above the greatly swollen base.

Fig. 292. Leafy branch of *Cupressus macrocarpa* with ripe cones, about one-half natural size.

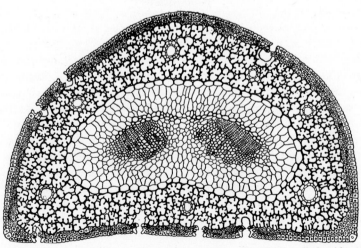

Fig. 293. Cross section of a leaf of *Pinus nigra*, ×75. The thick-walled epidermal and hypodermal layers surround the mesophyll, with infolded cell walls, and containing several resin ducts. The endodermis encloses the transfusion tissue and two vascular bundles, in which the xylem lies below the phloem.

largely secondary in origin, show a collateral arrangement. They are enclosed by a zone of "transfusion tissue."

The stem of the Coniferales is an ectophloic siphonostele and exhibits an advanced type of vascular anatomy (Fig. 294). It has a small pith, a thick vascular cylinder, and a thin cortex. The organization of the conducting tissues is collateral and endarch. Only traces of mesarch structure remain, as in the cotyledons of certain genera. There is a great

Fig. 294. Cross section of a six-year-old stem of *Pinus monophylla*, showing small pith, thick vascular cylinder, and thin cortex, ×11. The phloem occupies a narrow zone outside the xylem, the latter showing radiating vascular rays and numerous resin ducts.

development of secondary wood, which consists almost entirely of tracheids. The tracheids have bordered pits, those of the Araucariaceae being mostly in two or three rows, instead of in a single row as in the other conifers. In *Taxus* the tracheids bear spiral thickenings in addition to the bordered pits. The phloem of conifers consists chiefly of sieve tubes. There are no companion cells. The leaf traces may be double, as in the Abietaceae, or single, as in the Cupressaceae. The conifers are characterized by the presence of resin canals, which are long intercellular cavities lined with resin-secreting cells. They commonly occur in all parts of the plant, being especially abundant in the leaves and in the cortex of the stem. In *Pinus* and many other genera they may also be present in the wood. In *Taxus* resin canals are lacking.

The strobili are normally monosporangiate. The majority of conifers are monoecious, but some are dioecious, e.g., *Juniperus, Araucaria, Podocarpus*, the Taxaceae, and a few others. The arrangement of the sporophylls follows that of the leaves, being cyclic in the Cupressaceae and spiral in the other families.

Staminate Strobilus. In all the Coniferales the staminate strobilus is simple, with few to many microsporophylls arising directly from the cone axis (Fig. 295*A*). Bracts are not present. The stamen is a reduced structure, generally consisting of a slender stalk and an expanded sterile tip. The microsporangia are abaxial and most commonly borne in pairs (Fig. 295*B*, *C*). Each stamen bears 2 microsporangia in the Abietaceae and Podocarpaceae, 2 to 5 in the Taxodiaceae, 2 to 6 in the Cupressaceae, 6 to 15 in the Araucariaceae, and 4 to 8 in the Taxaceae. In the Araucariaceae and Taxaceae the microsporangia are pendent on a peltate stamen, as in *Ginkgo*. The microsporangia of conifers are eusporangiate, developing either from a single hypodermal initial or from a layer of initials. The wall is composed of several layers of cells, the innermost layer forming the tapetum.

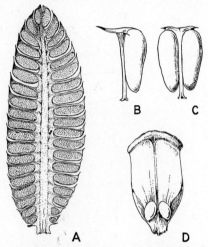

Ovulate Strobilus. A definite ovulate cone is present in all the families of Coniferales except the Podocarpaceae and Taxaceae, where it is greatly reduced, in some of the Podocarpaceae to one or two ovules and in most of the Taxaceae to one.

FIG. 295. *Pinus nigra.* *A*, longitudinal section of staminate strobilus, each microsporophyll bearing a pair of abaxial microsporangia, ×4; *B*, side view of a microsporophyll, ×10; *C*, abaxial view of same; *D*, ovuliferous scale, showing two adaxial ovules, natural size.

The ovulate strobilus differs from the staminate in being compound, that is, the ovules are borne on secondary axes, as in the Cordaitales. The main axis of the cone bears a number of bracts and in the axil of each is an "ovuliferous scale" (Figs. 295*D* and 296*A*). The bract is homologous with the microsporophyll of the staminate cone, but the nature of the scale is puzzling. The view most generally held is that it represents a greatly reduced axillary shoot bearing a pair of leaves that are fused along their margins. In fact, in abnormal cones the ovuliferous scale is sometimes replaced by a spur shoot bearing two leaves. In the Abietaceae the bract and scale are free, being united only at the base. Although in the mature cone the bract is usually smaller than the scale and inconspicuous, in some cases, as in *Pseudotsuga* and species of *Larix* and *Abies*, it is large and very prominent. In the Taxodiaceae, Cupressaceae, and Araucariaceae the bract and scale are coalescent.

In families having a well-developed ovulate strobilus, this nearly always becomes dry and woody at maturity but, in some genera, as in *Juniperus*, the ripe cone is berry-like. In the Abietaceae each cone scale bears two basal ovules on the adaxial side (Fig. 295*D*), but in the other families the number is variable, being two to seven in the Taxodiaceae, one to many in the Cupressaceae, and only one in the Araucariaceae.

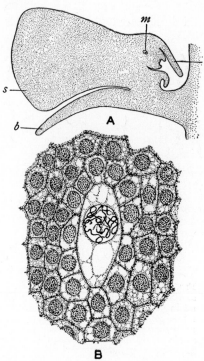

The ovules are inverted in the Abietaceae, Araucariaceae, and almost all the Podocarpaceae; they are erect in the Cupressaceae, Taxaceae, and almost all the Taxodiaceae.

The ovule has a single integument (Fig. 297*A*). In the Abietaceae the integument is fused to the nucellus below but is free at the apex, while in the other families, with few exceptions, the integument and nucellus are either entirely free or slightly united below. The ovule of the Coniferales does not develop a nucellar beak and pollen chamber, their absence being related to the fact that swimming sperms are not produced. The integument consists of an outer fleshy layer, a middle stony layer, and an inner fleshy layer. The outer layer is thin and usually disappears as the seed ripens. Both inner and outer sets of vascular strands have been eliminated. The megaspore mother cell is solitary and deepseated (Fig. 296*B*). It forms a linear tetrad. As in other gymnosperms, the innermost megaspore alone is functional.

Fig. 296. *Pinus nigra. A*, longitudinal section of young ovule, showing integument (*i*), ovuliferous scale (*s*), bract (*b*), and megaspore mother cell (*m*), deeply embedded in the nucellus, ×25; *B*, megaspore mother cell surrounded by nucellar tissue, its nucleus in prophase of the first reduction division, ×400.

In the Podocarpaceae and Taxaceae an outer fleshy covering grows up around the ovule, uniting with it in *Podocarpus* and *Torreya*, but remaining separate in *Taxus*. This fleshy structure has been interpreted by some botanists as a second integument, by others as the ovuliferous scale.

Female Gametophyte. As in the Cycadales and Ginkgoales, the development of the female gametophyte involves several stages, as follows: (1) free-nuclear division accompanied by the formation of a large central vacuole that results in parietal placing of the nuclei; (2) wall formation;

(3) centripetal growth until the gametophyte is cellular throughout. A deeper region of nutritive tissue is usually differentiated from a micropylar region of smaller cells in which the archegonia develop. The number of archegonia is highly variable. In the Abietaceae it is usually 2 to 5, but in the other families the number may be much higher, reaching 200 in extreme cases.

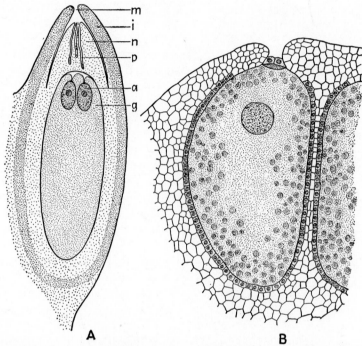

A   **B**

Fig. 297. Ovule and archegonium of *Pinus lambertiana*. *A*, longitudinal section of ovule, showing female gametophyte with two archegonia, ×10; *B*, mature archegonium with two neck cells, a small ventral canal cell, and a large egg with a conspicuous nucleus and many small food bodies, ×85; *m*, micropyle; *i*, integument; *n*, nucellus; *p*, pollen tube; *a*, archegonium; *g*, female gametophyte.

Archegonial development follows the same pattern as in the Cycadales. Sometimes only two neck cells are formed but generally there are many more, the number varying from 4 cells in one tier to about 12 or more in several tiers. In the Abietaceae a definite ventral canal cell is formed that soon disorganizes (Fig. 297*B*). In the other families there is only a ventral canal nucleus. In *Torreya* it is doubtful whether even this is present, the nucleus of the central cell apparently functioning directly as the egg nucleus. A special feature of the Taxodiaceae and Cupressaceae is the formation of an "archegonium complex," an organization of several archegonia in contact with one another and enclosed within a common jacket.

Male Gametophyte.   The amount of vegetative tissue arising in the male gametophyte varies according to the family.   The most primitive condition is seen in the Araucariaceae and Podocarpaceae, where two prothallial cells are cut off, these soon dividing to form a tissue of many

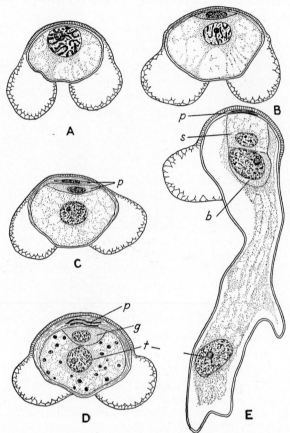

Fig. 298.   Male gametophyte of *Pinus nigra*, ×600.   *A*, microspore; *B*, *C*, *D*, successive stages in development of the pollen tube; *E*, pollen tube; *p*, prothallial cells; *t*, tube nucleus; *g*, generative cell; *s*, stalk cell; *b*, body cell.   (*After Coulter and Chamberlain.*)

cells.   In the Abietaceae two prothallial cells are formed but both of them are ephemeral (Fig. 298*A–C*).   Finally, in the Taxodiaceae, Cupressaceae, and Taxaceae, no prothallial cells are formed.   The generative and tube cells are nearly always differentiated before the pollen is shed (Fig. 298*D*).   All the conifers are wind-pollinated.   In the Abietaceae, with the exception of a few genera, *e.g.*, *Larix*, *Tsuga*, and *Pseudotsuga*, the pollen grains develop a pair of wings that grow out from the wall (Fig. 298).   The Podocarpaceae (except *Dacrydium*) also have winged pollen grains, but those of the other families are wingless.

The young ovulate cone is ready for pollination soon after emerging from the bud (Fig. 291). Its scales separate slightly and a pollination droplet exudes through the micropyle of each ovule. This droplet catches some of the pollen grains and, upon evaporating, draws them down into contact with the nucellus. Following pollination, the scales close and the cone begins a long period of growth. The pollen grains soon germinate. The apical end of each pollen tube grows downward into the nucellus, not laterally as in the cycads.

The tube nucleus moves into the pollen tube, while the generative cell, remaining at its basal end, soon gives rise to the stalk cell and body cell (Fig. 298*E*). These pass into the tube and considerably later the body cell divides to form two male cells that are usually equal in size and are always nonciliated (Fig. 299*A*). In the Abietaceae the two male nuclei are surrounded by cytoplasm derived from the body cell but are without a cell wall. They remain inside the body cell until just before the time of fertilization.

The pollen tube comes in close contact with the archegonium and the tip ruptures, discharging its contents into the egg. One of the male nuclei approaches the egg nucleus and the two come together (Fig. 299*B*). If the second male nucleus also enters the egg, it soon disintegrates. The cytoplasm surrounding the male nucleus mingles with the egg cytoplasm. In conifers with highly organized male cells, after entering the egg, the protoplast escapes from the cell wall and the cytoplasm remains in contact with the male nucleus, finally forming a conspicuous sheath around the fusing nuclei. The male and female nuclei do not fuse in the resting condition, but each forms a group of chromosomes that become arranged on a common spindle (Fig. 299*C*, *D*). Completion of the mitosis gives rise to the first two nuclei of the proembryo.

In *Pinus* and *Juniperus* the interval between pollination and fertilization is slightly more than a year, but in most other conifers it is less, sometimes only a month or two. During this time the development of the female gametophyte and the growth of the pollen tube take place.

Embryo. In *Pinus* four free nuclei are formed within the fertilized egg as a result of two successive mitotic divisions (Fig. 300*A*, *B*). These nuclei move to the base of the egg, where they become arranged in a horizontal plane. Each nucleus divides and walls come in, forming two tiers of four cells each (Fig. 300*C*, *D*). The cells of the upper tier, which remain open above, divide again and then the cells of the lower tier divide. The proembryo now consists of four tiers of cells with four cells in each tier (Fig. 300*E*, *F*). The lowest tier gives rise to four embryos; the next tier forms the primary suspensor cells; the next one constitutes the "rosette tier," which may later give rise to four embryos also; while the four upper cells are part of the general cytoplasm of the egg, which serves as a large food reservoir. The nuclei of the upper cells soon disintegrate.

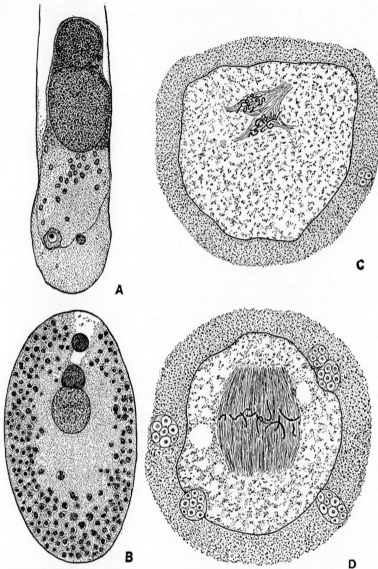

Fɪɢ. 299.   Fertilization in *Pinus*.   *A*, lower end of pollen tube, showing small tube nucleus, stalk cell, and two large male nuclei, ×250; *B*, two male nuclei within the egg, the larger one in contact with the egg nucleus, ×95; *C*, male and female chromatin groups inside egg nucleus; ×360; *D*, chromosomes derived from male and female nuclei on a common spindle, ×360.   (*From Haupt.*)

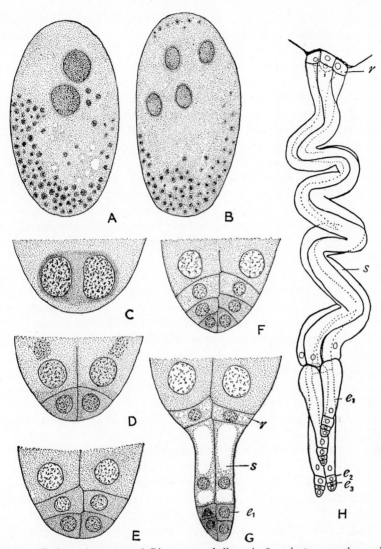

Fig. 300. Early embryogeny of *Pinus monophylla*. *A*, 2-nucleate proembryo; *B*, 4-nucleate stage; *C*, two of the four nuclei at base of egg; *D*, 8-celled proembryo; *E*, three tiers of four cells each; *F*, four tiers of four cells each; *G*, cells of suspensor tier elongating; *H*, later stage of *Pinus banksiana*, the four proembryos separating; *r*, rosette cells; *s*, primary suspensor cells; *e₁, e₂, e₃*, secondary suspensor cells; *A* and *B*, ×75; *C* to *G*, ×125; *H*, ×90. (*H, after Buchholz.*)

Following the establishment of the embryonal, suspensor, and rosette tiers, the four cells of the lowest tier divide and interpose another tier between them and the primary suspensor cells, thus forming secondary suspensor cells (embryonal tubes). This behavior may be repeated once or twice again. The primary suspensor cells elongate and thrust the lower cells into the female gametophyte tissue. The four rows of lower cells now separate and the secondary suspensor cells elongate. Elongation of the suspensors, both primary and secondary, continues to such an extent that they become coiled and twisted (Fig. 300*H*).

Each of the four terminal cells gives rise to a separate embryo. Meanwhile one or more cells of the rosette tier may divide to form a rosette embryo. These ordinarily do not develop very far, however, before they disintegrate. As a result of receiving unequal amounts of food, the four primary embryos grow at different rates. The largest finally survives and the others become aborted. Thus the mature seed, with rare exceptions, has only one embryo.

In the Abietaceae, Taxodiaceae, and Cupressaceae four free nuclei are formed in the egg before walls appear. In the other families a larger number of nuclei are produced—as many as 32 or 64 in the Araucariaceae. After the appearance of walls, the proembryo, as a rule, consists of four tiers of cells in the Abietaceae, but of only three tiers in the Taxodiaceae, Cupressaceae, and Araucariaceae. In many conifers the cells of the lowest tier of the proembryo do not separate to form four embryos, as they do in *Pinus*, but remain together to form a single embryo, while the cells of the rosette tier collapse instead of giving rise to rosette embryos. In these conifers several embryos usually begin to develop in the same ovule, but each comes from a different fertilized egg.

Thus polyembryony in the Coniferales is of two types: (1) *cleavage polyembryony*, where multiple embryos arise from the splitting of a single embryo; and (2) *simple polyembryony*, where more than one fertilized egg in the same ovule gives rise to an embryo. Each type is characteristic of particular genera. In the Abietaceae, for example, cleavage polyembryony is a feature of *Pinus*, *Cedrus*, and *Tsuga*, while simple polyembryony is characteristic of *Larix*, *Picea*, *Pseudotsuga*, and *Abies*. In both types of polyembryony only one embryo in each seed reaches maturity, the others degenerating.

When mature, the conifer embryo consists of a hypocotyl terminating in a radicle at the suspensor end and a minute plumule at the opposite end, the plumule being surrounded by two or more cotyledons (Fig. 301). The number of cotyledons ranges from 2 to 18, but more conifers are dicotyledonous than polycotyledonous. The Abietaceae show the largest number and the greatest variability. The ripe seed of conifers is generally brown. The outer and inner fleshy layers of the integument become very thin, the outer one often disappearing entirely. Thus the seed coat consists essentially of the middle stony layer. The embryo goes into a condition of dormancy in which it usually remains for many months, although the seeds of many conifers will germinate without undergoing a resting period. As in the cycads and *Ginkgo*, food is stored in the vegetative tissue of the female gametophyte, generally designated as *endosperm*. In germination the entire embryo emerges from the seed coat, which is carried out of the ground on the tips of the cotyledons.

Summary. The Coniferales were probably derived from the Cordaitales during the Paleozoic and represent a parallel line of evolution to the Ginkgoales, which seem to have had a similar origin. These three orders, comprising the coniferophytes, constitute a line of descent as old as the cycadophytes. The Coniferales have retained fewer primitive reproductive features than the Ginkgoales, their chief advance being in ovule structure and the loss of swimming sperms. In both orders the stem, freely branching, is an endarch siphonostele with almost no mesarch structure

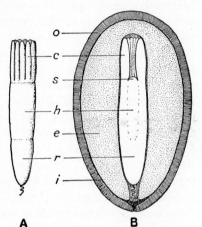

Fig. 301. Embryo (*A*) and longitudinal section of the seed (*B*) of *Pinus edulis*, ×4; *o*, outer seed coat; *i*, inner seed coat; *c*, cotyledons; *s*, stem tip; *h*, hypocotyl; *r*, root tip; *e*, endosperm.

left. Moreover, the pith is small and the vascular cylinder thick. The leaves of conifers are characteristically small and without dichotomous venation. Although the microsporophylls are grouped to form a simple strobilus, the ovulate strobilus, except where greatly reduced, is compound, a feature also of the Cordaitales.

The six families of conifers represent various degrees of progress from a common ancestry. Their advance has been in different directions, as follows:[1] (1) The arrangement of leaves and sporophylls is spiral in all the families except the Cupressaceae, where it is cyclic. (2) All families have distinct ovulate cones except the Podocarpaceae and Taxaceae. (3) The bract and scale in the ovulate cone are separate in the Abietaceae but united in the other families. (4) Winged pollen grains are present only in the Abietaceae and Podocarpaceae. (5) A considerable amount of vegetative tissue is present in the male gametophyte of the Araucariaceae and Podocarpaceae. Two ephemeral prothallial cells are formed in the Abietaceae, none in the three other families. (6) A ventral canal cell is formed in the Abietaceae, only a ventral canal nucleus in the other fami-

[1] In each case the condition to be regarded as primitive is stated first.

lies.   (7) An archegonium complex is present only in the Taxodiaceae and Cupressaceae.   This is an advanced character.

The oldest families of conifers are the Abietaceae and Araucariaceae. Although it is uncertain which is the more ancient, much evidence from the vascular anatomy of both living and extinct forms indicates that the Abietaceae are the ancestral stock of conifers.   The Araucariaceae seem to have given rise to the Podocarpaceae and Taxaceae.   The Taxodiaceae and Cupressaceae are younger than the other families and have probably sprung from the Abietaceae.

7. Gnetales

This is the highest order of gymnosperms.   It includes 3 peculiar genera of diverse habit and distribution.   *Ephedra*, with about 35 species, inhabits arid parts of the Mediterranean region, tropical and temperate Asia, and western North and South America.   *Welwitschia*, with a single species, is found only in arid parts of western South Africa.   *Gnetum*, with 30 species, occurs in the tropics of South America, Asia, and Africa.   The fossil record of the Gnetales is very fragmentary and does not extend beyond the Tertiary.

Sporophyte.   The species of *Ephedra* are low, much-branched shrubs, seldom exceeding 2 m. in height, with long-jointed green stems bearing opposite or whorled scale-like leaves (Fig. 302*A*).   Some of the species are trailing.   *Welwitschia* is a large turnip-shaped plant with a tuberous stem about 1 m. in diameter and about one-third as tall (Fig. 303).   It bears a single pair of terminal, elongated, strap-shaped leaves with parallel venation.   They trail along the ground, reaching a length of 3 m. or more and becoming split into numerous segments.   Except for the cotyledons, these are the only leaves the plant ever has.   Most of the species of *Gnetum* are woody vines, but a few are shrubs or small trees.   They have oval, leathery, opposite leaves that are net-veined and 5 to 8 cm. long (Fig. 304*A*).   All three genera are cyclic in the arrangement of their leaves and sporophylls.

The most distinctive feature of the vascular anatomy of all three genera is the occurrence of true vessels (tracheae) in the secondary wood.   These are present in addition to tracheids.   Resin canals are absent.   The endarch condition prevails throughout the plant body, all traces of mesarch structure apparently having been eliminated.

The strobili of *Ephedra* and *Gnetum* are usually monosporangiate and, as a rule, the two kinds occur on separate plants.   The strobili of *Welwitschia* are also functionally monosporangiate but, in the staminate strobilus, each set of stamens surrounds an abortive ovule, thus indicating an ancestral bisporangiate condition (Fig. 305*C*).   In all three genera both kinds of strobili are compound, the sporophylls arising on secondary axes borne in the axils of bracts.

Staminate Strobilus.   The staminate strobilus consists of an axis bearing a series of bracts arranged in opposite pairs.   These are connate in

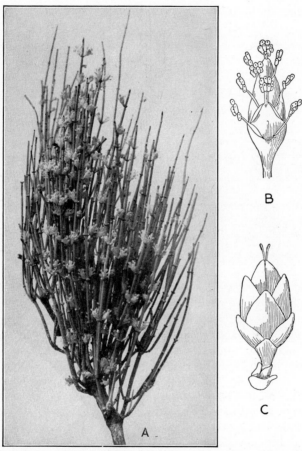

Fig. 302.   *A, Ephedra viridis,* showing portion of staminate plant with strobili, two-fifths natural size; *B* and *C, Ephedra antisiphilitica,* showing a staminate *(B)* and an ovulate *(C)* strobilus, enlarged.   *(B and C, after Watson.)*

Gnetum and imbricate in the two other genera.   In the axil of each bract, except the lower ones, is a "staminate flower," representing a simple strobilus.   This consists, in *Ephedra* and *Gnetum,* of a stalk bearing two (or, in *Ephedra,* up to six or eight) terminal microsporangia and a pair of basal scales (Figs. *302B* and *304C*).   In *Welwitschia* the staminate flower is composed of two opposite pairs of basal scales investing a whorl of six

united stamens that surround a sterile ovule (Fig. 305*A*, *C*). Each stamen bears three terminal microsporangia forming a synangium. In all
three genera the scales at the base of each staminate flower are sometimes
designated as a "perianth."

Ovulate Strobilus. The ovulate strobilus of *Ephedra* is simpler than
that of either of the other genera, consisting of an axis bearing several

Fig. 303. *Welwitschia mirabilis.* Female plant in foreground; male plant in background.
(*From a photograph furnished by the Chicago Natural History Museum.*)

opposite pairs of bracts and an erect terminal ovule or, in some species, of
two or more ovules (Fig. 302*C*). In *Welwitschia* and *Gnetum* the strobilus
has a long axis with many ovules borne in the axils of bracts (Figs. 304*E*
and 305*B*). In each genus an "ovulate flower" includes a single ovule
invested by a pair of scales that constitute a "perianth." The ovule has
two integuments, the inner one forming a long tubular micropyle (Figs.
305*D* and 306*A*). The outer integument has an outer fleshy layer and an
inner stony layer. There is a set of vascular strands in the fleshy layer of
the outer integument. In *Ephedra* a pollen chamber is formed by the
breaking down of some of the nucellar tissue but there are no swimming
sperms. In *Gnetum*, but not in *Welwitschia*, there is a slight tendency
toward the formation of a pollen chamber.

Female Gametophyte. The female gametophyte differs greatly among
the three genera of Gnetales. In *Ephedra* it develops as in the Coniferales,

with free-nuclear division followed by the formation of compact, small-celled, nutritive issue (Fig. 306). The archegonia, usually numbering two or three, appear in the micropylar region. They have many tiers of neck cells. A ventral canal nucleus is cut off but a wall does not separate it from the egg nucleus.

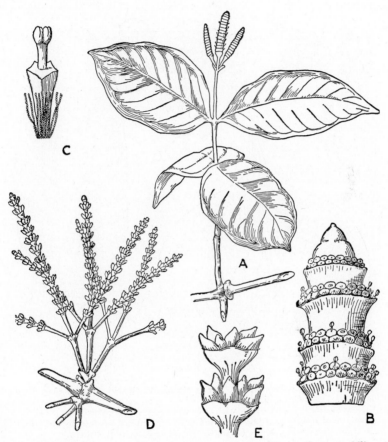

Fig. 304. Strobili of *Gnetum latifolium.* *A*, leafy branch with staminate strobili, natural size; *B*, part of staminate strobilus, enlarged; *C*, an expanded staminate "flower," ×5; *D*, branches with ovulate strobili, natural size; *E*, part of ovulate strobilus, enlarged. (*After Blume.*)

In *Welwitschia* the development of the female gametophyte proceeds as far as the formation of walls, but this is incomplete and the cells are multi-nucleate. Nuclear fusions are said then to occur in most of the cells until they become uninucleate. No archegonia are formed. The cells in the micropylar region are multinucleate and become free eggs, sending out tubes into which their nuclei pass. These tubes penetrate the nucellus, where they meet the pollen tubes.   Then an egg nucleus fuses with one of the male nuclei, after which it passes back into the female gametophyte. The cells in the lower region, after becoming uninucleate, continue to multiply, even after fertilization has taken place.   They form a nutritive tissue.

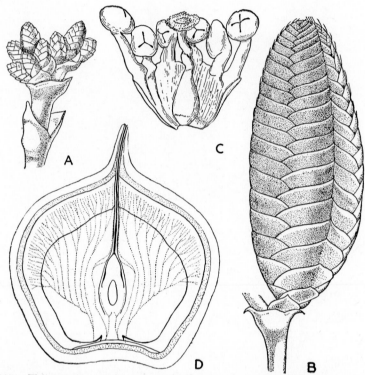

Fig. 305.   *Welwitschia mirabilis.   A*, young staminate strobili, natural size; *B*, ovulate strobilus, natural size; *C*, staminate "flower" with bracts removed, showing the six stamens united below and the sterile ovule with a long twisted micropylar tube, ×8; *D*, longitudinal section of ovule, showing inner integument forming micropylar tube and outer integument forming a wing, ×3.   (*A, B, C, after Hooker; D, after Church.*)

In *Gnetum* the female gametophyte begins its development with free-nuclear division.   However, there is no wall formation except, in some species, in the basal region, where a small-celled nutritive tissue is formed. Each nucleus in the micropylar region is a potential egg nucleus, several usually becoming organized as eggs but only one being fertilized.   After fertilization, the gametophyte becomes cellular throughout.   At first the cells are multinucleate but later become uninucleate, as in *Welwitschia*.

Male Gametophyte.   In *Ephedra* the microspore cuts off two prothallial nuclei but only the first is organized as a cell (Fig. 307).   These are persistent. The generative nucleus and tube nucleus are differentiated, the former giving rise to the stalk and body nuclei. These are not formed as cells. In this condition the pollen grain is shed. In the pollen tube two male nuclei are formed. The pollen grains of *Gnetum* and *Wel-*

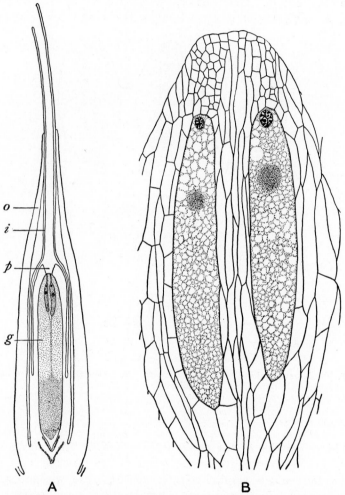

Fig. 306. *Ephedra trifurca.* *A*, longitudinal section of an ovule, showing outer integument (*o*), inner integument (*i*) forming a long micropylar tube, pollen chamber (*p*), and female gametophyte (*g*) with two archegonia, ×42; *B*, two archegonia just before division of the central-cell nucleus, ×112. (*After Land.*)

witschia contain an ephemeral prothallial nucleus, a tube cell, and a generative cell. A stalk cell and body cell are not formed, but later the nucleus of the generative cell gives rise directly to two male nuclei, as in angiosperms.

Embryo. In all three genera of the Gnetales the embryo is dicotyle-donous but its development varies. In *Ephedra* the division of the fertilized egg nucleus results in the formation of eight free nuclei, around each of which there is organized a cell that becomes an independent proembryo (Fig. 308*A*). Only one or, rarely, two of these reach maturity. The proembryo sends out a suspensor tube, at the tip of which a cell is cut

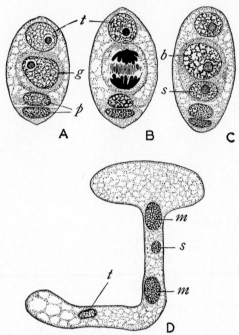

Fig. 307. Male gametophyte of *Ephedra trifurca*. *A*, pollen grain with two prothallial nuclei (*p*), generative nucleus (*g*), and tube nucleus (*t*); *B*, division of generative nucleus; *C*, shedding condition with two prothallial nuclei, stalk nucleus (*s*), body nucleus (*b*), and tube nucleus; *D*, pollen tube with tube nucleus (*t*), stalk nucleus (*s*), and two male nuclei (*m*); *A*, *B*, *C*, ×1,500; *D*, ×500. (*After Land.*)

off. This gives rise to the embryo (Fig. 308*B*). In *Welwitschia* and *Gnetum* the fertilized egg behaves as one of the proembryonal cells of *Ephedra*, the embryo arising from the fertilized egg without any free-nuclear division. This condition is characteristic of angiosperms.

Summary. The occurrence of vessels in the secondary wood, of compound staminate strobili, and the prolongation of the inner integument of the ovule into a micropylar tube are unique features that distinguish the Gnetales from all other gymnosperms. The presence of true vessels is an angiosperm character. Others include the elimination of archegonia and formation of free eggs (except in *Ephedra*), the elimination of free-nuclear division in the embryogeny (except in *Ephedra*), the formation of two male nuclei directly from the generative nucleus (except in *Ephedra*), and the presence of compound strobili with simple strobili ("flowers") bearing a "perianth." Such strobili suggest the inflorescences of certain angiosperms. The origin of the Gnetales is unknown. They are not

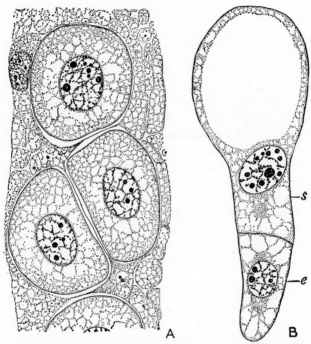

Fig. 308. Proembryonal cells of *Ephedra trifurca*, ×440. *A*, three of the eight free proembryonal cells; *B*, a proembryonal cell in which the embryo initial cell (*e*) is differentiated from the suspensor cell (*s*). (*After Land*.)

closely related to any of the other gymnosperms, while any direct relationship to the angiosperms is very doubtful, although both groups may have had a common ancestry. The three genera do not seem to be closely related to one another and may have had a separate origin. *Ephedra* shows certain resemblances to the Cordaitales that suggest its derivation from that group.

CHAPTER IX

SPERMATOPHYTA (CONTINUED)

2. ANGIOSPERMAE

The angiosperms are the largest and most conspicuous group of modern plants, numbering about 195,000 species. They are also the youngest group, and are thought to have been derived from the gymnosperms, or possibly to have had an independent origin from the pteridophytes. They appeared in the Lower Cretaceous and from the Upper Cretaceous to the present time have been the dominant group of land plants (Fig. 258). Angiosperms are found in practically all terrestrial habitats where plants may exist. Some occur in fresh water and even in the sea, the aquatic habit being secondarily acquired. A relatively few forms, having little or no chlorophyll, are saprophytic or parasitic.

Although many angiosperms are woody, the majority are herbaceous. The woody condition is considered to be the more primitive, and the herbaceous one to have been derived from it. The seeds of angiosperms are borne in a closed vessel, the ovary, and not, as in gymnosperms, on the exposed face of an open carpel (or equivalent structure). The ovary represents the basal portion of a single closed carpel or of two or more united carpels. It ripens to form a fruit, which contains the seeds. Angiosperms are often called "flowering plants," as the presence of flowers is one of their most outstanding features.

The two great groups (subclasses) of angiosperms are the Dicotyledoneae and the Monocotyledoneae, distinguishable on the basis of the following combination of characters, but with individual exceptions to each: The dicotyledons have seeds with two cotyledons, stems with a hollow cylinder of vascular tissue and with a functioning cambium, leaves with netted veins forming an open system, and floral parts chiefly in fours or fives. The monocotyledons have seeds with one cotyledon, stems with scattered vascular bundles and without a functioning cambium, leaves with parallel veins forming a closed system, and floral parts typically in threes.

The Dicotyledoneae include 240 families and approximately 155,000 species, the Monocotyledoneae 45 families and about 40,000 species. The Dicotyledoneae comprise the Archichlamydeae, whose flowers are naked, apetalous, or choripetalous, and the Metachlamydeae, whose flowers are sympetalous. The Archichlamydeae include some members having floral parts more or less spirally arranged, while the flowers of the Metachlamydeae are all definitely cyclic. The Archichlamydeae are generally regarded as the ancestral stock from which both the Metachlamydeae and the Monocotyledoneae have been derived.

Vegetative Organs

The sporophyte of angiosperms presents an enormous diversity in size and habit, ranging from tiny herbs to tall trees 100 m. in height. Most angiosperms grow erect upon the ground, but some are trailing, climbing,

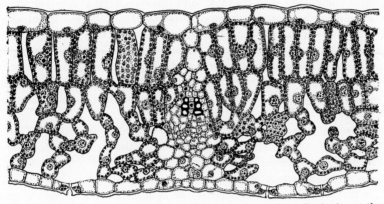

FIG. 309. Cross section of a leaf of lilac (*Syringa vulgaris*), ×250. Beginning at the top, the tissues are the upper epidermis, the palisade layer, the spongy tissue with numerous intercellular spaces, the lower epidermis in which three stomata are seen, and, in the center, a small vein.

or epiphytic. Their stems are usually branched, but may be unbranched; they are generally aerial, but may be subterranean. As in gymnosperms, branching of the stem is lateral, never dichotomous. The leaves are typically broad and thin, but display extreme variation in size, shape, and other features. Their arrangement on the stem may be either spiral or cyclic. They may be simple or divided into leaflets (compound), petiolate or sessile, net-veined or parallel-veined, deciduous or evergreen. In net-veined leaves the veins form an obvious reticulum and their ultimate veinlets end freely to form an open system. In parallel-veined leaves the larger veins run parallel to one another and, if connected by cross veinlets, these form a closed system.

Leaf Structure. In spite of their diversity in external features, the leaves of angiosperms are rather uniform in structure. Leaves arise as lateral outgrowths from the embryonic region of a stem tip and develop by intercalary growth. A cross section of a typical mature leaf reveals the following tissues (Fig. 309): the *epidermis*, usually a single external layer of colorless cells with cutinized outer walls and containing numerous stomata; the *palisade tissue*, generally comprising one or two layers of green cells, vertically elongated, and lying beneath the upper epidermis; the *spongy tissue*, a loose region of green cells and large intercellular spaces; the *veins*, vascular bundles that traverse the spongy tissue. The arrangement of the conducting tissues in the veins is collateral, the xylem lying above the phloem. Cambial activity, if present, is weak. The mesophyll, including the palisade and spongy tissues, is the photosynthetic tissue of the leaf.

Root Tip. The root tip comprises the rootcap, embryonic region, region of elongation, and region of maturation. The rootcap is a protective sheath. The embryonic region includes the apical meristem, of very limited extent, characterized by active cell division. In the region of elongation the newly formed cells increase in length, while in the region of maturation they become differentiated to form permanent tissues. In many roots three or four distinct growing regions, or *histogens*, can be recognized (Fig. 310). The outermost layer of cells, nearly continuous around the embryonic region, is the *dermatogen*, which gives rise to the epidermis. Inside the dermatogen is the *periblem*, consisting of several layers that form the cortex. In the center of the root tip is the *plerome*, which produces the stele. In the monocotyledons a *calyptrogen* forms the rootcap and lies just behind it.

The plerome arises from a group of initials situated at its very tip. Just beyond lie another group of initials, often constituting a single layer. In the dicotyledons these form the periblem, while a third layer, beyond and in contact with it, gives rise to both the dermatogen and rootcap. In the monocotyledons the middle group of initials produce both the periblem and dermatogen, while the outermost layer of initials, the calyptrogen, independently forms the rootcap (Fig. 310).

Root hairs, arising in the region of maturation, are slender tubular extensions of the epidermal cells. They greatly increase the absorbing surface of the root. New ones are formed as the root increases in length. The older ones finally disappear.

Mature Root. The structure of the mature root is rather uniform throughout the angiosperms (Fig. 311). As in other vascular plants, the root represents a primitive type of vascular organization, being typically an exarch radial protostele. The stele is surrounded by an extensive cortex whose innermost cells, the endodermis, have more or less thickened walls. Lying immediately inside the endodermis is a layer of parenchyma, or occasionally several layers, forming the pericycle.

The process of lignification, progressing centripetally from the protoxylem strands, often does not reach to the center of the root, whose cells then remain parenchymatous and form a pith. Such a condition is common in monocotyledons, while in dicotyledons a pith is typically absent.

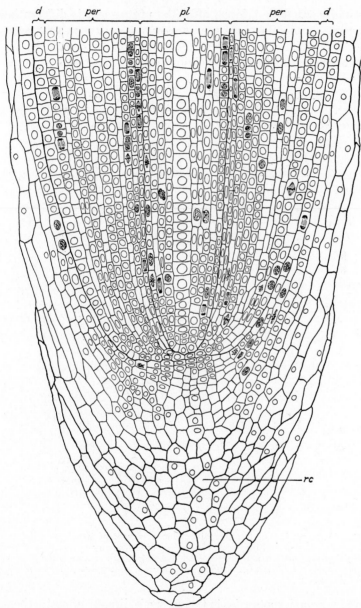

Fig. 310. Median longitudinal section of a root tip of onion (*Allium cepa*), showing histogens, ×170; *d*, dermatogen; *per*, periblem; *pl*, plerome; *rc*, rootcap. At the tip of the plerome is a layer of cells that gives rise to the periblem and dermatogen. Below this layer is the calyptrogen, which produces the rootcap.

The primary wood that forms after the protoxylem is differentiated is metaxylem. In dicotyledons the number of protoxylem strands is commonly 4 or 5, while in monocotyledons it is generally more, often 15 or 20. Phloem occurs as separate strands lying between the groups of protoxylem

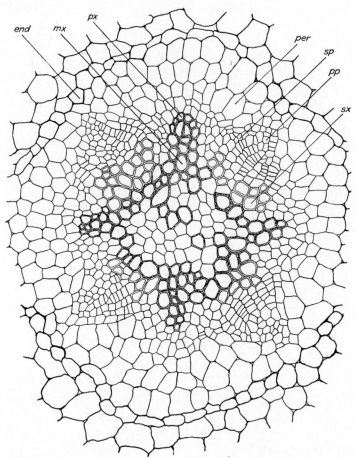

Fig. 311. Cross section of the central portion of a root of baneberry (*Actaea alba*), showing primary tissues and beginning of formation of secondary tissues by the cambium, which lies between the secondary xylem and phloem, ×200; *end*, endodermis; *per*, pericycle; *pp*, primary phloem; *sp*, secondary phloem, *px*, protoxylem; *mx*, metaxylem; *sx*, secondary xylem.

elements. Branch roots arise in the pericycle directly opposite the protoxylem strands. They then grow outward through the cortex (Fig. 312).

Except in fibrous roots, a cambium arises between the primary xylem and phloem and cuts off secondary vascular tissues—secondary xylem on the inside and secondary phloem on the outside (Fig. 311). Soon a more or less continuous cylinder of secondary vascular tissues is formed.

Stem Tip.   An embryonic region, a region of elongation, and a region of maturation are present in a stem tip, but are more extensive and much less clearly defined than in a root tip, overlapping to a considerable extent.   Immediately behind the apical meristem the leaf primordia arise superficially as lateral outgrowths and develop in acropetal succes-

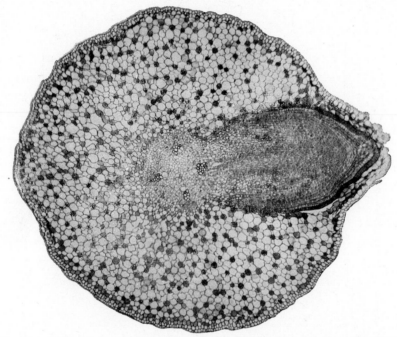

Fig. 312.   Cross section of a root of willow (*Salix*), showing a branch root pushing outward through the cortex, ×55.

sion (Fig. 313).   A meristem may arise in the axil of each leaf primordium while it is still very small, giving rise to a lateral bud, or the meristem may not appear until later.

Generally the dermatogen is clearly recognizable, but often the line of demarcation between the periblem and plerome is not.   For this reason, and because it is usually difficult or impossible to relate the origin of the epidermis, cortex, and stele to distinct cell regions or "histogens," a newer and more satisfactory concept of the structure and growth of the stem apex is that it is made up of two distinct "growth zones."   The outer zone, or *tunica*, consists of one or more (up to four or five) superficial layers of small uniform cells that divide anticlinally, so that each layer remains distinct.   Periclinal divisions occur only in connection with leaf and bud formation.   The inner zone, or *corpus*, comprises the central tissue, the cells of which are larger and divide in all planes and so are irregular in size and arrangement.   Thus the two zones differ both in position and mode of growth.   Surface growth predominates in the tunica, while volume growth is characteristic of the corpus.   Frequently these zones are not clearly marked off from each other and vary consider-

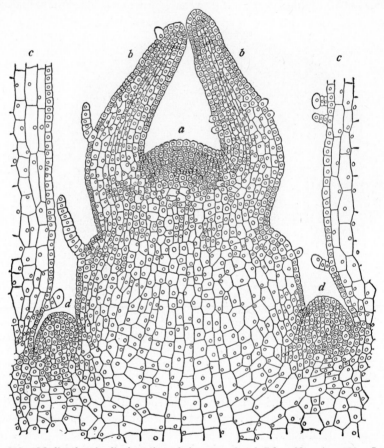

Fig. 313.   Median longitudinal section of the stem tip of *Coleus blumei*, ×200.   In the center is the apical meristem (*a*) with a leaf primordium (*b*) on either side.   In the axil of each of the older leaves (*c*) is a lateral meristem (*d*) that will produce an axillary bud.

ably in form and relative extent.   Moreover, the relative contributions of the tunica and corpus to the three regions of the mature stem are usually difficult to determine and differ according to the species.

Mature Stem.   As in the leaf, the epidermis of the young stem becomes cutinized and contains many stomata.   The cortex consists mainly of green parenchyma, but sclerenchyma may be differentiated as development proceeds.   In some stems a well-marked endodermis is present, but generally this layer is not clearly differentiated.   In stems that increase in diameter a cork cambium or *phellogen* arises beneath the epidermis, forming cork tissue. This finally replaces the epidermis as a protective covering. Communication between the atmosphere and the living tissues beneath the cork is maintained through lenticels.

The stele is bounded externally by the pericycle, which usually consists of several layers of cells. Some of these may remain parenchymatous,

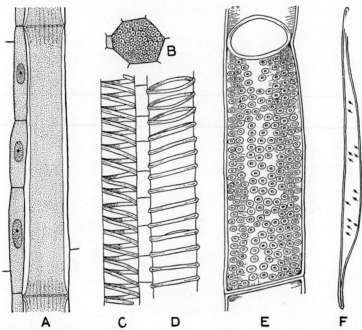

Fig. 314. Conducting tissues, ×200. Phloem elements: a sieve tube and a row of companion cells from a squash stem, as seen in longitudinal (*A*) and transverse (*B*) sections. Xylem elements: spiral (*C*), annular (*D*), and pitted vessels (*E*), and a wood fiber (*F*) from a stem of castor bean.

while others become sclerenchymatous. The development of the primary xylem is endarch. Among gymnosperms, with the exception of the Gnetales, tracheids are the only conducting elements present in the xylem, but in angiosperms *vessels* are the chief elements. Tracheids are derived from single cells, vessels from a row of cells whose end walls break down. Both are lignified, the lignin being localized to form spirals, rings, an irregular network, or it may be so abundant that the walls are pitted (Fig. 314*C–E*). Spiral and annular elements are characteristic of protoxylem, reticulate and pitted elements of metaxylem and secondary xylem. In addition to vessels, the secondary xylem of angiosperms may consist, largely or in part, of tracheids, wood fibers, and wood parenchyma (Fig. 314*F*). The phloem is made up of sieve tubes, companion cells, and often also of fibers and parenchmya (Fig. 314*A*, *B*).   Companion cells do not occur in pteridophytes and gymnosperms.   As in the Filicinae and gymnosperms, leaf gaps are formed in the vascular cylinder in connection with the departure of leaf traces.

Stelar Types.   The stem of most woody dicotyledons is like that of gymnosperms in being an ectophloic siphonostele, the vascular tissues

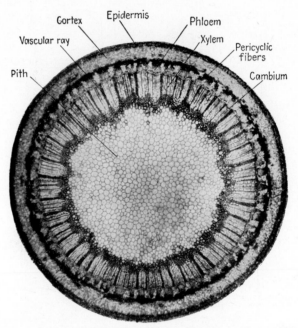

Fig. 315.   Cross section of a young stem of magnolia (*Magnolia grandiflora*), showing vascular cylinder surrounded by the cortex and enclosing the pith, ×17.

forming a nearly continuous cylinder enclosing the pith (Fig. 315).   This cylinder, consisting of xylem and phloem in collateral arrangement, is traversed by numerous vascular rays.   As in the root, the cambium, a meristematic layer of cells, arises between the primary xylem and phloem. Through cambial activity, the stems of woody dicotyledons undergo a great deal of secondary thickening, increasing in diameter from year to year.

The stems of herbaceous dicotyledons are like those of woody dicotyledons except that the vascular tissues are greatly reduced in amount, either as a result of diminished cambial activity, resulting in a continuous but narrow vascular cylinder, or by the breaking up of the cylinder into separate bundles to form a dictyostele.   In such stems the vascular bundles are at first separated by wide bands of parenchyma connecting the pith with the cortex.   The cambium may extend across these "pith rays" and later give rise to secondary xylem and phloem, thus forming a continuous vascular cylinder, or it may produce only parenchyma between the bundles, which then remain separate.   In many herbs the interfascicular cambium fails to develop at all, the secondary vascular tissues then being produced within the bundles.

Thus the stems of herbaceous dicotyledons illustrate various degrees of reduction from the more highly organized but more primitive condition

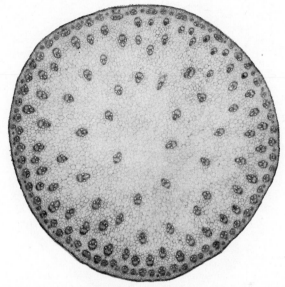

Fig. 316.   Cross section of a young stem of Indian corn (*Zea mays*), showing scattered vascular bundles, ×8.

seen in the stems of typical woody dicotyledons.   This strongly indicates that the woody stem is the more ancient type from which the herbaceous stem has been derived, probably in response to climatic changes.

The stems of most monocotyledons display a characteristic type of dictyostele with scattered vascular bundles (Fig. 316).   With rare exceptions, a cambium is wanting, and so no secondary thickening ordinarily occurs.   In a few monocotyledons, such as *Dracaena*, *Aloe*, and *Yucca*, a special kind of secondary thickening takes place.   Here a cambium arises in the pericycle or inner cortex and forms a cylinder of new vascular tissues.

In most monocotyledons the arrangement of the conducting tissues in each vascular bundle is collateral, as in dicotyledons, but frequently it is *amphivasal*, the xylem surrounding the phloem (Fig. 317).   The young stem of a monocotyledon is usually a siphonostele with collateral bundles. The monocotyledons represent, in their stem structure, the final stages in a reduction series that begins with the gymnosperms and woody dicotyledons and passes through the herbaceous dicotyledons, where every intermediate condition is seen.   This reduction series indicates the general trend of evolution as it seems to have taken place in the spermatophytes.

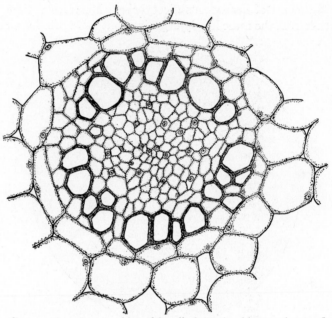

FIG. 317.   Cross section of an amphivasal bundle from the rhizome of sweet flag (*Acorus calamus*), a monocotyledon, showing the xylem completely surrounding the phloem, ×500.

The Flower

A strobilus is a group of sporophylls borne on a more or less elongated axis.   A flower is essentially a strobilus in which the sporophylls (stamens and carpels) are usually borne on a shortened axis (receptacle) and are usually surrounded by a perianth.   This distinction is untenable, however, because some flowers have an elongated receptacle and some have no perianth.   For convenience, any organization of sporophylls may be designated as a strobilus in pteridophytes and gymnosperms and as a flower in angiosperms.   Such a distinction is arbitrary.   A flower and a strobilus are morphologically equivalent structures.

Practically all gymnosperms, except the Bennettitales, have monosporangiate strobili, while most angiosperms have bisporangiate ("perfect") flowers.   In many cases the monosporangiate ("imperfect") condition has arisen by the suppression of stamens in the one kind of flower and of carpels in the other, the reduced organs often being represented by

vestiges.   The two kinds of flowers may occur on the same plant (monoecious condition) or on separate plants (dioecious condition).

The Perianth.   In a typical flower the perianth consists of two differentiated sets of parts, the outer set being the *calyx* and the inner set the

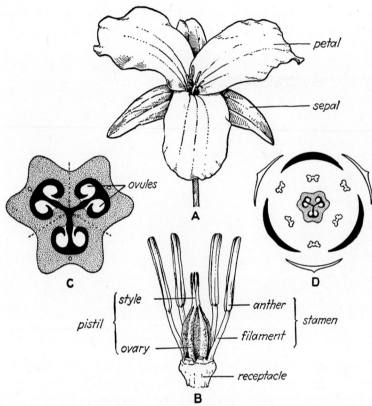

Fig. 318.   Floral structure of the large-flowered trillium (*Trillium grandiflorum*).   *A*, a
single flower, two-thirds natural size; *B*, four of the stamens and the pistil, twice natural
size; *C*, cross section of the ovary, the dotted lines indicating the junction of the carpels,
$\times 10$; *D*, the floral diagram.

corolla (Fig. 318).   The calyx is made up of *sepals*, the corolla of *petals*.
Ordinarily the sepals are scale-like and green, while the petals are larger
and either white or of some other color than green.   Both may be small
and inconspicuous, however, as in the rushes (*Juncus*), or large and
showy, as in the lilies (*Lilium*).   In some flowers the perianth consists of a
single set of parts.   These may be greenish and scale-like, as in the beet
(*Beta*), or large and showy, as in the anemone.   In either case the flower
is said to be *apetalous* and the single whorl is arbitrarily designated as the
calyx.   This is based on the assumption that the corolla is the missing

set, which may or may not be true. In fact, the single whorl apparently often represents a perianth that has never become differentiated into a calyx and corolla. *Naked* flowers are those which are entirely without a perianth. It may have been lost through degeneration or may never have been developed.

Sepals and petals are leaf-like in both form and structure. Phylogenetically they may either have been derived by sterilization from sporophylls,

FIG. 319. Flower of *Magnolia grandiflora*, a primitive type, with numerous stamens and carpels borne in spiral arrangement on an elongated receptacle, one-half natural size.

may represent modified foliage leaves, or possibly, at least in some flowers, the sepals may have evolved from leaves and the petals from stamens. Often the foliage leaves and perianth parts intergrade, making it difficult to delimit the flower from the vegetative shoot that bears it. In some flowers, notably in the water lily (*Nymphaea*), the petals intergrade with the stamens.

Most flowers have a regular (*actinomorphic*) corolla, composed of petals alike in size and shape, the flower as a whole exhibiting radial symmetry (Fig. 318). This represents a relatively primitive condition. Many flowers have an irregular (*zygomorphic*) corolla, with not all the petals alike, thus showing bilateral symmetry. This tendency reaches its highest expression in flowers having spurs, sacs, or pouches, as in the Leguminosae, Labiatae, and Orchidaceae.

Establishment of Whorls and Definite Numbers. Primitive flowers, like those of the magnolia and buttercup (*Ranunculus*), have a convex, elongated receptacle bearing indefinitely numerous stamens and carpels in spiral arrangement (Fig. 319). Such a condition is similar to that of a strobilus. In most flowers, however, the receptacle does not elongate but generally broadens at the apex, the floral parts arising from it in a series of whorls. The members of one whorl usually alternate with those of the next whorl (Fig. 318*D*). Commonly there are two whorls of perianth parts, two whorls of stamens, and one whorl of carpels. Such flowers are said to be *pentacyclic*. Where one whorl of stamens is wanting, this being nearly always the inner one, the flower is *tetracyclic*. With the establishment of a cyclic arrangement of floral parts, the members of each set are reduced to a definite number that is often the same in all whorls. In monocotyledons the number of parts in each whorl is generally three, while in dicotyledons it is usually five but often four. In many flowers the number of carpels is less than the number of parts in any of the other whorls.

Zonal Development. A striking feature of floral evolution has been the tendency for the members of the same whorl to develop as a single organ. Thus, in some flowers, the carpels are separate, each forming a simple pistil, while in most flowers the carpels are organized to form a compound pistil (Figs. 318*B*, *C*, and 326). Similarly, in many flowers, the petals are wholly or partly united to form a corolla tube and the sepals are united to form a calyx tube. Obviously a *syncarpous* flower (one with united carpels) is more advanced than an *apocarpous* one (one with separate carpels), and a *sympetalous* flower (one with united petals) is more advanced than a *choripetalous* one (one with separate petals). In some flowers the stamens are united to form a tube, but this condition is uncommon.

It should be understood that, in all flowers where members of the same set are united, the parts do not arise separately and later fuse, but originate together from a common meristem and develop as a single organ. There is a zonal development from the receptacle that involves all members of the same set, so that they are united from the beginning. Sometimes the primordia of the individual members arise separately but are soon carried upward by zonal development from below. This results in a compound pistil with separate styles or in a corolla tube with free tips.

Hypogyny, Perigyny, and Epigyny. In most sympetalous flowers the stamens are free above but are attached below to the corolla tube. Here zonation involves the members of two different sets. A still more advanced condition occurs where the receptacle enters into a zonal development with other floral sets. In *hypogynous* flowers all the sets arise independently from a more or less convex receptacle, the ovary being entirely free and situated above the place of attachment of the sepals, petals, and stamens (Fig. 320). In *perigynous* flowers the ovary is also free, but the receptacle is more or less concave, forming a disk-like or cup-like structure from the rim of which the sepals, petals, and stamens arise.

Here zonation involves the three outer floral sets.   In *epigynous* flowers the upward growth of the receptacle involves the ovary as well as the other floral parts, so that the ovary is embedded in the receptacle and the sepals, petals, and stamens seem to arise from its summit.   In hypogynous and perigynous flowers the ovary is *superior*, while in epigynous flowers it is *inferior*.   Hypogyny represents the most primitive and most common condition, epigyny the most advanced.   Perigyny is intermediate and least common.

In perigynous and epigynous flowers the structure surrounding the ovary and bearing the sepals, petals, and stamens on its rim is generally

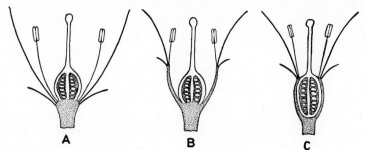

Fig. 320.   Diagrams illustrating hypogyny (*A*), perigyny (*B*), and epigyny (*C*).   In each flower the receptacle is stippled.

regarded as a zonal upgrowth of the receptacle because, in the development of the flower, such an upgrowth actually occurs.   Another view, supported by evidence from vascular anatomy, is that the structure referred to is made up of the fused basal portions of the sepals, petals, and stamens, to which, in epigynous flowers, the carpels are also united. Although such fusion cannot be seen in floral development (ontogeny), it is assumed to have occurred during the course of floral evolution.

Floral Development.   A longitudinal section through a very young flower bud reveals the fact that the floral parts arise at the tip of the receptacle as rounded protuberances of meristematic tissue.   They arise in much the same way as foliage leaves from a vegetative stem tip.   Ordinarily their appearance is acropetal, the sepals coming first, next the petals, then the stamens, and finally the carpels.   This sequence is shown in the buttercup (*Ranunculus*), for example, a primitive flower that is apocarpous and hypogynous and one in which the stamens and carpels arise in spiral succession on an elongated receptacle (Fig. 321).   As in all flowers, the apical meristem does not continue to grow indefinitely, but sooner or later becomes transformed into carpels.

The usual order of appearance of floral parts is modified in certain flowers, especially where one set is being suppressed.   In the shepherd's-purse (*Capsella*), one of the Cruciferae, the petals appear after the other

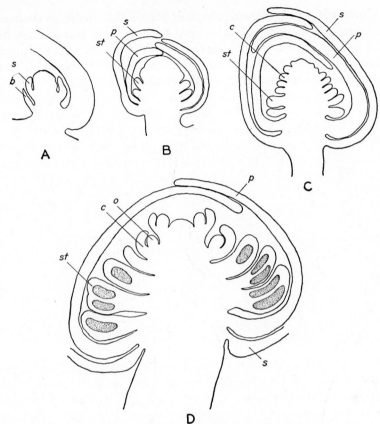

FIG. 321. Floral development in the buttercup (*Ranunculus*), ×50. *A* to *D*, successively older stages; *b*, bract; *s*, sepal; *p*, petal; *st*, stamen; *c*, carpel; *o*, ovule.

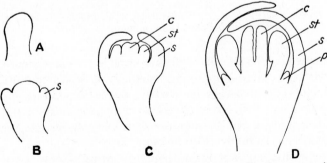

FIG. 322. Floral development in shepherd's-purse (*Capsella bursa-pastoris*), ×100. *A* to *D*, successively older stages; *s*, sepal; *st*, stamen; *c*, carpel; *p*, petal. The order of appearance differs from that of a typical flower in that here the petals appear last.

parts have arisen but, of course, in their proper place between the sepals
and stamens (Fig. 322).   This flower, when mature, has small petals.
In the fleabane (*Erigeron*) and other members of the Compositae the
sepals are the last members to appear.   They remain vestigial.   This
flower shows the epigynous type of development (Fig. 323).

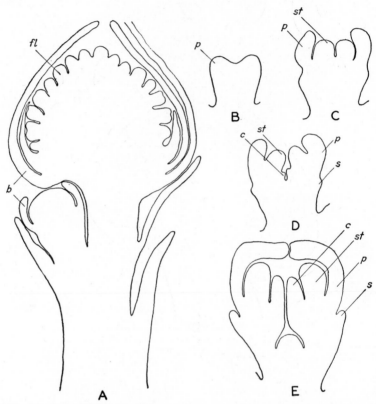

FIG. 323.   Floral development in fleabane (*Erigeron*).   *A*, very young and older inflorescence, the flowers arising on the convex receptacle, ×75; *B* to *E*, successive stages in the
development of a single flower, ×200; *b*, bract; *fl*, flower; *p*, corolla; *st*, stamen; *c*, carpel;
s, calyx.

The Stamen.   The stamen of angiosperms is the same structure as in
gymnosperms, a microsporophyll.   Generally it is differentiated into a
terminal, club-like, spore-bearing portion, the *anther*, and a slender stalk,
the *filament* (Fig. 318*B*).   A cross section of a young anther usually shows
four microsporangia, but the number may vary among different angiosperms from one to many (Fig. 324*A*).   As a rule, the microsporangia
extend the entire length of the anther.   Later, by the breaking down of
the intervening tissue between each pair of microsporangia, two large
cavities may be formed (Fig. 324*B*); or the four microsporangia may

remain separate. When the stamen is mature, the microsporangia, regardless of their number, are called *pollen sacs*.

As in gymnosperms, the development of the microsporangia is eusporangiate. A very young anther is made up of uniform meristematic tissue

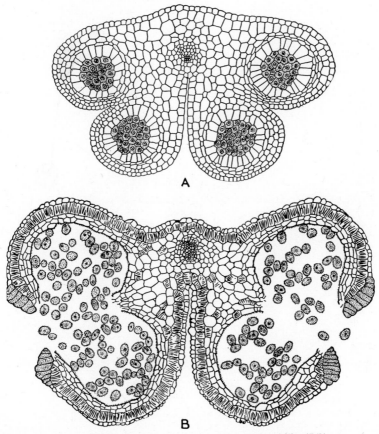

Fig. 324. Cross section of a young and of a mature anther of lily (*Lilium*). *A*, young anther, the four microsporangia with sporogenous tissue, ×60; *B*, mature anther with two pollen sacs containing pollen grains, ×30. The tapetum, surrounding the sporogenous tissue and conspicuous in *A*, has broken down in *B*, while the endothecium has developed bands of thickening. (*B, after Chamberlain.*)

surrounded by an epidermis. As seen in cross section, four lobes soon appear and a conducting strand becomes differentiated in the center. The cells forming the hypodermal layer are probably all potentially sporogenous but, as a rule, are actively so only in four regions, *viz.*, under the lobes. Only one longitudinal row of hypodermal cells may be differentiated under each lobe as sporangium initials, as in the Malvaceae and

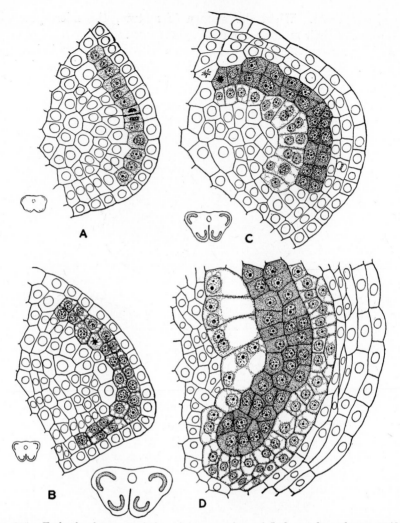

Fig. 325. Early development of the microsporangium of *Iochroma lanceolatum*, ×400.
Each stage also shows outline of entire anther, ×32.   *A*, cross section of portion of young
anther with hypodermal initial cells (shaded); *B*, division of initials to form primary
parietal cells (outer shaded layer) and primary sporogenous cells; *C*, later stage, showing
two layers of parietal and of sporogenous cells (latter heavily shaded) and differentiation
of inner portion of tapetum (lightly shaded); *D*, later stage, showing anther wall composed
of epidermis, endothecium, and middle layers; also sporogenous tissue (heavily shaded)
surrounded by tapetum (lightly shaded).

most members of the Compositae, but ordinarily a plate including several
or many hypodermal cells appears (Fig. 325*A*).

In the development of a microsporangium, the formation of a periclinal
wall in each initial separates the outer *primary parietal cells* from the inner
primary sporogenous cells (Fig. 325*B*).   The former, lying immediately

beneath the epidermis, then undergo further periclinal divisions, usually forming about three to five layers of parietal tissue (Fig. 325*C, D*). The outermost parietal layer, lying next to the epidermis, is the *endothecium*. As a rule, by the development of fibrous bands of thickening, the endothecium becomes hygroscopic and assists in the dehiscence of the anther (Fig. 324*B*). The innermost layer of parietal tissue forms part of the tapetum, the rest of which is derived from the cells immediately in contact with the sporogenous cells on their inner side. Sometimes the tapetum becomes two- or three-layered. An interesting feature is the division of the tapetal nuclei to form two or more free nuclei in each cell (Fig. 325*D*). The middle layers and tapetum generally disappear before the maturing of the spores, the ripe sporangium wall usually consisting only of the epidermis and endothecium. A tapetal plasmodium, surrounding the microspores, is seen in several groups, such as the Compositae and Helobiales.

The cells forming the primary sporogenous layer generally undergo two or three divisions to form the microspore mother cells, which then greatly enlarge and assume a spherical form. The next two divisions, during which the number of chromosomes is reduced one-half, result in the formation of tetrads. At this time the tapetum disorganizes. The tetrads are mostly tetrahedral in dicotyledons and isobilateral in monocotyledons. A linear arrangement of microspores is rare, but occurs in the milkweeds (*Asclepias*) and a few other forms.

Upon separation from the tetrads, the microspores have developed a two-layered cell wall consisting of an outer *exine* and an inner *intine* (Fig. 334). Although commonly the exine is thickened, the cell wall usually has one or more thin places where the exine is not formed and through which the pollen tube may later emerge. Its outer surface usually bears warts or spines, or is variously sculptured. Ordinarily the microspores become free from one another at maturity, but in some angiosperms (*e.g.*, *Typha* and *Rhododendron*) the members of the tetrad do not separate, while in a few others, notably in the milkweeds (*Asclepias*) and certain orchids, all the spores in a sporangium cling together and escape as a mass, which is called a *pollinium*.

As a rule, the anther dehisces by means of two longitudinal slits (Figs. 318*B* and 324*B*), but sometimes by terminal slits or pores, by hinged valves, or irregularly.

The Carpel. The carpel of angiosperms is really a megasporophyll but, instead of bearing the ovules freely exposed, as in gymnosperms, it surrounds them. Where two or more carpels are wholly or partly united, forming a compound pistil, the flower is said to be *syncarpous*. Where the carpels are free, each constituting a simple pistil, the flower is *apocarpous*. The enlarged, hollow, lower portion of the pistil, the *ovary*, encloses one or more ovules (Fig. 318*B*).   Generally a slender stalk-like *style* arises from the ovary.   In some compound pistils the styles as well as the ovaries are united, while in others the styles are wholly or partly free (Fig. 326).   The style may be hollow but usually is solid.   The tip of the style, termed the *stigma*, is not a morphological unit, but merely an exposed and often expanded portion of the tissue that lines the ovarian cavity and extends upward through the style.   In some flowers the stigmatic surface extends down the outside of the style.

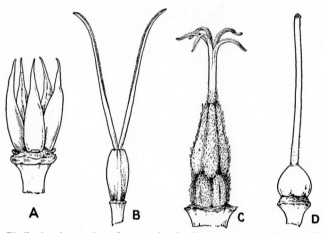

Fig. 326.   Pistils showing various degrees of union between the carpels.   *A*, five separate carpels in the flower of stonecrop (*Sedum*), ×3; *B*, pistil of garden pink (*Dianthus*) with two carpels having united ovaries and free styles, ×3; *C*, pistil of geranium (*Pelargonium*) with five united carpels having free stylar tips, ×6; *D*, pistil of nightshade (*Solanum*) with two completely united carpels, ×6.

An ovary may contain a single cavity (*locule*) or two or more cavities separated from one another by partitions.   The ovules may be attached to the walls of the ovary or to the partitions between the locules, in either case being foliar in origin.   In some cases the receptacle grows upward into the ovarian cavity and bears the ovules either terminally, laterally, or in both ways.   Such ovules are cauline in origin.

The carpel of angiosperms is generally regarded as the equivalent of an infolded leaf bearing ovules along its fused margins.   In fact, in many apocarpous flowers the carpel arises as an open structure that encloses the ovules as development proceeds.   Although a foliar organ, the carpel is not a transformed foliage leaf.   It is a sporophyll—an organ with its own evolutionary history reaching far back into a pteridophyte ancestry. Sporophylls and foliage leaves have undergone a parallel evolutionary development.   Another view regarding the nature of the carpel is that it is a greatly reduced branch system.   This theory is based on its supposed evolution from the sporangium-bearing leaf of the ferns, which is often interpreted as a modified branch system (see page 305).

The Ovule. In the development of an ovule, at first a small rounded protuberance appears (Fig. 327). This is the nucellus, or megasporangium proper. At its base an integument then arises as a ring of tissue, the nucellus meanwhile increasing in prominence. Later, if a second integument is to be formed, it arises outside the first one. The integument or integuments grow out beyond the nucellus, leaving a narrow passageway,

FIG. 327. Successive stages in the development of an anatropous ovule, the last representing a section through a mature ovule. (*After Gray.*)

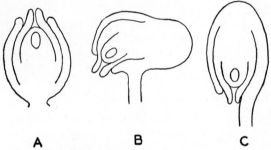

A   B   C

FIG. 328. Directions of ovules: *A*, orthotropous; *B*, campylotropous; *C*, anatropous. (*After Coulter.*)

the micropyle. In the Archichlamydeae and Monocotyledoneae two integuments are generally present, but in nearly all the Metachlamydeae there is a single massive one. As a rule, the ovule is borne on a short stalk, the *funiculus*, the part of the ovary to which it is attached being the *placenta*. The basal portion of the ovule is called the *chalaza*.

When mature, ovules may be erect (*orthotropous*), curved (*campylotropous*), or inverted (*anatropous*) (Fig. 328). There are also intermediate conditions. The first represents the most primitive condition and is characteristic of most cauline ovules. It is found among the Urticaceae, Polygonaceae, Xyridaceae, and a few other relatively primitive families of Archichlamydeae and Monocotyledoneae. The second type is also uncommon, being found among the Chenopodiaceae, Caryophyllaceae, Cruciferae, and Gramineae. The third condition is most advanced and most common. Anatropous ovules are found in many of the Archichlamydeae and Monocotyledoneae, and almost exclusively in the

Metachlamydeae.   In anatropous ovules having two integuments, the outer one is united on one side with the funiculus.

The development of the ovule is eusporangiate.   Generally a single hypodermal initial is differentiated at the apex of the nucellus, but occasionally there are two or more initials, especially among the lower families of Archichlamydeae.   Ordinarily the initial, by a periclinal division, gives rise to an outer *primary parietal cell* and an inner *primary sporogenous cell*, as in the microsporangium (Fig. 329).   The parietal cell may divide periclinally once or twice again, or it may remain undivided. In practically all the Metachlamydeae, and exceptionally in the two other groups of angiosperms, wall tissue is eliminated, the hypodermal initial functioning directly as the megaspore mother cell (Figs. 330*A* and 333*A*).   In all other angiosperms the primary sporogenous cell is the megaspore mother cell.   It gives rise, by two successive divisions, usually to a linear tetrad, the reduction in the number of chromosomes taking place at this time (Fig. 330*B–D*).   A T-shaped arrangement of the megaspores is not infrequent.

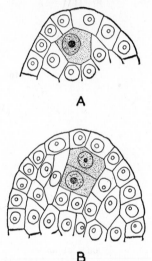

Fig. 329.   Early development of the megasporangium of the willow (*Salix*), showing single hypodermal initial (*A*) and the two cells derived from it (*B*): the primary parietal cell (outer shaded one) and the primary sporogenous cell.   (*After Chamberlain.*)

The Female Gametophyte.   As in gymnosperms, the female gametophyte (embryo sac) develops within the tissues of the ovule and similarly is nearly always formed by the innermost megaspore, the other three degenerating.   The functional megaspore greatly enlarges, encroaching upon and absorbing the abortive megaspores as well as more or less of the surrounding nucellar tissue (Fig. 330*E*).   Typically the megaspore nucleus gives rise to eight nuclei by three successive divisions (Figs. 330*F–H* and 331).   Thus, as in gymnosperms, the development of the female gametophyte is initiated by free-nuclear division, but in angiosperms the nuclei are almost always definitely eight in number.   There is no wall formation at this stage, but the free nuclei exhibit a striking polarity, four being at one end of the embryo sac and four at the other end.   This polarity is established after the first nuclear division, when a large vacuole appears between the daughter nuclei (Fig. 330*G*).

One nucleus from each polar group now comes to the center of the embryo sac.   These two nuclei, called *polar nuclei*, come in contact with each other and generally unite at once to form the *fusion nucleus*, or some-

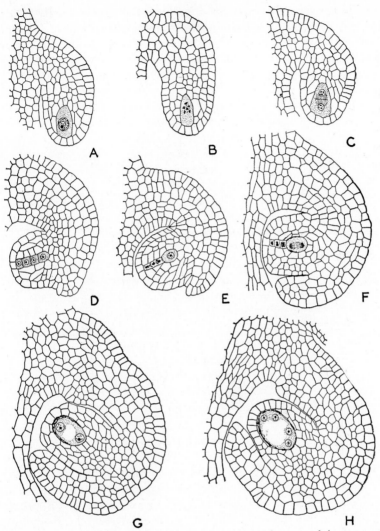

FIG. 330. Megasporogenesis and early development of the embryo sac of *Anemone patens*, ×200. *A*, young ovule with megaspore mother cell; *B*, first meiotic division; *C*, completion of first division; *D*, linear tetrad of megaspores; *E*, functional megaspore enlarging; *F*, division of megaspore nucleus; *G*, 2-nucleate embryo sac; *H*, 4-nucleate embryo sac. (*From preparations supplied by Dr. George H. Conant.*)

times remain distinct (Fig. 331). The three nuclei left at the micropylar end of the embryo sac become organized as naked cells, forming the *egg apparatus*. Of these, one is the *egg* and the two others are *synergids*. Ordinarily the egg lies between the synergids and slightly exceeds them in size; its nucleus is farther from the micropyle than their nuclei are. Usually the three cells forming the egg apparatus are pyriform. The synergids are generally interpreted as potential eggs normally incapable of being fertilized. The three nuclei at the chalazal end of the embryo sac, which is the one opposite the micropylar end, are usually organized as small naked or walled cells called *antipodals*. The antipodals, sometimes ephemeral, are usually somewhat persistent, rarely giving rise later

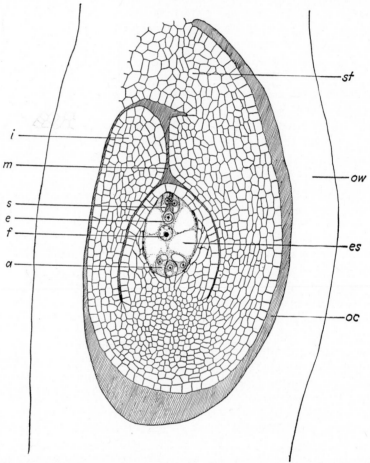

Fig. 331. Ovule of *Anemone patens* with mature embryo sac, ×200; *ow*, ovary wall; *oc*, ovary cavity; *st*, stalk of ovule; *i*, integument; *m*, micropyle; *es*, embryo sac; *s*, synergid; *e*, egg; *f*, fusion nucleus; *a*, antipodal cell.

to an extensive tissue. The antipodals are said to be nutritive in function and probably represent vegetative cells of the female gametophyte in various stages of disappearance.

Variations in Embryo-sac Development. The development of the ordinary type of embryo sac is characterized by two important features:

(1) Five successive nuclear divisions intervene between the megaspore mother cell and the formation of the egg. (2) The embryo sac is derived from a single megaspore, the innermost one. Numerous deviations from this type of development are seen throughout the angiosperms. The principal ones are as follows (Fig. 332):

Oenothera. In *Oenothera* and other members of the Onagraceae, a linear tetrad of megaspores is formed in the usual way but, with few exceptions, the outermost (micropylar) megaspore, rather than the innermost (chalazal) one develops into the embryo sac. Only four successive nuclear divisions intervene between the megaspore mother cell and the egg. The nucleus of the functional megaspore gives rise to two nuclei, both of which remain at the micropylar end of the embryo sac, a vacuole appearing below them. Each again divides and, of the four nuclei thus formed, three are organized into the egg apparatus, while the fourth becomes a polar nucleus. Because of the absence of a fifth nuclear division, there is no second polar nucleus and there are no antipodals.

Allium. This type of embryo sac occurs not only in certain other genera of Liliaceae, such as *Scilla* and *Trillium*, but also in numerous genera belonging to many other families. The megaspore mother cell divides into two cells of which the upper one soon degenerates, while the lower one undergoes three successive free-nuclear divisions to form the embryo sac. When mature, this displays the usual kind of eight-nucleate organization. It is apparent that only four nuclear divisions occur between the megaspore mother cell and the egg and that two megaspore nuclei participate in the formation of the embryo sac.

Peperomia. In this genus, one of the Piperaceae, all four megaspore nuclei are involved in the formation of the embryo sac, no walls being formed between them. The four nuclei are arranged in a cross-like manner, with a large vacuole between them; two successive nuclear divisions follow, the resulting 16 free nuclei being arranged in various ways, depending on the species. The egg apparatus consists of the egg and a single synergid. In *Peperomia pellucida* eight nuclei form the fusion nucleus and six degenerate, while in *Peperomia hispidula* 14 nuclei form the fusion nucleus.

Various modifications of the *Peperomia* type are seen in certain other families. Thus, in *Gunnera*, three nuclei form the egg apparatus, seven unite to form the fusion nucleus, and six degenerate. In the Penaeaceae and certain species of *Euphorbia* the 16 free nuclei are arranged in four groups of four each. One member of each group becomes a polar nucleus, the four polar nuclei fuse, while the three remaining nuclei in each group become organized as cells. The three cells at the upper end of the embryo sac constitute the egg apparatus, the other cells finally degenerating.

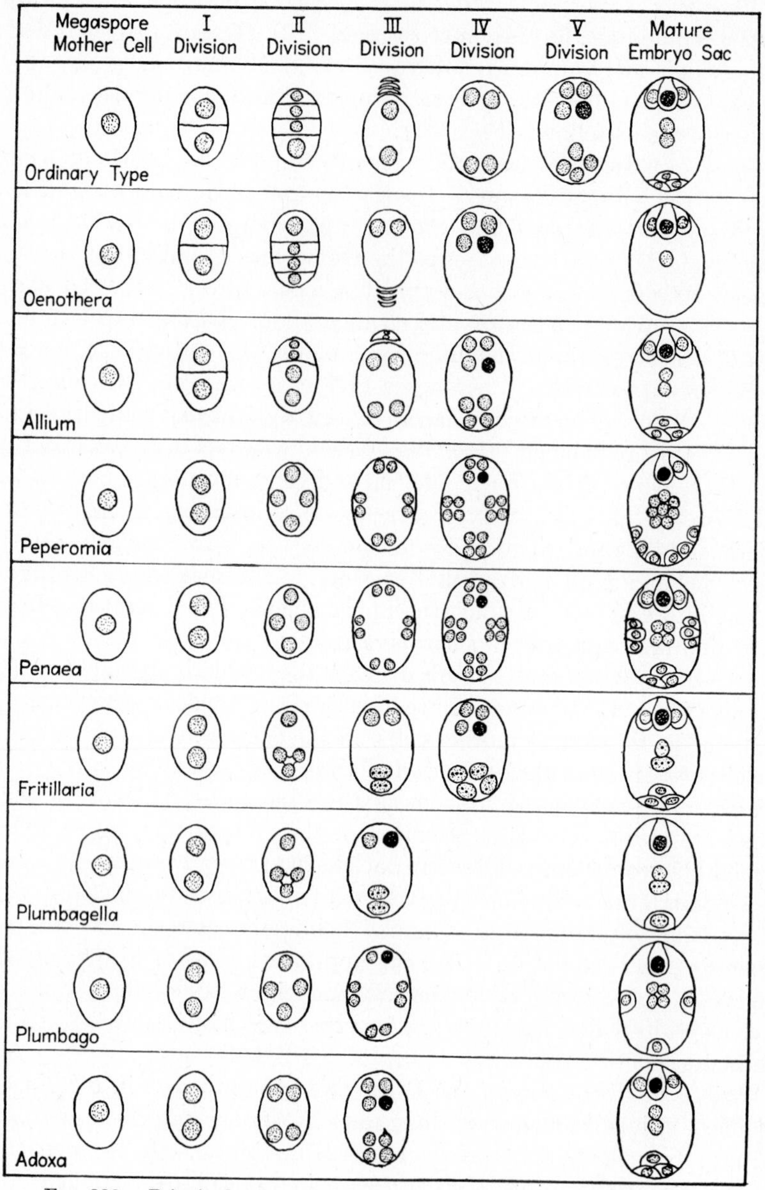

Fig. 332.   Principal types of embryo-sac development in angiosperms.

Fritillaria. In *Fritillaria, Tulipa, Lilium,* and certain other Liliaceae, as well as members of other families, a characteristic development occurs (Fig. 333). The four megaspore nuclei, arranged in a linear row, are not separated by walls. As the embryo sac enlarges, the three lower megaspore nuclei migrate to the chalazal end. All four nuclei now begin to divide, but before the division is complete, the three lower nuclei fuse. As a result, a second four-nucleate stage appears, the two micropylar nuclei being separated from the two chalazal ones by a large vacuole. The micropylar nuclei are haploid, the chalazal ones triploid. After another free-nuclear division occurs, the upper group of four nuclei give rise to the egg, two synergids, and a haploid polar nucleus, the lower group to three antipodals and a triploid polar nucleus. Sometimes only two antipodals are formed.

Plumbagella. The embryo sac of *Plumbagella,* one of the Plumbaginaceae, closely resembles that of *Fritillaria.* Four megaspore nuclei arise without any wall formation. The three lower nuclei pass to the chalazal end of the embryo sac, a large vacuole appearing between them and the micropylar nucleus. The three chalazal nuclei fuse. Both nuclei now divide and the embryo sac usually remains four-nucleate. The egg is organized from one of the two haploid nuclei, an antipodal cell from one of the two triploid nuclei. The fusion nucleus is formed by the union of the two remaining nuclei, one of which is haploid and the other triploid.

Plumbago. In *Plumbago* and several other genera of the Plumbaginaceae, a unique type of embryo sac is seen. The four megaspore nuclei, formed without the appearance of walls and arranged in a cross-like manner, undergo one more division. One of each pair of nuclei becomes a polar nucleus, the second member of the micropylar pair is organized into the egg, while the three other nuclei degenerate. The mature embryo sac has only two nuclei—that of the egg and a fusion nucleus formed by the union of the four polar nuclei.

Adoxa. The type of development seen in this genus and in *Sambucus,* both members of the Caprifoliaceae, has been reported in members of many other families, but some of these (*e.g., Lilium*) have been shown to belong to other types, while many others are doubtful. In *Adoxa* no cell-wall formation accompanies the two divisions of the megaspore mother cell, the four nuclei dividing again to form an eight-nucleate gametophyte. Thus the egg is separated from the megaspore mother cell by only three free-nuclear divisions and all four megaspore nuclei participate in the formation of the embryo sac. This has the ordinary type of mature organization.

Male Gametophyte. In angiosperms the male gametophyte is reduced even more than in gymnosperms. No prothallial cells are produced. Before the anther dehisces, the microspore nucleus divides to form the

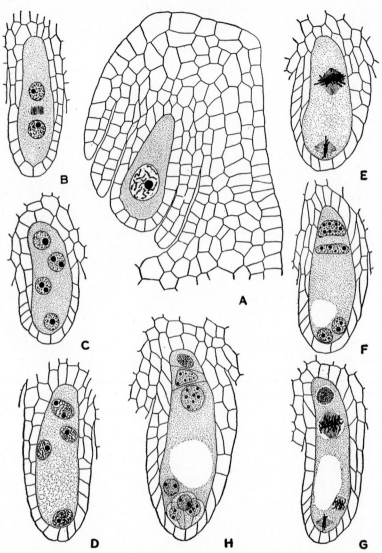

FIG. 333. Development of the embryo sac of *Fritillaria biflora* ×200. *A*, entire ovule with megaspore mother cell; *B*, 2-nucleate stage; *C*, first 4-nucleate stage; *D*, the four megaspore nuclei beginning to divide; *E*, completion of division, resulting in second 4-nucleate stage; *F*, the two micropylar nuclei being haploid and the two chalazal ones triploid; *G*, the two micropylar nuclei and one of the chalazal nuclei dividing again; *H*, mature embryo sac with egg, two synergids, and haploid polar nucleus at micropylar end and triploid polar nucleus and two antipodal cells at chalazal end.

generative nucleus and tube nucleus, the former becoming organized as a small, naked generative cell lying within the larger tube cell (Fig. 334). The generative cell is usually elliptical, lenticular, or spindle-shaped. The tube nucleus is generally large, with a large nucleolus and little chromatin. The generative nucleus is usually smaller, with a small nucleolus or none, and with considerable chromatin. The generative cell gives rise directly to two male cells, dividing either within the pollen grain or, somewhat more frequently, in the pollen tube. The male cells show considerable variation in form but are never ciliated. In most angiosperms the male cells remain intact, while in some the membrane around each seems to disappear, leaving their nuclei free. The male nuclei often become vermiform, especially after entering the embryo sac.

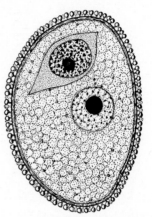

Fertilization. As in gymnosperms, pollination must precede fertilization but, because the ovules of angiosperms are enclosed in an ovary, the pollen grains cannot come in contact with them. Pollen is transferred by various agencies from the anther to the receptive surface of the style (the stigma), where it germinates, putting forth a long pollen tube that grows down the inside of the style and into the cavity of the ovary. Branching pollen tubes, characteristic of gymnosperms, are found in only a few angiosperms, notably among members of the amentiferous orders.

FIG. 334. Section of a pollen grain of lily (*Lilium auratum*) in the shedding condition, ×750. The smaller, naked generative cell lies within the larger tube cell, each having its own nucleus.

Where there is a stylar canal, the pollen tube usually grows down through it, but where the style is solid, as is more commonly the case, the tube secretes enzymes that digest a passageway to the ovary. The nucleus and cytoplasm of the tube cell, as well as the generative cell, pass down the pollen tube as it develops. The tube nucleus usually lies at the tip of the advancing pollen tube and apparently is concerned with its development. While the tube is developing, or frequently before the pollen grain is shed, the generative cell gives rise to two male cells.

Upon reaching the cavity of the ovary, the pollen tube grows along the ovary wall until it reaches one of the ovules, which it then enters, ordinarily through the micropyle. After penetrating the intervening nucellar tissue, the tip of the pollen tube ruptures and its contents are discharged into the embryo sac. The tube nucleus soon disintegrates, but both male cells (or male nuclei, as the case may be) enter the embryo sac. One of the male nuclei penetrates the egg and unites with the female nucleus, thus effecting fertilization (Fig. 335). Although distinct male cells may be present in the pollen tube, or even in the embryo sac, there is evidence indicating that, in most angiosperms, only a male nucleus enters the cytoplasm of the egg. Immediately after fertilization, the egg becomes surrounded by a cell wall.

The second male nucleus entering the embryo sac now unites with the nucleus resulting from the fusion of the two polar nuclei, thus forming the *primary endosperm nucleus.* This unique behavior, which has been called "double fertilization," has been observed in so many angiosperms that it must be regarded as characteristic of the group as a whole. Usually one of the synergids is destroyed by the entrance of the pollen tube, while the other synergid, as well as the antipodal cells, generally disappear soon after fertilization has taken place.

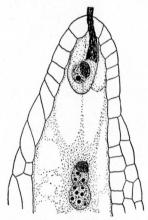

Fig. 335. Fertilization in *Fritillaria biflora*, ×250. One male nucleus is in contact with the egg nucleus, while the other has joined the two polar nuclei.

Although ordinarily the pollen tube enters the ovule through the micropyle (*porogamy*), in some of the more primitive Archichlamydeae it may penetrate the lower end of the ovule. This behavior, known as *chalazogamy,* has been observed in the Casuarinaceae, Juglandaceae, Corylaceae, Urticaceae, and Euphorbiaceae. In certain other angiosperms the pollen tube may follow an intermediate route, entering the ovule through the integument (*mesogamy*).

The behavior of the polar nuclei is variable, depending on the species. Generally they unite before the pollen tube enters the embryo sac, forming the fusion nucleus (Fig. 331). To this the male nucleus later is added. Sometimes, as in *Fritillaria* and *Lilium,* the fusion of the polar nuclei is delayed until the male nucleus has joined them, all three then fusing simultaneously (Fig. 335). Sometimes the polar nuclei remain at opposite ends of the embryo sac until the pollen tube has entered. Then the male nucleus fuses with the micropylar polar nucleus, the other one joining them later.

Because typically a male nucleus unites with two haploid polar nuclei, the primary endosperm nucleus, of course, is triploid. In some forms, however, as in the Onagraceae, it is diploid, being formed by a union between the male nucleus and one polar nucleus; while in such genera as *Peperomia, Fritillaria, Lilium, Plumbago,* and *Penaea* various degrees of polyploidy are attained, the primary endosperm nucleus arising from the fusion of four or more nuclei of the embryo sac, with the addition of the male nucleus.

Following fertilization, the petals and stamens wither and drop off, and often the sepals do likewise. As the ovules are transformed into seeds, the ovary enlarges to form a fruit. Thus normally fertilization provides a stimulus that has far-reaching effects.

Endosperm. Typically endosperm arises from a triple-fusion nucleus, division of which usually precedes that of the fertilized egg. Sometimes each of the nuclear divisions is accompanied by the formation of a wall, so that a tissue is formed at once (Fig. 336*A*). More commonly, however, the formation of endosperm is initiated by free-nuclear division (Fig. 336*B*). These free nuclei are usually parietally placed but sometimes fill the embryo sac. Unless the endosperm is absorbed by the embryo while still in the free-nuclear stage, wall formation then takes place, often simultaneously throughout the endosperm, resulting in a compact tissue without intercellular spaces. Reserve food becomes stored in its cells, generally in large quantities. This may be deposited as hemicel-

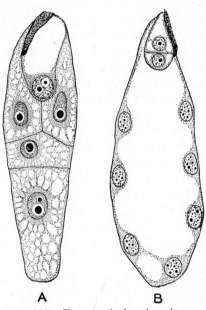

A   B

FIG. 336. Two methods of endosperm formation. *A*, *Silphium laciniatum*, nuclear division followed immediately by wall formation, ×300; *B*, *Fritillaria biflora*, endosperm arising by free-nuclear division, ×150. In *A*, the fertilized egg (above) has not yet divided; in *B*, it has divided once.

lulose on the cell walls, which often become very thick, as in the date and many other palms. In some angiosperms, as in many of the Podostemaceae and Orchidaceae, the endosperm is absent or greatly reduced, often being represented by only a few free nuclei. The endosperm may persist in the seed as a food-storage tissue or may be entirely absorbed by the developing embryo.

The integument or integuments of the ovule are transformed into the testa of the seed. The nucellus is almost or entirely destroyed during the development of the seed, but in such forms as the Centrospermales it persists and gives rise to a tissue, called *perisperm*, which becomes the chief food-storage region. In the Nymphaeaceae the seed contains both endosperm and perisperm.

The nature of the endosperm in angiosperms is very confusing. In gymnosperms it is obviously vegetative tissue of the female gametophyte, and thus necessarily arises before fertilization. In angiosperms it arises after fertilization, ordinarily from a triple fusion of nuclei, one of which is male, another female (since it is sister to the egg nucleus), and a third vegetative. Some have regarded endosperm as gametophyte tissue stimulated to develop by nuclear fusions. Others have considered it to be sporophyte tissue, the twin of the embryo. Since it is ordinarily triploid, however, it cannot be either gametophyte or sporophyte in the strict sense of the terms. It might better be regarded as undifferentiated tissue continuing the growth of the female gametophyte and stimulated to develop by nuclear fusions. The union of the male nucleus with the polar nuclei cannot be regarded as an act of fertilization because (1) the effect of the fusion is merely to furnish a growth stimulus; (2) more than a single male and female nucleus is involved; and (3) the product of the triple fusion is not a new individual.

Embryo. The development of the embryo from the fertilized egg does not, as in nearly all gymnosperms, begin with free-nuclear division, but each division is accompanied by the formation of a cell wall. Since embryogeny differs in dicotyledons and monocotyledons, except in the earliest stages, a representative example of each will be described.

Capsella. The sequence of embryonic stages can be followed easily in the common shepherd's-purse (*Capsella*), a dicotyledon belonging to the Cruciferae. Here the zygote, by a series of transverse divisions, gives rise to a proembryo of varying length (Fig. 337A, B). The terminal cell (the one farthest from the micropyle) forms practically all the embryo, while the other cells give rise to the suspensor. The basal cell of the suspensor is much larger than the others. The terminal cell undergoes three successive divisions, each at right angles to the preceding one, thus resulting in the formation of octants (Fig. 337C, D). The first division is always vertical but the second vertical and the horizontal divisions may occur in either order. Of the eight cells now constituting the embryo, the upper tier of four cells eventually gives rise to the cotyledons and stem tip, the basal tier to all the hypocotyl except its tip.

The suspensor elongates, becoming 8 to 10 cells in length and pushing the embryo downward. A peripheral layer of primary epidermal cells, the *dermatogen*, is now cut off by periclinal walls appearing in all 8 cells of the embryo (Fig. 337E). Additional longitudinal and transverse divisions occur in the inner cells and soon the *periblem*, comprising the cells eventually to produce the cortex, is differentiated from the *plerome*, which gives rise to the stele (Fig. 337F). The plerome is complete at the tip of the hypocotyl but the periblem and dermatogen are not. They are completed at the expense of the adjacent cell of the suspensor. This divides

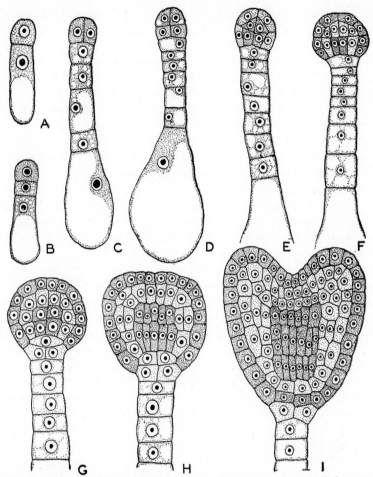

FIG. 337. Successive stages in early development of the embryo of *Capsella bursa-pastoris*, a dicotyledon, ×500. *A*, two-celled proembryo; *B*, three-celled proembryo; *C*, proembryo with longitudinally divided terminal cell and enlarged basal cell; *D*, terminal cell divided to produce octants, four cells lying beneath the four shown; *E*, cutting off of dermatogen by periclinal walls; *F*, differentiation of periblem and plerome, the former indicated by lighter shading; the cell at the upper end of the suspensor is the hypophysis; *G*, completion of periblem by cell cut off the hypophysis; *H*, later stage, showing cell divisions throughout the embryo; *I*, completion of dermatogen from middle tier of cells derived from the hypophysis.

transversely into two cells. The upper cell, called the *hypophysis*, contributes to the embryo, while the lower one is added to the suspensor.

The hypophysis divides transversely, the cell next to the embryo completing the periblem and the other cell undergoing two longitudinal divisions at right angles to each other to form a plate of four cells (Fig. 337*G*, *H*). In a later stage, each of these four cells divides transversely, the upper tier completing the dermatogen and the lower tier forming the first layer of the rootcap (Fig. 337*I*).   This stage is further marked by the appearance of the two cotyledons, one on each side of the stem tip, which lies at the upper end of the hypocotyl.   Thus the stem tip is terminal and the cotyledons are lateral.

Many dicotyledons follow the general course of embryogeny as seen in *Capsella*, but there are a number of departures from it.   In the Nymphae-aceae, for example, a globular proembryo is developed and generally no suspensor is formed.   In the Myrtaceae a massive proembryo fills the micropylar end of the embryo sac and several embryos may be differentiated from it.   In the Rubiaceae and Leguminosae the suspensor is enormously elongated.

Sagittaria.   The development of the embryo of *Sagittaria*, one of the Alismaceae, is representative of the more primitive families of monocotyledons.   Here the proembryo is a filament of three cells—a large basal cell, a middle cell, and a terminal cell (Fig. 338*A*, *B*).   The basal cell enlarges considerably but does not divide, constituting the greater part of the suspensor.   The middle cell, by a series of transverse and vertical divisions, forms the stem tip, hypocotyl, root tip, and the rest of the suspensor (Fig. 338*C–F*).   The terminal cell gives rise to the cotyledon.   It divides first by a vertical wall and then by walls in the two other planes, thus forming octants (Fig. 338*D*, *E*).   The dermatogen arises in the cotyledon by the formation of periclinal walls and proceeds toward the root end of the embryo (Fig. 338*G*).   Later the periblem and plerome are differentiated. The stem tip arises as a depression in the side of the embryo, thus being lateral in position rather than terminal as in the dicotyledons (Fig. 338*H*, *I*).

A number of modifications of the *Sagittaria* type of embryogeny have been noted.   For example, the Araceae have a massive proembryo and lack a suspensor.   The Liliaceae have a filamentous proembryo that soon becomes massive.   In the Orchidaceae the body regions are not differentiated and, in many forms, a large suspensor becomes a haustorial organ.

In *Agapanthus*, a member of the Liliaceae, dicotyledonous embryos are occasionally produced.   The proembryo is more or less massive.   Its tip broadens and a peripheral cotyledonary zone gives rise to two growing points.   The entire zone then grows upward, resulting in the formation of a cotyledonary ring surrounding a depression from which the stem tip develops.   If both growing points continue to develop equally, a dicotyledonous embryo results, but if only one continues, a monocotyledonous embryo is formed.   This indicates that dicotyledony is more primitive than monocotyledony.   It also suggests that the stem tip is really terminal and the cotyledons lateral, even though only one cotyledon is produced.

Apomixis. Irregularities in the normal process of sexual reproduction occur occasionally in some angiosperms, constantly in others. *Apomixis* is a condition in which sexual reproduction in the flower is replaced by some form of asexual reproduction. It may take the form of *partheno-*

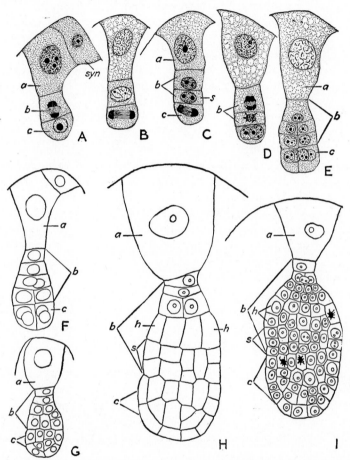

Fig. 338. Successive stages in early development of the embryo of *Sagittaria variabilis*, a monocotyledon. *A* and *B*, three-celled proembryos, showing synergid (*syn*), basal cell (*a*), middle cell (*b*), and terminal cell (*c*) from which the cotyledon is derived; *C*, division of middle cell into two cells, one of which (*s*) gives rise to the stem tip; *D*, slightly older stage; *E*, formation of four cells from the terminal cell; *F*, further development of the middle region; *G*, differentiation of dermatogen in the terminal region; *H*, further development of dermatogen and differentiation of middle region into hypocotyl (*h*) and stem tip (*s*); *I*, later stage. (*After Schaffner.*)

genesis, which is the development of an embryo from an unfertilized egg. This has been observed in a number of angiosperms, such as *Thalictrum, Antennaria, Alchemilla, Erigeron,* and *Taraxacum.* In all these and similar cases the reduction of chromosomes fails to take place in connection with megaspore formation.   Consequently the egg is a diploid cell and fertilization is unnecessary.   Haploid parthenogenesis is very rare, having been reported in only a few plants.

The development of an embryo from other cells of the embryo sac than the egg, called *apogamy*, has been observed in *Antennaria, Alchemilla, Allium, Iris,* and other forms, but is not known to occur constantly in nature.   Here a synergid or an antipodal gives rise to an embryo, which may be diploid or haploid, depending on whether or not meiosis occurred in the division of the megaspore mother cell.   *Sporophytic budding* occurs when cells of the nucellus or integument project into the embryo sac and give rise to embryos.   It has been reported in *Citrus, Coelebogyne, Funkia,* and other angiosperms, where it frequently accompanies apogamy.

The Fruit.   The fruit develops as the seeds ripen and always encloses them.   Like the flower, it has no morphological individuality.   A *true fruit* consists merely of a ripened ovary, while an *accessory fruit* includes in addition one or more associated parts of the flower, such as the calyx or receptacle.   The ripened ovary wall is the *pericarp*.   When a fruit develops from an inferior ovary, its wall consists of the pericarp united with the receptacle.   At maturity, fruits may be dry or fleshy; when dry, they may be dehiscent or indehiscent.   Sometimes the pericarp becomes fleshy on the outside and stony within.   Some fruits develop from simple pistils, others from compound pistils.   An *aggregate fruit* arises from a group of separate ovaries, belonging to a single flower, that become more or less consolidated.   A *multiple fruit* is similar, except that it is derived from the ovaries of a number of flowers.   The development of a fruit without fertilization is called *parthenocarpy*.   Parthenocarpic fruits are nearly always seedless.

The Seedling.   In practically all angiosperms the embryo goes into a state of dormancy as the seed matures, this being accomplished by the withdrawal of most of the water present and by important chemical changes.   In the presence of favorable external conditions, germination occurs by the resumption of growth of the embryo and of other processes within the seed.

In many seeds, particularly those of dicotyledons, the endosperm is completely absorbed by the embryo while the seed is ripening, the reserve food being thus transferred to the embryo itself, principally to the cotyledons.   In seeds containing endosperm, this is absorbed by the embryo in germination.

When germination begins, the root tip pushes through the testa and grows downward into the ground, giving rise to the primary root.   The hypocotyl may remain short or may elongate considerably, depending on the kind of germination.   Where it remains short, the cotyledon or cotyledons remain inside the testa, the plumule soon giving rise to a shoot that pushes upward. Where the development of the primary root is accompanied by elongation of the hypocotyl, the cotyledon or cotyledons are pulled out of the testa and are carried above the ground, where they often expand and function as foliage leaves. In such seedlings the development of the plumule into the shoot is usually considerably delayed.

Chief Orders of Angiosperms

It would be beyond the scope of the present work to include an extensive account of the classification of angiosperms, a subject of concern mainly to the taxonomist. A general survey of the chief orders, however, will demonstrate the complexity of the group and illustrate its principal evolutionary trends, many of which have already been mentioned. The orders in each of the three series do not represent a phylogenetic sequence but merely different levels of progress. The interrelationships of many groups is obscure, so that the tracing of lines of descent is difficult and will not be attempted here.

1. ARCHICHLAMYDEAE

The Dicotyledoneae include the Archichlamydeae and Metachlamydeae. The Archichlamydeae are the primitive stock of angiosperms from which both the Metachlamydeae and Monocotyledoneae have been derived. Their flowers are naked, apetalous, or choripetalous, the parts being usually cyclic but frequently more or less spiral.

Piperales. The Piperales comprise 4 families and about 1,200 species of mostly tropical herbs and shrubs, nearly all belonging to the Piperaceae. The peppers (*Piper*) and peperomias are the best-known examples. The flowers, borne in spikes, are perfect or imperfect, mostly naked, typically trimerous but usually reduced, hypogynous, and mostly apocarpous.

Salicales, Juglandales, and Fagales. These orders, with several others of minor importance, were once grouped together as the Amentiferae, because their flowers are borne in aments or catkins. The Salicales include a single family, the Salicaceae, to which belong the willows (*Salix*) and poplars (*Populus*). The Juglandales also comprise a single family, the Juglandaceae, including the walnuts (*Juglans*) and hickories (*Carya*). The Fagales contain two families, the Corylaceae and Fagaceae. To the Corylaceae belong the birches (*Betula*), alders (*Alnus*), etc., and to the Fagaceae the beeches (*Fagus*), chestnuts (*Castanea*), and oaks (*Quercus*). The Amentiferae are woody plants with imperfect flowers. In the Salicaceae and Corylaceae both kinds of flowers are in aments, but in the Juglandaceae and Fagaceae only the staminate flowers are. In all families except the Salicaceae, the flowers of some members have a simple bractlike perianth. The pistillate flowers are hypogynous in the Salicaceae and epigynous in the other families; they are syncarpous in all.

Urticales. This is an order of about 1,500 species distributed among 4 families: the Ulmaceae and Moraceae, which are mostly woody, and the Cannabinaceae and Urticaceae, which are mostly herbaceous. Representative members of the Ulmaceae are the elms (*Ulmus*); of the Moraceae, the mulberries (*Morus*) and figs (*Ficus*); of the Cannabinaceae, hemp (*Cannabis*) and hop (*Humulus*); of the Urticaceae, the nettles (*Urtica*). The flowers are mostly imperfect, apetalous, hypogynous, and syncarpous. The stamens equal the perianth segments in number. The ovary is unilocular, usually having a single ovule.

Santalales. These are parasitic herbs and woody plants, numbering about 1,200 species, mostly tropical. The Loranthaceae and Santalaceae are the largest of 8 families. The mistletoes belong to the Loranthaceae. The flowers are perfect or imperfect and epigynous, mostly with a petaloid perianth consisting of a single whorl but sometimes differentiated into a calyx and corolla. The stamens equal the sepals in number. There are generally three united carpels, mostly forming a unilocular ovary.

Aristolochiales. This is a small order of herbs and woody plants, the principal family, the Aristolochiaceae, numbering about 200 species. The chief genus is *Aristolochia*. The flowers are perfect and epigynous, with a highly developed petaloid perianth consisting of a single whorl of united parts. The ovary is multilocular and has an indefinite number of ovules.

Polygonales. This is a small order of 800 species of herbs and woody plants, all belonging to the Polygonaceae. Representative genera are smartweed (*Polygonum*), dock (*Rumex*), rhubarb (*Rheum*), and buckwheat (*Fagopyrum*). The small flowers, mostly borne in spikes, are perfect or sometimes imperfect, regular, hypogynous, and syncarpous. The perianth, consisting of a single whorl, is bract-like. The unilocular ovary contains a single ovule.

The preceding orders, with some others of less importance, constitute the apetalous series of the Archichlamydeae. They are characterized by flowers that, with few exceptions, have a simple perianth which is not differentiated into a distinct calyx and corolla but consists of a single whorl of parts. Some members have naked flowers. Most of these orders are of uncertain relationships. Some may be primitive, while others are doubtless reduced.

The following orders, constituting the choripetalous series of the Archichlamydeae, typically have a perianth consisting of two distinct whorls—calyx and corolla—the members of which are separate and distinct.

Centrospermales. This assemblage is often broken up into two orders, the Chenopodiales and Caryophyllales. It includes about 3,500 species of herbs grouped into 10 families, of which 4 are of greatest interest, *viz.*, the Chenopodiaceae, to which belong the goosefoots (*Chenopodium*), beet (*Beta*), spinach (*Spinacia*), etc.; the Amaranthaceae, including pigweed (*Amaranthus*) and coxcomb (*Celosia*); the Portulacaceae, represented by *Portulaca*; and the Caryophyllaceae, containing the carnation and pinks (*Dianthus*), catchfly (*Silene*), chickweed (*Stellaria*), etc.

The flowers are mostly perfect, regular, mostly hypogynous, syncarpous, and usually pentamerous. The perianth may consist of either one or two whorls. The ovary is mostly unilocular. The Centrospermales represent a transition between the apetalous and choripetalous dicotyledons, as the lower families have a bract-like undifferentiated perianth, while the higher families have a distinct calyx and corolla, the latter being very showy. A characteristic feature is the presence of abundant perisperm in the seed. This takes the place of endosperm as a food-storage region. The Centrospermales show some resemblances to the Polygonales, and the two orders may be related.

Ranales. The Ranales are a great genetic order, comprising 16 families and about 5,000 species of herbs, shrubs, and trees. The largest family, the Ranunculaceae, has 1,200 species, and includes such common forms as buttercup (*Ranunculus*), *Hepatica*, *Anemone*, *Clematis*, columbine (*Aquilegia*), larkspur (*Delphinium*), and peony (*Paeonia*). Other important familes are the Nymphaeaceae, Berberidaceae, Magnoliaceae, and Lauraceae.

This order is ill defined. The flowers are perfect and mostly regular, but some are irregular. The perianth, usually consisting of a distinct calyx and corolla, is often undifferentiated and petaloid. Although the floral parts are often indefinitely numerous and wholly or partly spiral, there is a strong tendency toward the establishment of a cyclic condition with definite numbers, especially in the perianth. Hypogyny and apocarpy are features of the order, perigyny and syncarpy being infrequent. In the Berberidaceae and Lauraceae the carpels are reduced to one. The Ranales are generally regarded as a primitive order that has given rise both to the more specialized orders of dicotyledons and to the monocotyledons.

Papaverales. This order represents a specialized offshoot from the Ranales. There are 6 families and about 3,600 species, the principal families being the Papaveraceae, Fumariaceae, and Cruciferae. The Cruciferae, with 3,000 species, includes such well-known forms as the mustards (*Brassica*), radish (*Raphanus*), *Alyssum*, stocks (*Matthiola*), shepherd's-purse (*Capsella*), etc. The flowers of the Papaverales are mostly regular, hypogynous or sometimes perigynous, and syncarpous. The flowers are cyclic except that the stamens are spiral in some members. The pistil usually consists of two united carpels, syncarpy being the chief point of difference between this order and the Ranales. The Cruciferae are a distinct family whose members can be recognized by the floral formula 4-4-6-2.

Sarraceniales. This is a small order of insectivorous plants, comprising 3 families, and represented by the pitcher plants (*Sarracenia* and others) and the sundews (*Drosera*). As in the Papaverales, the flowers are regular, hypogynous, and syncarpous. The two orders seem to have undergone a parallel development, the chief difference between them being the placentation.

Rosales. The Rosales constitute the great central order of Archichlamydeae. They include 16 families and 15,000 species of herbs, shrubs, and trees distributed throughout the world. The three chief families are the Saxifragaceae, Rosaceae, and Leguminosae. The Leguminosae, with 12,000 species, is the second largest family of dicotyledons. The Saxifragaceae are represented by the saxifrages (*Saxifraga*), gooseberries and currants (*Ribes*), and *Hydrangea*. The Rosaceae include the roses (*Rosa*), strawberries (*Fragaria*), raspberries and blackberries (*Rubus*), cherries and plums (*Prunus*), hawthorns (*Crataegus*), pear and apple (*Pyrus*), etc. The Leguminosae include the acacias, locust (*Robinia*), lupines (*Lupinus*), clovers (*Trifolium*), beans (*Phaseolus*), peas (*Pisum*), etc.

The Rosales overlap the Ranales, on the one hand, with regularity, hypogyny, apocarpy, and indefinite numbers of stamens and carpels, but advance far beyond them, on the other hand, with irregularity, epigyny, syncarpy, and definite numbers. The perianth is typically pentamerous. The Rosaceae have regular flowers that are perigynous or epigynous and usually have several carpels. The Leguminosae have mostly irregular flowers that are hypogynous or somewhat perigynous and have a single carpel.

Geraniales. This large order of herbs and woody plants, containing about 9,000 species, is broken up into 20 families. Half of the species belong to the Euphorbiaceae, of which the largest genus is *Euphorbia*. Some familiar genera belonging to other families are *Geranium, Pelargonium, Oxalis, Linum,* and *Citrus.* The flowers are regular or irregular, hypogynous, syncarpous, and pentamerous throughout or often reduced. In the Euphorbiaceae the flowers are imperfect and apetalous, while in some members they are naked. The stamens of the Geraniales are rarely more than twice as many as the petals and usually equal to them in number. This is the first definitely cyclic and isocarpic order in the Archichlamydeae, but it shows a tendency to reduce the number of carpels.

Sapindales. The Sapindales, with about 3,000 species, most of which are woody, are separated into 21 families. Here belong the sumacs (*Rhus*), hollies (*Ilex*), maples (*Acer*), buckeyes (*Aesculus*), balsams

(*Impatiens*), etc. The flowers are regular or irregular, mostly hypogynous, and syncarpous. The perianth is mostly pentamerous but the stamens are usually reduced to eight. Most members are isocarpic. This order has developed parallel with the Geraniales, being distinguished from it chiefly by certain obscure ovule characters.

Rhamnales. This order includes about 1,100 species of woody plants belonging to 2 families, the Rhamnaceae, represented by the buckthorns (*Rhamnus*) and *Ceanothus*, and the Vitaceae, including the grapes (*Vitis*) and Virginia creeper (*Parthenocissus*). The flowers are regular, mostly hypogynous, syncarpous, and tetracyclic. The perianth is trimerous or tetramerous. The Rhamnales have developed parallel with the Geraniales and Sapindales, differing from them chiefly in having the stamens opposite the petals instead of alternate with them.

Malvales. This is an order of 8 familes and about 2,300 species of herbs and woody plants. The best-known families are the Tiliaceae, represented by the basswood (*Tilia*), and the Malvaceae, to which belong the mallows (*Malva*), hollyhock (*Althaea*), cotton (*Gossypium*), etc. The flowers are regular, hypogynous, syncarpous, and have a pentamerous perianth. The stamens are usually indefinitely numerous (rarely five) and more or less united. The placentation is axial.

Parietales. The Parietales, containing 30 families and about 5,000 species of herbs and woody plants, is an order representing an extremely confused classification. The most familiar forms are the violets (*Viola*). The order is characterized by parietal placentation, its other characters being rather inconstant. The flowers are regular or irregular; hypogynous, perigynous, or epigynous; and mostly syncarpous. They are typically pentamerous, but the stamens may be 3, 5, 10 or indefinitely numerous.

Opuntiales. Here belongs a single family, the Cactaceae, with about 1,100 species indigenous to America. The flowers are regular, epigynous, and syncarpous; they are peculiar in being spiral and polymerous. Thus the group represents a combination of primitive and advanced features.

Myrtales. This is a large tropical order of herbs and woody plants. It contains about 7,500 species grouped into 19 families, of which the Myrtaceae and Onagraceae are well known. The myrtles (*Myrtus*), *Eugenia*, and *Eucalyptus* belong to the Myrtaceae, while the fireweeds (*Epilobium*), evening primroses (*Oenothera*), and *Fuchsia* are familiar members of the Onagraceae. The flowers are mostly regular, perigynous or epigynous, and syncarpous. The perianth is mostly pentamerous and the stamens often indefinitely numerous. The carpels vary from two to many. This order resembles the Rosales in many ways, but here the carpels are never free.

Umbellales.   The Umbellales constitute the highest order of the Archichlamydeae.   They include 3 families and about 3,000 species, nearly all herbaceous.   Of these, 2,500 species belong to the Umbelliferae, where are found such familiar forms as carrot (*Daucus*), celery (*Apium*), parsnip (*Pastinaca*), and dill (*Anethum*).   The order is characterized by regular, epigynous flowers having a tetramerous or pentamerous perianth, a reduced calyx, a single whorl of stamens, and usually a bicarpellary, bilocular ovary with a single ovule in each locule.   The floral formula of the Umbelliferae, 5-5-5-2, is an advanced one.

2. Metachlamydeae

The Metachlamydeae are characterized chiefly by their sympetalous corollas, and so are often called the Sympetalae.   The entire group has reached a condition of definite numbers for all the floral sets, and therefore is constantly cyclic.   The stamens are generally attached to the corolla.

Ericales.   The Ericales comprise about 2,000 species of woody plants, mostly shrubs.   Of its 6 families, the Ericaceae, with about 1,500 species, is by far the largest.   It includes such well-known genera as azalea (*Rhododendron*), wintergreen (*Gaultheria*), heather (*Calluna*), heath (*Erica*), and blueberry (*Vaccinium*).   The flowers of the Ericales are regular or nearly so, tetramerous or pentamerous, pentacyclic or sometimes tetracyclic, mostly isocarpic, hypogynous or often epigynous, and syncarpous.   In tetracyclic flowers the stamens are opposite the petals.   The ovary is multilocular.   Some of the Ericaceae are choripetalous and in nearly all the stamens are free from the corolla.   Thus this order serves to connect the Archichlamydeae and Metachlamydeae.

Primulales.   The Primulales constitute an order of about 1,100 species of herbs grouped into 4 families, of which the Primulaceae is of chief interest.   The representative genus is primrose (*Primula*).   The flowers are regular, pentamerous, tetracyclic, isocarpic, mostly hypogynous, and syncarpous.   The single whorl of stamens stands opposite the petals and not, as in the higher tetracyclic orders, alternate with them.   The outer whorl of stamens is often vestigial.   The ovary is unilocular and has free-central placentation.   In some respects this order resembles the Centrospermales.

Ebenales.   This is an order of about 1,000 species of tropical trees and shrubs.   There are 4 small families, the characteristic one being the Ebenaceae, of which the ebony and persimmon (*Diospyros*) are examples.   The flowers are regular, tetramerous or pentamerous, pentacyclic, isocarpic, mostly hypogynous, and syncarpous.   The ovary is multilocular.   The floral parts show some variation in number, with an occasional increase in stamens and carpels.

The preceding orders constitute the pentacyclic isocarpic series of

Metachlamydeae, in which the floral formula is typically 5-5-10-5. They are more primitive than the other sympetalous orders and more closely related to the Archichlamydeae. They are, with few exceptions, regular and hypogynous.

The following orders comprise the tetracyclic anisocarpic series of Metachlamydeae, in which the floral formula is generally 5-5-5-2. Here belong three hypogynous and two epigynous orders.

Gentianales. This is a genetic order. It comprises about 5,000 species of herbs and woody plants separated into 5 families, the principal ones being the Oleaceae, Gentianaceae, and Asclepiadaceae. The Oleaceae is represented by the olive (*Olea*), ashes (*Fraxinus*), lilacs (*Syringa*), and privets (*Ligustrum*); the Gentianaceae by the gentians (*Gentiana*); and the Asclepiadaceae by the milkweeds (*Asclepias*). The flowers are regular, tetramerous or pentamerous, tetracyclic, anisocarpic, hypogynous, and apocarpous or syncarpous. They have two carpels. The Oleaceae have the peculiar floral formula of 4-4-2-2.

Tubiflorales. This great central order of Metachlamydeae is closely related to the Gentianales and difficult to separate from it. It includes 20 families and about 16,000 species, most of which are herbs. The eight principal families, with several representative genera, are as follows: Convolvulaceae—bindweed (*Convolvulus*), morning-glory (*Ipomoea*), and dodder (*Cuscuta*); Polemoniaceae—*Polemonium, Phlox*, and *Gilia*; Hydrophyllaceae—*Hydrophyllum, Nemophila*, and *Phacelia*; Boraginaceae—forget-me-not (*Myosotis*), bluebells (*Mertensia*), and *Heliotropium*; Verbenaceae—*Verbena* and *Lantana*; Labiatae—sage (*Salvia*) and mint (*Mentha*); Solanaceae—nightshade (*Solanum*), tobacco (*Nicotiana*), and *Petunia*; Scrophulariaceae—mullein (*Verbascum*), foxglove (*Digitalis*), and snapdragon (*Antirrhinum*).

The flowers of the Tubiflorales are regular or irregular, mostly pentamerous, tetracyclic, anisocarpic, hypogynous, and syncarpous. They have two carpels (three in Polemoniaceae). The corolla is mostly regular in all families except the Verbenaceae, Labiatae, and Scrophulariaceae, where it is almost always irregular. These three families have only four stamens, or sometimes only two, while the others have five. The ovary is unilocular or bilocular in the Hydrophyllaceae; mostly bilocular in the Convolvulaceae, Solanaceae, and Scrophulariaceae; mostly trilocular in the Polemoniaceae; and mostly tetralocular in the Boraginaceae, Verbenaceae, and Labiatae.

Plantaginales. These are the plantains, comprising one family of about 200 species of herbs. The principal genus is *Plantago*. The flowers are regular, tetramerous, tetracyclic, anisocarpic, hypogynous, and syncarpous. They have two carpels. The corolla is dry and membranaceous. This order is related to the Tubiflorales.

Rubiales. This order consists of over 5,000 species of herbs and woody plants distributed among 5 families, by far the largest being the Rubiaceae, to which belong coffee (*Coffea*) and *Cinchona*. The Caprifoliaceae, another family, is represented by the honeysuckles (*Lonicera*), *Viburnum*, and the elders (*Sambucus*). The flowers are regular or irregular, tetramerous or pentamerous, tetracyclic, anisocarpic, epigynous, and syncarpous. They have usually two or three carpels. The calyx is reduced. This order shows a resemblance to the Umbellales.

Campanulales. This is the culminating order of Metachlamydeae. It includes 8 families and 16,000 species, about 13,000 of which belong to the Compositae, the largest family of dicotyledons. A few well-known genera are goldenrod (*Solidago*), *Aster*, sunflower (*Helianthus*), *Chrysanthemum*, thistle (*Cirsium*), dandelion (*Taraxacum*), lettuce (*Lactuca*), etc. Other familiar families are the Cucurbitaceae, Campanulaceae, and Lobeliaceae. The flowers are regular or irregular, pentamerous, tetracyclic, anisocarpic, epigynous, and syncarpous. They have two or three carpels. The calyx is reduced. A special feature is the tendency of the five stamens to be united in various ways. The flowers of the Compositae are organized to form a compact head surrounded by an involucre of many bracts. The head is usually composed of peripheral ray flowers and central disk flowers.

3. Monocotyledoneae

The monocotyledons are generally regarded as having been derived from the Ranales region of the Archichlamydeae. In the lower orders the floral parts fluctuate in number and are more or less spiral in arrangement, while in the higher orders they are constant and cyclic.

Pandanales. This is a very primitive order of about 450 species grouped into 3 families. Many are hydrophytes. The screw pine (*Pandanus*) of the tropics is the representative form, but the most familiar member in temperate regions is the cattail (*Typha*). The flower clusters are usually surrounded, when young, by a conspicuous sheathing bract. The flowers are imperfect and mostly naked, but sometimes a simple bract-like perianth is present. The stamens and carpels show great variation in number and are mostly spiral. Both hypogyny and apocarpy are features of the order.

Helobiales. Here belong about 300 species of primitive aquatic and marsh plants comprising 6 families. Familiar genera are *Potamogeton*, *Sagittaria*, *Elodea*, and *Alisma*. The Helobiales are a genetic group, showing several lines of descent. A sheathing bract surrounds the inflorescence, as in the Pandanales, but the flowers are usually perfect. The flowers may be naked, apetalous, or choripetalous, are usually hypogynous but, in one family, are epigynous. The stamens range from indefinite to definite in number, the pistils from apocarpy to syncarpy. The numerous stamens and apocarpous pistils suggest a relationship to the Ranales.

Glumales. The Glumales include the Cyperaceae, or sedges, and the Gramineae, or grasses, together numbering about 8,000 species. The flowers are surrounded by scale-like bracts, called glumes, the perianth being either wanting or represented by minute scales. The flowers, which are mainly perfect, have six stamens or less (mostly three), and a unilocular ovary with a single ovule. The pistil, commonly said to consist of a single carpel, really is formed of three completely united carpels. All members are hypogynous. There is much evidence indicating that the Glumales are not primitive but reduced from lily-like ancestors.

Palmales. This order includes only the Palmaceae, with about 1,200 species, mostly of tropical and subtropical trees. The flowers are small, mostly imperfect, and borne in a massive inflorescence at first surrounded by a large sheathing bract. The presence of a perianth is a constant feature of the group; it is inconspicuous and composed of two similar whorls of three members each. The flowers are mostly trimerous, hypogynous, and mostly syncarpous. They commonly have six stamens (often more) and three carpels.

Arales. This order, of about 1,500 species, comprises 2 families of herbs, the principal one being the Araceae. Most of its members are tropical, some familiar ones being jack-in-the-pulpit (*Arisaema*), calla lily (*Zantedeschia*), and elephant's-ear (*Calocasia*). The flowers, which are small and inconspicuous, are borne on a fleshy axis, the *spadix*, surrounded by a conspicuous bract, the *spathe*. They are perfect or imperfect, hypogynous, and syncarpous. A simple scale-like perianth is sometimes present, its absence in most forms being a result of reduction. The number of stamens and carpels, although variable, is small.

The preceding orders constitute the spiral series of Monocotyledoneae. They are characterized, for the most part, by fluctuating numbers of floral parts, a simple perianth or none, apocarpy, and the development of sheathing bracts. In the Glumales the bracts appear in connection with the individual flowers, in the other orders, in connection with the inflorescence.

The following orders constitute the cyclic series of Monocotyledoneae. Here the flowers are typically trimerous, pentacyclic, and syncarpous. The perianth consists of a distinct calyx and corolla. In a relatively few members the perianth parts are more or less united; otherwise they are separate.

Farinales. The Farinales comprise an order of about 2,500 species of mostly grass-like herbs distributed into 13 families. The most familiar member is the spiderwort (*Tradescantia*), but the pineapple (*Ananas*) belongs here and also the "long moss" (*Tillandsia*) of the Southern United States. The flowers are regular or nearly so, mostly trimerous and pentacyclic, hypogynous or sometimes epigynous, and syncarpous. The perianth may or may not be differentiated into a calyx and corolla and the latter may be bract-like or petaloid. A special feature is the presence of mealy (farinose) endosperm.

Liliales. The Liliales are the great central order of monocotyledons. They number about 5,000 species, most of which are herbs. They are grouped into 9 families, the principal ones being the Juncaceae, Liliaceae, Amaryllidaceae, and Iridaceae. The Juncaceae include the rushes (*Juncus*). The Liliaceae contain such well-known genera as *Trillium*, *Erythronium*, lily (*Lilium*), tulip (*Tulipa*), hyacinth (*Hyacinthus*), onion (*Allium*), and *Yucca*. The Amaryllidaceae are represented by the tuberose (*Polianthes*), *Agave*, and *Narcissus*. The Iridaceae comprise the flags (*Iris*), *Crocus*, *Gladiolus*, etc.

The flowers are mostly regular and have a perianth consisting of two trimerous whorls that are nearly always alike, being bract-like in the Juncaceae and petaloid in the other families. They have mostly six stamens (three in the Iridaceae) and a tricarpellary pistil. The flowers are either hypogynous (Juncaceae and Liliaceae) or epigynous (Amaryllidaceae and Iridaceae).

Scitaminales. Here belong 4 families and about 1,000 species of mostly tropical herbs, including *Canna*, banana (*Musa*), and ginger (*Zingiber*). The perianth, displaying a special type of irregularity, is composed of two whorls that are often entirely petaloid. All members are epigynous. Generally only one fertile stamen is present. The pistil is tricarpellary and the ovary trilocular.

Orchidales. This is the highest order of monocotyledons as well as the largest. It comprises 2 families and about 15,000 species of herbs, nearly all of which belong to the Orchidaceae. The orchids reach their greatest display in the tropics, where most of them are epiphytes. The flowers of the Orchidaceae are irregular, epigynous, and syncarpous. The irregularity is of a special type. The perianth consists of two trimerous whorls, one petal being strikingly different from the others. The stamens are reduced to three, but these do not belong to the same whorl; usually only one stamen is fertile. The pistil is tricarpellary and the ovary unilocular. The seeds are without endosperm.

COMPARISON OF GYMNOSPERMS AND ANGIOSPERMS

The most important distinguishing characters of the Gymnospermae and Angiospermae are as follows:

GYMNOSPERMAE	ANGIOSPERMAE
Plants woody	Plants woody or herbaceous
Wood without vessels (except in Gnetales)	Wood almost always with vessels
Sporophylls borne in strobili (except in Cycadofilicales); perianth absent	Sporophylls borne in flowers; perianth generally present
Ovules freely exposed, not in a closed ovary	Ovules in a closed ovary formed by one or more megasporophylls
Female gametophyte with abundant vegetative tissue and with archegonia (except in *Welwitschia* and *Gnetum*)	Female gametophyte with little or no vegetative tissue, consisting typically of an eight-nucleate embryo sac; archegonia absent
Pollen coming in direct contact with ovules	Pollen not coming in direct contact with ovules
Male gametophyte usually with one or more prothallial cells; generative cell producing a stalk cell and a body cell, the latter giving rise to two male cells that may or may not be organized as ciliated sperms	Male gametophyte without prothallial cells; generative cell directly producing two male cells that are never ciliated
Endosperm formed from vegetative tissue of female gametophyte	Endosperm arising after fertilization, generally from a triple fusion of nuclei
Development of embryo initiated by free-nuclear division (except in *Welwitschia* and *Gnetum*)	Development of embryo without a free-nuclear stage
Cotyledons two to many	Cotyledons one or two

GENERAL CONCLUSIONS

The two most outstanding features of the spermatophytes are the presence of seeds and the development of the flower. They excel the pteridophytes in the complexity of their vegetative organs, while the gametophyte is subordinated to the sporophyte to such an extent that it is always dependent upon it. The microsporangia and megasporangia are borne by sporophylls that, with few exceptions, are considerably less leaf-like than the sporophylls of most pteridophytes. Almost invariably the megasporangium (nucellus of the ovule) produces only one functional megaspore, which always gives rise to the female gametophyte without being shed. In all spermatophytes the development of the sporangia is eusporangiate, as among the lower pteridophytes, but the initials are hypodermal rather than epidermal in origin.

In gymnosperms the archegonia are more reduced than in pteridophytes, while in angiosperms they are eliminated. The male gametophyte produces only two sperms, or male cells, and true antheridia are not present. Among existing groups, ciliated sperms occur only in the Cycadales and *Ginkgo*. Fertilization, accomplished with the aid of a pollen tube, results in an embryo that develops inside the ovule.

The Seed. The adaptation to life on land is more nearly perfect in the spermatophytes than in any other group of plants. This has come about partly through the greater complexity of their vegetative organs, but chiefly by the development of the seed. The development of the seed is a result of three conditions—heterospory, retention of the megaspore within the megasporangium, and formation by the zygote of a dormant embryo.

Both the bryophytes and pteridophytes are handicapped in their adjustment to the land habit by two basic requirements: (1) In order to reach the egg and effect fertilization, the sperm must swim through water, a handicap persisting from aquatic ancestors. (2) After fertilization has taken place, the embryo must continue its development whether external conditions are favorable or not.

The seed overcomes both these handicaps. The necessity for external water as a means by which the sperm may reach the egg is obviated by the transportation, through air, of the male gametophyte, inside a pollen grain, to the vicinity of the female gametophyte and the development of a pollen tube through which the male gamete can pass. In this way fertilization is made more certain. Following fertilization, the passing of the embryo into a state of dormancy, as well as the formation of a protective seed coat, enables the embryo to live until conditions become favorable for its continued growth.

The Flower. The flower is difficult to define because every possible transition exists between a typical strobilus and a typical flower. It is apparent, therefore, that the strobilus is the forerunner of the flower and that the changes involved in passing from the one to the other represent an important evolutionary advance. The perianth probably arose as a protective envelope for the sporophylls, but later came to have additional functions, such as the attraction of insects. In gymnosperms the transfer of pollen is precarious, depending upon the vagaries of the wind. To increase the chances of success, an enormous excess of pollen must be produced, thus involving a tremendous waste. The transfer of pollen by insects, to which the flowers of most angiosperms are highly adapted, is more certain and consequently much less wasteful than wind-pollination. Probably the most important factor responsible for the evolutionary progress made by the angiosperms has been the development of the flower in adaptation to insect pollination.

Associated with the development of the flower and its specialization for insect pollination has been the enclosure of the ovules. Originally the carpels of seed plants must have been leaf-like structures bearing marginal ovules, a condition preserved in such existing gymnosperms as *Cycas revoluta*. The change from the open carpel with its ovules freely exposed to the closed carpel with its ovules inside a cavity marks another great advance which the angiosperms have made over the gymnosperms. This change led to the development of the fruit.

Interrelationships. The fossil record gives no evidence as to which of the two great Paleozoic groups of gymnosperms—the Cycadofilicales and the Cordaitales—is the older. Except for the presence of seeds, however, the Cycadofilicales are so fern-like as to leave little doubt that they have been derived from some ancient fern stock. The Cordaitales, less fern-like, may have branched off from the Cycadofilicales early in the Paleozoic, although it seems more likely that both groups have had a common origin. The Cycadofilicales very probably gave rise to two divergent lines of descent, one represented by the Bennettitales of the Mesozoic, a specialized offshoot that became extinct, the other leading to the Cycadales, a group that still survives.

There is strong evidence that the Cordaitales were ancestral to both the Ginkgoales and the Coniferales, orders that reached a climax in the Mesozoic. Except for *Ginkgo biloba*, the Ginkgoales are extinct, while the Coniferales are still so abundant as to constitute the largest order of living gymnosperms. The Gnetales are a group of obscure origin. They may represent a specialized offshoot from the Coniferales, but any relationship to the angiosperms is very doubtful.

The oldest undoubted angiosperms appear in the deposits of the Lower Cretaceous. Their characters are so distinct that they must have originated at a much earlier time, but it is not known when or from what older group they arose. There is a possibility that the angiosperms originated independently from the pteridophytes, but this is remote in view of the many common features existing between gymnosperms and angiosperms. There is no convincing evidence, however, indicating from what group of gymnosperms the angiosperms may have sprung.

One theory holds that the angiosperms have been derived from the Gnetales. Their compound strobili resemble the inflorescences of certain angiosperms with monosporangiate (imperfect) flowers and a simple undifferentiated perianth. The presence of vessels in the secondary wood is a character shared by both groups. If the resemblances between the Gnetales and angiosperms are a result of parallel evolution, there can be no direct relationship between them, although they may have come from a common ancestry.

Another theory claims the derivation of the angiosperms from the Bennettitales. Their strobilus, which is bisporangiate, somewhat resembles the flower of a magnolia, but the stamens, and particularly the carpels, are very different in the two groups. On the whole, the cycadeoid strobilus is so specialized that it is very unlikely that an angiosperm flower could have evolved from it. It seems more reasonable to suppose that the resemblance between them is a result of parallel development and does not denote any direct relationship. The fossil record has not produced transitional forms connecting the gymnosperms and angiosperms. In their absence, speculation concerning the ancestry of the angiosperms seems futile.

CHAPTER X

EVOLUTION OF THE PLANT KINGDOM

The doctrine of evolution states that all forms of life, living and extinct, have been derived from preexisting forms by a process of gradual change. This principle of "descent with modification," supported by an overwhelming mass of evidence, has been fully established as a fundamental axiom of biology. The method by which evolution has taken place, however, is imperfectly understood and considerable uncertainty exists as to the relative importance of the various factors involved.

These factors are of two kinds: primary or causative and secondary or directive. Causative factors give rise to heritable variations, which are the raw materials of evolution. These are built up into new species under the influence of directive factors, which determine the course of evolution. Heritable variations arise both from new combinations of genes in fertilization and by mutation, a process involving changes in the chromosomes of reproductive cells, the causes of which are largely unknown. The addition or loss of one or more chromosomes by irregularities in meiosis may cause changes affecting several or many characters simultaneously. Much more common and of greater importance are changes involving individual genes, these giving rise to innumerable small variations that supply most of the raw material upon which the directive factors of evolution operate. Thus evolution is mainly dependent upon the appearance of mutations, especially gene mutations.

The general trend of evolution is toward greater fitness to the conditions of existence. Some of the variations arising by recombination of genes or by mutation are adaptive, while others are not. By natural selection, favorable variations having survival value are preserved and accumulated through successive generations, thus bringing about greater adaptation to the environment. Natural selection determines which individuals among a diversified population shall survive in the "struggle for existence." It is generally regarded as the most important directive factor yet discovered.

Theories dealing with the causes of evolution are concerned chiefly with the origin of species. One of the great problems of morphology is the determination of the origin and phylogenetic development of the larger plant groups. The fossil record demonstrates that groups once dominant on the earth have been replaced by others more advanced, but it seldom indicates from which older group a younger one has been derived. Inter-relationships among the larger groups must be inferred principally from evidence based on studies in comparative morphology. The "lower" groups of plants are merely those which have undergone relatively little modification, the "higher" groups, a vastly greater amount. Existing groups are usually represented as twigs on a phylogenetic tree. The larger branches denote divergent lines of descent. These are often obscure and difficult to trace, but become clear as knowledge advances.

Specialization. The general trend of evolution toward greater adaptation to the environment has resulted in the development of specialized forms from generalized forms. Structural complexity is always a result of evolution from a simpler condition of organization, but simplicity does not always represent a primitive state. Often it denotes reduction from a more highly developed ancestry. Sometimes there is structural evidence of such reduction, especially in ontogeny, but usually this evidence is obscure or wanting. Consequently it is often difficult to ascertain whether structural simplicity is a primary or a derived condition.

Higher types have arisen from generalized members of lower groups, not from specialized members. Highly specialized groups, like the red algae and the mosses, represent blindly ending lines of descent. They may change in the direction of greater specialization, but cannot revert to a generalized condition and then become specialized in another direction.

In many groups evolutionary advance has not affected all parts of the plant to the same extent and, as a consequence, advanced features are often combined with primitive ones. For example, although the cycads are seed plants, they have retained swimming sperms, an extremely ancient character, the phylogenetic continuity of which can be traced back to the algae. Sometimes the development of one character is associated with the suppression of another. Thus, in the Compositae, the formation of an involucre has resulted in a reduction of the calyces of the individual flowers in the head. Similarly the strong development of mechanical tissues in the stems of many large herbaceous angiosperms is related to the weak development of xylem and might be regarded as a compensation for it. Such instances of compensation are common throughout the plant kingdom.

Parallel Development. The same evolutionary tendency, acting independently in different groups of plants, may bring about similar changes, thus resulting in parallel development or homoplasy. For example, heterogamy has arisen independently in a number of widely separated algal groups and heterospory in various groups of vascular plants. Epigyny has developed independently in many different families of angiosperms. Structural similarity resulting from parallel development is no indication of phylogenetic relationship. It merely signifies that evolution in two or more different groups has occurred in the same general direction and often in response to the same influence.   Instances of parallel development are numerous.   Unless they are recognized, false conclusions regarding relationships may be drawn.

Real relationships among different kinds of plants are shown by the presence of similar characters derived from a common ancestry.   The members of every natural group, despite superficial differences, are built according to the same basic pattern.   This is expressed by the characters that distinguish it from other groups.   Related plants display many structural resemblances because of a common origin, while their differences are a result of divergent evolutionary tendencies.   The greater the degree of basic resemblance between any two kinds of plants, the closer is their relationship and the less remote their common ancestry.

Homologous Structures.   In any natural group the various members possess certain structures that are considered as homologous, or morphologically equivalent.   Such structures may display considerable diversity in form or function, but have a similar ontogeny and so bear the same relation to the plant as a whole.   In liverworts, for example, spores and elaters are homologous, since they develop from the same mass of undifferentiated sporogenous tissue.   In angiosperms stamens and carpels are homologous with leaves, as well as with the sporophylls of other vascular plants.   Tendrils and thorns may be homologous either with stems or leaves, depending on their place of origin on the plant.   Cladophylls are homologous with stems, while bracts and scales are homologous with leaves.

Recapitulation.   Developmental stages not only reveal homology between different kinds of structures, but frequently furnish other evidence of evolutionary changes.   In the early development of many plants, stages appear that correspond to adult stages in less highly specialized plants.   This suggests that such developmental stages may represent ancestral conditions.   The theory that "ontogeny recapitulates phylogeny" cannot be regarded as a principle of broad application, however, for in many plants embryonic or juvenile stages have no apparent evolutionary significance.   On the other hand, the theory receives support from many sources.   For example, among kelps *Laminaria* is a generalized type, the simplest species consisting of a holdfast, stipe, and an undivided blade.   Most of the other kelps are more highly differentiated when mature, but in early development pass through a *Laminaria*-like stage.   This indicates that *Laminaria* represents the ancestral condition.

The occurrence of a protonemal stage in the life history of a moss recalls an algal stage in the ancestry.   The presence of needle-like leaves on the seedlings of certain conifers and of scale-like leaves on older plants suggests that the juvenile foliage represents the ancestral type.   The seedlings of some species of *Acacia* have bipinnate leaves that are soon replaced by phyllodia, the adult form of foliage. In such species transitional stages are common. In the development of the common bracken fern (*Pteridium aquilinum*), the young plant passes through a protostelic and then a siphonostelic stage before the dictyostelic or permanent condition is reached. These stages represent a phylogenetic series. In the seedlings of most monocotyledons the stem is at first a siphonostele, gradually becoming a dictyostele with scattered vascular bundles. This indicates that the siphonostelic condition is the more primitive one.

PROMINENT EVOLUTIONARY TENDENCIES

Comparative morphology furnishes abundant evidence of evolution along determinate lines. Changes that have taken place in definite directions are apparent throughout the plant kingdom. Because some members are more advanced than others, it is possible, within a group, to construct a series of forms showing various degrees of modification. Such a series may indicate either an advance or a decline, depending on whether evolution has been progressive or retrogressive. The species of *Lycopodium* display various stages in the organization of a strobilus, while the genera of Fucales show a reduction series with respect to the number of eggs produced in an oögonium. Often an advance in one direction has been accompanied by a decline in another. The development of an irregular corolla in certain families of angiosperms, such as the Labiatae and Scrophulariaceae, has resulted in a reduction in the number of stamens from five to four or two. Evolutionary tendencies, whether progressive or retrogressive, usually continue as long as the group displaying them persists. Some of the more conspicuous evolutionary tendencies seen in the major groups of green plants will be briefly summarized.

Algae. Among the algae vegetative advance has been marked by the organization of single cells into colonies and the development of multicellular bodies into filamentous, plate-like, and massive types. Progress is also shown by the beginning of cellular differentiation, resulting in specialization of different parts of the body for particular functions.

From a condition where reproduction is wholly asexual, an advance is seen in the establishment of sexual reproduction and in its change from isogamy to heterogamy. The tendency to interpose a vegetative growth phase between gametic union and meiosis has resulted in the establishment of an alternation of haploid and diploid generations. Some algae show a tendency to develop the sporophyte at the expense of the gametophyte. The algae are a polyphyletic group representing a number of parallel evolutionary lines whose connections are very uncertain. Most groups seem to have arisen independently from a flagellate ancestry.

Bryophytes. The contributions of the bryophytes to the evolution of the plant kingdom include the establishment of the land habit, the appearance of archegonia and multicellular antheridia, and the development of a distinct alternation of unlike generations as a constant feature of the group. Prominent evolutionary trends include a differentiation of the gametophyte in internal structure, the development of a leafy gametophyte from a thallus, and a tendency of the sporophyte to become partially independent of the gametophyte. From a sporophyte almost wholly sporogenous, progress has been made by ever-increasing sterilization of tissue and its diversion to other functions. This is seen in the development of a foot and seta, elaters, and a dehiscence mechanism, in the formation of a columella, and in the development of green tissue.

Relationships between the bryophytes and green algae are mainly conjectural, there being no direct fossil connection between the two groups. However, the bryophytes seem clearly to have been derived from aquatic ancestors, their structural advances being correlated with the establishment of the land habit. These include a compact plant body, absorptive rhizoids, jacketed sex organs, heavy-walled aerial spores, etc.

Pteridophytes. The advance of the pteridophytes over the lower groups is shown by the establishment of an independent sporophyte, evolution of a vascular system, organization of a strobilus, and appearance of heterospory. With few exceptions, the sporophyte consists of roots, stem, and leaves. In one line of descent the leaves have remained small, undivided, and single-veined; in the other line they have become large, divided, and many-veined. In the evolution of the vascular system the trend has been from exarch to mesarch xylem and then to endarch, also from a protostelic to a siphonostelic condition and then to a dictyostelic one. The presence of leaf gaps in the ferns is regarded as an advanced feature, their absence in other pteridophytes being primitive.

Lycopods show an advance from those with every leaf a sporophyll to those with a compact strobilus. Both lycopods and ferns show a trend from homospory to heterospory. Heterospory has accelerated the reduction of the gametophyte generation and sex organs. Among homosporous forms, subterranean gametophytes have been derived from aerial ones. Ferns show evolutionary tendencies affecting the sporangia, such as a change from the eusporangiate to the leptosporangiate type, reduction in the thickness of the wall and in the output of spores, development of an annulus, etc.

The origin of pteridophytes is uncertain, a direct connection with either the algae or the bryophytes being hypothetical. Some paleontological evidence indicates that the major groups have been derived independently from the Psilophytales.

Spermatophytes. The spermatophytes reach the culmination of evolution in the development of the seed, development of pollen tubes, ultimate enclosure of the seed by the carpel (angiospermy), ultimate elimination of swimming sperms and later of archegonia, a great reduction in the gametophyte generation, and the evolution of the flower.

The abandonment of ciliated sperms by the conifers resulted in a change in the pollen tube from a branched haustorial organ to a carrier of the male cells. The male gametophyte has undergone a reduction in the number of male cells to two and of prothallial cells to two or one and finally to none. Throughout gymnosperms the female gametophyte exhibits various stages in reduction that reach an extreme in angiosperms. The tendency for eggs to mature earlier and earlier in the development of the gametophyte has finally resulted in the elimination of archegonia.

A marked feature of evolution in the seed plants has been the development of the strobilus into a flower. Among angiosperms floral evolution has been marked by a number of evolutionary tendencies, among which are the following: floral parts numerous and spiral to few and cyclic, pentacyclic to tetracyclic, free to united; perianth undifferentiated to differentiated into a distinct calyx and corolla; corolla regular to irregular; flowers hypogynous to perigynous and epigynous; ovules with two integuments to only one; embryo dicotyledonous to monocotyledonous; endosperm abundant to little or none; fruit simple to aggregate and multiple. Angiosperms also show trends from a woody to an herbaceous habit, from erect types to vines, from perennials to annuals, from a spiral to a cyclic arrangement of leaves, from simple to divided leaves, and from net-veined to parallel-veined leaves.

It is clearly evident that the gymnosperms have been derived from the pteridophytes and are a much older group than the angiosperms, whose origin is obscure. If the angiosperms have not come from the gymnosperms, the presence of seeds, pollen tubes, and many other common features are a result of parallel development.

EVOLUTION OF SEX

There are two primary types of reproduction in the plant kingdom, sexual and asexual. The distinctive feature of sexual reproduction is the fusion of two cells to form a zygote. In asexual or vegetative reproduction no such fusion occurs.

Asexual Reproduction. Cell division is the simplest and oldest method of reproduction and in many unicellular plants it is the only method. In multicellular plants cell division does not result in reproduction but in growth. To make reproduction possible, a cell or group of cells must become detached from the parent plant. A spore shares with ordinary vegetative cells its ability to divide, but does so only after being liberated. It differs from other cells not in power but in opportunity. Asexual reproduction by means of spores is a feature of nearly all the green algae and of most fungi, occurring even in some of the unicellular forms.

It should be understood that the formation of vegetative spores never involves a reduction of chromosomes. In fact, with few exceptions, they are borne on a haploid plant body. Vegetative spores always give rise to the same kind of plant body as the one that produced them. Spores formed by meiosis from a diploid cell, like tetraspores in the red algae, ascospores and basidiospores in the fungi, and all spores in the higher plants, are not vegetative spores but meiospores and belong to the sexual life cycle.

In plants above the thallophyte level, asexual or vegetative reproduction is carried on by various means, such as gemmae, bulbils, bulbs, tubers, runners, isolated branches, etc. Each of these consists of a group or mass of vegetative cells isolated from the parent and capable of reproducing it.

Origin of Sex. Most algae producing vegetative zoospores, whether unicellular or multicellular, also bear gametes on the same kind of vegetative body. Gametes not only resemble zoospores structurally but, in isogamous forms, commonly intergrade with them. This indicates that gametes have been derived from zoospores. It is not known what induced reproductive cells to first unite in pairs, but the tendency soon became a fixed habit.

The fact that the zygote becomes a thick-walled resting cell in most green algae suggests that the original function of sexual reproduction was protection over a period of unfavorable conditions. In fact, experiments have shown that the advent of such conditions induces gamete formation. When conditions for vegetative growth are at their best, reproduction does not occur. When they become somewhat less favorable, vegetative activity begins to wane and spores are formed. As conditions become more severe and the plant approaches the end of its growing season, gametes appear. The conditions favoring gamete production in the green algae are those that inhibit germination of the zygote and result in its dormancy. When it germinates at the beginning of the next season, conditions are usually not conducive to maximum vegetative activity. It is possible that the formation of spores by the zygote, a feature of so many green algae, is merely a response to these conditions.

Differentiation of Gametes. In isogamy all the gametes are alike in appearance and behavior. The fact that they pair, however, implies a mutual attraction and indicates that a difference exists between them. Each of the pairing gametes must represent an opposite sex. In heterogamy the differences between the two kinds of gametes merely become apparent, so that they are recognizably male and female.

Isogamy represents the original condition of gametic union. It has been retained by many green and brown algae. These groups display various degrees of heterogamy, however, indicating that this condition has been derived from isogamy by a differentiation of gametes into sperms and eggs. In isogamy, as a rule, both kinds of gametes are motile and equally small, neither containing much food. In heterogamy there is a division of labor, the sperm providing motility and remaining small, the egg providing food and becoming large. Its advantage lies in the greater supply of food available for the zygote and the young plant that develops from it. In the red algae, where heterogamy is universal, the sperm is nonmotile but much smaller than the egg. Heterogamy is established in all the higher plants, with swimming sperms occurring in all bryophytes, all pteridophytes, and a few gymnosperms.

Evolution of Sex Organs. The production of gametes in ordinary vegetative cells is characteristic of most of the green algae. In isogamous forms these cells remain unchanged, while in nearly all heterogamous forms they become modified in size and shape. Thus there are not only two kinds of gametes but two kinds of gametangia, the sperms arising in antheridia and the eggs in oögonia. A differentiation of gametes has been accompanied by a differentiation of sex organs, but the gametes develop from the protoplasts of vegetative cells.

In a few green algae, such as *Vaucheria*, in the Charophyceae, and in nearly all the brown and red algae a more advanced condition has been reached. Here the gametes are borne in sex organs that have never been a part of the vegetative body, but arise as special reproductive branches. A differentiation has taken place between cells that remain entirely vegetative in function and those that are strictly reproductive. Although this condition is found mainly among heterogamous algae, it occurs in a few isogamous members of the Phaeophyceae, such as *Ectocarpus*, where gametangia are developed on special branches.

Thus among the algae three stages may be recognized in the evolution of sex organs, depending upon whether gametes are produced in (1) an unmodified vegetative cell, (2) a transformed vegetative cell, or (3) a special reproductive cell distinct from the rest of the body. The first stage is characteristic of isogamous forms, the second and third of heterogamous forms.

The sex organs of the bryophytes and pteridophytes are more highly developed than those of the algae in that both kinds are multicellular and have an outer jacket of sterile cells usually forming a single layer. The sterile jacket, which protects the gametes from drying out, was probably developed as a response to air exposure.   Although the bryophytes are thought to have arisen from chlorophycean ancestors, existing green algae have unicellular sex organs.   Therefore it is necessary to assume that the ancestral forms had multicellular gametangia of the *Ectocarpus* type. The bryophyte antheridium could readily have been derived from such a gametangium by sterilization of the outer layer of cells.   The archegonium, having diverged more widely from its original condition, went through several stages in its evolution.   At first it may have resembled the antheridium, consisting of a group of fertile cells enclosed by a sterile jacket.   Further progress may have been marked by reduction of the fertile cells to a single row and then by sterilization of all of these except the lowest one, the other cells in the row becoming canal cells.   Evidence for this theory comes from the occasional appearance, in both liverworts and mosses, of reversionary archegonia with multiple eggs, with two rows of canal cells, or with some of the canal cells replaced by spermatogenous cells.

The sex organs of bryophytes and pteridophytes perform accessory functions related to gametic union and embryo development.   The sterile jacket of the antheridium not only protects the developing sperms but facilitates their dispersal.   Frequently dehiscence occurs suddenly and the sperms are discharged with considerable force.   The neck of the archegonium serves as a passageway for the entrance of sperms, the canal cells breaking down to form mucilage through which the sperms swim. The venter of the archegonium enlarges after fertilization, protecting the embryo and aiding in the transfer of food to it.

Antheridia with a large number of spermatogenous cells and archegonia with many neck canal cells are generally regarded as primitive. Throughout the bryophytes and pteridophytes the tendency to reduce the number of these cells reaches an extreme in the heterosporous pteridophytes, where the antheridium may produce only four sperms, as in *Isoetes*, and the archegonium has only one neck canal cell.   These trends are continued into the spermatophytes, where antheridia are not organized and only two sperms or their equivalent are formed and where archegonia, without any neck canal cells, are present only in the gymnosperms.

The embryo sac of angiosperms may have evolved from the typical female gametophyte of gymnosperms, but, except for the formation of free eggs in the Gnetales, intermediate stages are lacking.   Although most angiosperms possess an eight-nucleate embryo sac that develops in a characteristic way, many deviations from the typical pattern occur. These reveal several trends, such as the participation of more than a single megaspore nucleus in the formation of the embryo sac and a reduction in the number of nuclear divisions that intervene between the formation of the megaspore nuclei and the egg nucleus.

Further Expressions of Sexuality. In the evolution of sex the differentiation of gametes was soon followed by a differentiation of sex organs. A further stage was the differentiation of structures bearing the sex organs, while a final stage was a sexual differentiation of entire individuals.

In most liverworts belonging to the Marchantiales the antheridia are borne on male receptacles and the archegonia on female receptacles. These show a marked structural differentiation. In some members, such as *Marchantia*, there is also a differentiation of individuals, the male plants bearing antheridial receptacles and the female plants archegonial receptacles. In *Sphaerocarpus*, belonging to another group of liverworts, the male plants are much smaller than the female. Certain species of *Oedogonium* have dwarf male filaments consisting of only a few cells.

Although *Spirogyra* has not reached the level of heterogamy, some species show a differentiation of sexual individuals. This expresses itself only in the behavior of the gametes, those of one member of a pair of conjugating filaments being active, while those of the other are passive. The occurrence of distinct male and female individuals is a feature of many heterogamous algae, such as *Cutleria, Dictyota, Polysiphonia,* and many others.

In plants with an alternation of generations the gametophyte is commonly called the sexual generation and the sporophyte the asexual one. This misconception arises from failure to regard fertilization and meiosis as complementary processes, both of which are integral parts of a complete sexual life cycle. Vegetative spores are asexual but meiospores are not. Where the zygote directly gives rise to four meiospores, as in *Oedogonium*, it is easy to associate their formation with fertilization. Where meiospores are borne on a sporophyte, the time interval between fertilization and meiosis is longer, but the relation between them is the same.

In the bryophytes and homosporous pteridophytes the sporophyte does not express any sexual characters. But, with the establishment of heterospory, sexual differentiation becomes extended from the gametophyte to the sporophyte. The significance of heterospory lies in the production of a male gametophyte by the microspore and a female gametophyte by the megaspore. The occurrence of two kinds of gametophytes is reflected in a visible differentiation of the spores. This differentiation may be extended to the sporangia, sporophylls, strobili, and even to the entire sporophyte. In *Selaginella* the visible consequences of heterospory are not as far-reaching as in seed plants, where the organs associated with the production of microspores (stamens and pollen sacs) and of megaspores (carpels and ovules) are as highly differentiated as the sex organs of bryophytes and pteridophytes. Stamens and carpels are not sex organs, but their differences are associated with a sexual differentiation that has been extended to them from the gametes.

Among the gymnosperms a separation of microspore-bearing and megaspore-bearing structures to two kinds of cones is another expression of sexual differentiation.   In the cycads, *Ginkgo*, and some conifers this is extended to the entire sporophyte, so that there are male and female plants as well as male and female cones.   Most angiosperms bear flowers having both stamens and carpels, but some have two kinds of flowers, one with stamens and the other with carpels.   The two kinds may occur on the same plant or on separate plants, depending on the species.

Significance of Sex.   The most important feature of sexual reproduction is the union of the two gametic nuclei.   This brings together two haploid sets of chromosomes to form a diploid zygote nucleus.   Each set consists of innumerable genes that determine hereditary characters and each ordinarily represents a somewhat different assortment of genes. Meiosis, sooner or later following gametic union, provides a means of reshuffling the paternal and maternal chromosomes brought together in the previous act of fertilization, thus resulting in many new gene combinations.

It is evident that sexual reproduction, through fertilization and meiosis, creates great variation among individuals related by descent and so furnishes raw material for evolutionary processes to work upon.   Asexual reproduction results in organic similarity; sexual reproduction results in diversity.   The significance of sexual reproduction is not primarily the multiplication of individuals, but the production of heritable variations that accelerate the process of evolution.   It is in this feature that its great advantage lies.   In plants first reaching the level of sexuality, this advantage would tend to be perpetuated through natural selection and to become established as a permanent part of the life history.

ALTERNATION OF GENERATIONS

Many algae and fungi, as well as all plants above the thallophyte level, are characterized by an alternation of generations, in which the life cycle consists of two kinds of individuals that follow each other in alternate sequence.   One of these, the gametophyte, is haploid and produces gametes, while the other, the sporophyte, is diploid and produces spores. The diploid condition arises in the zygote, produced by gametic union. The zygote develops into a sporophyte, meiosis taking place when spores are formed.   The spore gives rise to the gametophyte.   The zygote is the first cell of the sporophyte generation, and the spore is the first cell of the gametophyte generation.

Types of Life Cycles.   Fertilization and meiosis are the two cardinal events in every life cycle involving sexual reproduction and each is a necessary consequence of the other.   Thus every plant with sexual reproduction displays both a haploid and a diploid phase, but in many thallophytes the life cycle includes only one kind of individual. In most green algae the vegetative body is haploid and meiosis occurs in connection with the germination of the zygote. Here a prolonged haploid growth phase alternates with a single diploid cell, the zygote. Although the zygote usually gives rise to four spores, it could hardly be regarded as a sporophyte, and so there is no true alternation of generations.

In many diatoms, Siphonocladiales, Siphonales, and in all the Fucales the vegetative body is diploid, meiosis occurring when gametes are formed, as in animals. Here a prolonged diploid growth phase alternates with a few haploid cells, the gametes, and again there is no true alternation of generations. Thus, where the life cycle includes only one vegetative phase, this may be either haploid, meiosis directly following fertilization, or diploid, meiosis immediately preceding fertilization.

An alternation of generations occurs wherever a diploid growth phase intervenes between fertilization and meiosis, and a haploid growth phase between meiosis and fertilization. Such a condition is displayed by *Ulva* and a few other green algae, by most brown and red algae, and by all bryophytes and pteridophytes. It is also characteristic of the spermatophytes, although in angiosperms the haploid phase (gametophyte) consists of only a very few cells or nuclei. Obviously this is a result of reduction, while in *Fucus*, for example, where a somewhat similar condition prevails, reduction may have taken place but evidence is lacking.

In *Fucus*, where spores are absent from the life cycle, a diploid plant body produces gametes. In *Ulothrix* and *Oedogonium*, on the other hand, a haploid body may produce either gametes or spores. Such spores are vegetative spores and are not homologous with the four spores derived from the zygote or with the spores borne by the sporophyte of the higher plants, both of which are meiospores and belong to the sexual life cycle. Either a haploid or a diploid plant body may be propagated vegetatively by various means without fertilization and meiosis being involved. Vegetative reproduction is always asexual.

Origin of Alternation of Generations. Regarding the origin of alternations, two different theories have been advanced, the homologous theory and the antithetic theory. The homologous theory was based originally on conditions in those algae in which a single plant can produce either spores or gametes. It assumes that these functions later became separated into two distinct individuals, sporophyte and gametophyte, alternating regularly in the life cycle. The theory furnishes a more adequate explanation of alternation where the two generations are alike vegetatively than where they are unlike. Against it may be urged the fact that vegetative spores produced by a haploid plant body and meiospores produced by a zygote or a sporophyte are not morphologically equivalent. Also, the homologous theory fails to account for the difference in chromosome numbers that exists between the gametophyte and sporophyte. The phenomena of apogamy and apospory have been cited as evidence in favor of this theory, but they are merely digressions from the normal life cycle.

The antithetic theory seems to be more in accord with actual conditions in the plant kingdom. It contends that the gametophyte is the original generation and the sporophyte a later one interpolated in the life history between fertilization and meiosis. It holds that the sporophyte has evolved from the zygote, an initial stage occurring in such algae as *Oedogonium*, where the zygote gives rise to four meiospores. A second stage might be represented by *Coleochaete*, where the zygote, after undergoing meiosis, forms a small group of spore-producing cells (up to 32). In a third stage, as seen in *Riccia*, the zygote develops into a very simple sporophyte in which meiosis is delayed until spores are formed. In the evolution of the plant kingdom, such a delay may have taken place in a single step by mutation.

Where the zygote becomes a thick-walled resting cell, its nucleus divides reductionally upon germination. This is a feature only of fresh-water green algae. Where the zygote germinates at once, it gives rise to a diploid vegetative body. This occurs in the marine green algae, in the brown algae, and in most of the red algae.[1] In most algae with a diploid vegetative phase, there is a distinct alternation of generations, exceptions being such forms as *Acetabularia*, *Codium*, *Bryopsis*, and the Fucales.

It is apparent that the behavior of the zygote is related to environmental conditions. Seasonal variations are more pronounced in bodies of fresh water than in the ocean. A resting zygote, usually formed near the close of the growing season, carries the plant over a period of unfavorable conditions. Algae with a resting zygote display no diploid vegetative phase. Thus the origin of alternation of generations may be sought in a determination of the factors that induce prompt germination of the zygote with an accompanying postponement of meiosis. Perhaps these factors have been responsible for a mutation that has resulted in the establishment of a diploid generation.

Alternation of generations, once established in a group of plants, conferred such advantages that it would tend to be retained as a permanent feature. These advantages are: (1) An increase in the number of individuals produced as a result of a single gametic union, thereby conferring on them any beneficial results of such a union which, in many of the lower plants, sometimes occurs with a great deal of rarity. Instead of produc-

---

[1] In the red algae the zygote always germinates promptly, but subsequent stages are variable and complicated by the formation of carpospores. These are haploid in the two lowest orders, where the zygote is the only diploid cell in the life cycle, and diploid in the other orders, where they give rise to sporophytes.

ing only one new plant, the zygote now indirectly produces, through the development of the sporophyte, a large number of new plants. (2) An increase in the possible range of variation. Where the zygote undergoes meiosis only two genetically different lines of descent are possible, since the segregation of genes takes place during the first reduction division. The development of a sporophyte results in meiosis in many spore mother cells, all descended from the same zygote, and so makes possible a great many new chromosome combinations. The advantages of alternation of generations are proportional to the size and length of life attained by the sporophyte and account, at least in part, for its dominance over the gametophyte in vascular plants.

The evolution of the sporophyte in the higher plants has been marked by a prolongation, through vegetative growth, of the interval between fertilization and meiosis. The sporophyte of *Riccia* represents a primitive condition in that its growth period is short and nearly all its cells produce spores. Throughout bryophytes and pteridophytes progressive sterilization of potentially sporogenous tissue has resulted in an elaboration of vegetative structures. At the same time, not only is relatively less and less tissue devoted to spore production, but it appears later and later in the life history.

As the sporophyte has achieved independence and become the dominant generation in all vascular plants, the gametophyte has undergone a progressive decline. This has been accentuated by the development of heterospory, first seen in the pteridophytes. In spermatophytes the gametophyte has become not only greatly reduced structurally, but actually is parasitic on the sporophyte, thus reversing conditions in the bryophytes, where the sporophyte is parasitic on the gametophyte throughout its entire existence.

SELECTED REFERENCES

General

Arnold, C. A., Introduction to Paleobotany. New York, 1947.
Brown, W. H., The Plant Kingdom. Boston, 1935.
Campbell, D. H., The Evolution of the Land Plants. Stanford University, 1940.
Darrah, W. C., Textbook of Paleobotany. New York, 1939.
Engler, A., and L. Diels, Syllabus der Pflanzenfamilien. Berlin, 1936.
Jeffrey, E. C., The Anatomy of Woody Plants. Chicago, 1917.
McLean, R. C., and W. R. Ivimey-Cook, Textbook of Theoretical Botany, vol. I. London, 1951.
Sharp, L. W., Fundamentals of Cytology. New York, 1943.
Walton, J., An Introduction to the Study of Fossil Plants. London, 1940.
Wettstein, R., Handbuch der systematischen Botanik, 2 vols. Leipzig and Vienna, 1933.

Algae

Cavers, F., The Interrelationships of Flagellata and Primitive Algae. *New Phytol.*, Reprint 7. 1913.
Chapman, V. J., An Introduction to the Study of Algae. Cambridge, 1941.
Fritsch, F. E., The Structure and Reproduction of the Algae, 2 vols. Cambridge, 1935 and 1945.
———, Present-day Classification of Algae. *Bot. Rev.* **10**:233–277. 1944.
Geitler, L., Reproduction and Life History in Diatoms. *Bot. Rev.* **1**:149–161. 1935.
Kniep, H., Die Sexualität der niederen Pflanzen. Jena, 1928.
Oltmanns, F., Morphologie und Biologie der Algen, 3 vols. Jena, 1922–1923.
Setchell, W. A., and N. L. Gardner, The Marine Algae of the Pacific Coast of North America. I. Myxophyceae. *Univ. Calif. Pubs. Bot.* **8**:1–138. 1919. II. Chlorophyceae, *ibid.* **8**:139–374. 1920. III. Melanophyceae, *ibid.* **8**:383–898. 1925.
Smith, G. M., The Fresh-water Algae of the United States. New York, 1950.
———, Cryptogamic Botany, vol. I. Algae and Fungi. New York, 1938.
———, Nuclear Phases and Alternation of Generations in the Chlorophyceae. *Bot. Rev.* **4**:132–139. 1938.
———, Marine Algae of the Monterey Peninsula, California. Stanford University, 1944.
Taylor, W. R., Marine Algae of Florida. *Carnegie Inst. Wash. Pub.* 379:1–219. 1922.
———, Marine Algae of the Northeastern Coast of North America. *Univ. Mich. Studies Sci. Ser.* **13**:1–427. 1937.
Tilden, Josephine E., The Algae and Their Life Relations. Minneapolis, 1935.

Fungi

Alexopoulos, C. J., Introductory Mycology. New York, 1952.
Bessey, E. A., Morphology and Taxonomy of Fungi. Philadelphia, 1950.
Fitzpatrick, H. M., The Lower Fungi—Phycomycetes. New York, 1930.

Gäumann, E. A., and C. W. Dodge, Comparative Morphology of Fungi. New York, 1928.

Gwynne-Vaughan, H. C. I., and B. Barnes, The Structure and Development of the Fungi. Cambridge, 1937.

Kniep, H., Die Sexualität der niederen Pflanzen. Jena, 1928.

Martin, G. W., The Myxomycetes. *Bot. Rev.* **6**:356–388. 1940.

Smith, G. M., Cryptogamic Botany, vol. I. Algae and Fungi. New York, 1938.

Wolf, F. A., and F. T. Wolf, The Fungi, vol. I. New York, 1947.

Bryophytes

Bower, F. O., Primitive Land Plants. London, 1935.

Campbell, D. H., Structure and Development of Mosses and Ferns. New York, 1918.

———, The Relationships of the Hepaticae. *Bot. Rev.* **2**:53–66. 1936.

Cavers, F., The Interrelationships of the Bryophyta. *New Phytol.*, Reprint 4. 1911.

Smith, G. M., Cryptogamic Botany, vol. II. Bryophytes and Pteridophytes. New York, 1938.

Pteridophytes

Bower, F. O., Ferns (Filicales), 2 vols. Cambridge, 1923–1926.

———, Primitive Land Plants. London, 1935.

Campbell, D. H., Structure and Development of Mosses and Ferns. New York, 1918.

Eames, A. J., Morphology of Vascular Plants. Lower Groups. New York, 1936.

Smith, G. M., Cryptogamic Botany, vol. II. Bryophytes and Pteridophytes. New York, 1938.

Gymnosperms

Chamberlain, C. J., Gymnosperms, Structure and Evolution. Chicago, 1935.

Coulter, J. M., and C. J. Chamberlain, Morphology of Gymnosperms. Chicago, 1917.

Johansen, D. A., Plant Embryology. Waltham, Mass., 1950.

Schnarf, K., Embryologie der Gymnospermen. Berlin, 1933.

Angiosperms

Coulter, J. M., and C. J. Chamberlain, Morphology of Angiosperms. New York, 1903.

Eames, A. J., and L. H. MacDaniels, Introduction to Plant Anatomy. New York, 1947.

Esau, Katherine, Origin and Development of Primary Vascular Tissues in Seed Plants. *Bot. Rev.* **9**:125–206. 1943.

Foster, A. S., Problems of Structure, Growth, and Evolution in the Shoot Apex of Seed Plants. *Bot. Rev.* **5**:454–470. 1939.

Johansen, D. A., A Critical Review of the Present Status of Plant Embryology. *Bot. Rev.* **11**:87–107. 1945.

———, Plant Embryology, Waltham, Mass., 1950.

Maheshwari, P., The Angiosperm Embryo Sac. *Bot. Rev.* **14**:1–56. 1948.

———, The Male Gametophyte of Angiosperms. *Bot. Rev.* **15**:1–75. 1949.

———, An Introduction to the Embryology of Angiosperms. New York, 1950.

Schnarf, K., Embryologie der Angiospermen. Berlin, 1929.

———, Vergleichende Embryologie der Angiospermen. Berlin, 1931.

Wilson, C. L., and T. Just, The Morphology of the Flower. *Bot. Rev.* **5**:97–131. 1939.

Evolution

Coulter, J. M., The Evolution of Sex Plants. Chicago, 1914.

Svedelius, N., Alternation of Generations in Relation to Reduction Division. *Bot. Gaz.* **83**:362–384. 1927.

Turrill, W. B., Taxonomy and Phylogeny. *Bot. Rev.* **8**:473–532; 655–707. 1942.

Wahl, H. A., Alternation of Generations and Classification with Special Reference to the Teaching of Elementary Botany. *Torreya* **45**:1–12. 1945.

GLOSSARY

Abaxial. Situated on the side away from the axis or stem.

Accessory fruit. A fruit consisting of a ripened ovary and other ripened parts, as the calyx or receptacle.

Acropetal. An order of development in which the youngest structures are at the apex and the oldest at the base.

Actinomorphic. Having flowers with radial symmetry, the parts extending outward from a common center like the spokes of a wheel.

Adaxial. Situated on the side toward the axis or stem.

Adventitious. Arising sporadically without order or out of the usual place, as a bud.

Aeciospore. In various rust fungi, one of the spores produced in an aecium.

Aecium. A cup-like structure in the life cycle of a typical rust, producing spores in chains.

Aerobic. Living or active only in the presence of free oxygen.

Aggregate fruit. A fruit consisting of a group of consolidated ripened ovaries derived from a single flower.

Akinete. In certain algae, a nonmotile, thick-walled resting spore derived from an entire vegetative protoplast whose wall becomes the wall of the spore.

Alternation of generations. The presence in the same life cycle of two distinct plant bodies or individuals that succeed each other, a haploid body (gametophyte) producing gametes and a diploid body (sporophyte) producing spores.

Ament. A catkin, or scaly spike.

Amphicribral. A vascular bundle with phloem surrounding the xylem.

Amphigastrium. One of the reduced ventral leaves in a leafy liverwort.

Amphiphloic. A siphonostele with phloem both external and internal to the xylem.

Amphithecium. In bryophytes, the outer layer of cells developed in the young sporophyte.

Amphivasal. A vascular bundle with xylem surrounding the phloem.

Anaerobic. Living or active in the absence of free oxygen.

Anatropous. Having the ovule inverted and straight, with the micropyle bent downward to the funiculus, to which the body of the ovule is united.

Androspore. In such algae as *Oedogonium*, a zoospore that produces a dwarf male filament.

Anisocarpic. Flowers in which the number of carpels is not equal to that of each of the other cycles.

Annulus. A ring or ring-like part, as in a mushroom, a moss capsule, or a fern sporangium.

Anther. The pollen-bearing part of a stamen.

Antheridium. The sperm-producing organ in thallophytes, bryophytes, and pteridophytes.

Anticlinal. Inclined in an opposite direction; a cell wall perpendicular to the outside surface.

Antipodal. Pertaining to the opposite end, as the cells or nuclei in an embryo sac at the end opposite the egg.

Apetalous. Without petals but with sepals.

Apical cell. A single cell at the tip of a structure from the segments of which all its cells are derived.

Aplanospore. In various algae, a nonmotile spore with a wall not derived from the wall of the cell in which it is formed.

Apocarpous. With separate carpels.

Apogamy. Development of an embryo from a cell of the gametophyte other than the egg.

Apomixis. A condition in which sexual reproduction is replaced by some form of asexual reproduction.

Apophysis. An enlargement at the base of the capsule of some mosses.

Apothecium. A cup-like or disk-like ascocarp.

Archegonium. The female sex organ of bryophytes, pteridophytes, and most gymnosperms.

Ascocarp. In most ascomycetes, a fruiting body producing asci.

Ascogenous hyphae. Hyphae that bear asci.

Ascogonium. The female sex organ of ascomycetes.

Ascospore. One of the spores borne in an ascus.

Ascus. In ascomycetes, a sac-like cell in which ascospores are produced.

Autoecious. Passing through all stages in the life cycle on the same host, as certain rust fungi.

Autotrophic. Self-nourishing; capable of making its own food, as a green plant.

Auxospore. In diatoms, a reproductive cell formed by the union of two cells or asexually.

Axil. The upper angle between a leaf or branch and the stem from which it arises.

Bacillus. A straight, rod-shaped bacterium.

Basidiocarp. In most basidiomycetes, a fruiting body producing basidia.

Basidiospore. One of the spores borne on a basidium.

Basidium. In basidiomycetes, a club-shaped structure that produces basidiospores.

Basipetal. An order of development in which the youngest structures are at the base and the oldest at the apex.

Biciliate. Having two cilia.

Bilocular. Having two locules or cavities.

Bisporangiate. With microsporangia and megasporangia borne in the same strobilus or flower.

Bract. A scale borne on a floral axis, especially one subtending a flower or inflorescence.

Calyptra. In bryophytes and pteridophytes, a covering developed from the venter of the archegonium and surrounding the sporophyte, at least when young, and in some mosses later carried on top of the capsule as a hood.

Calyptrogen. That part of the embryonic tissue of a root tip from which the rootcap is developed.

Calyx. The sepals of a flower, collectively; the outer whorl of perianth parts.

Cambium. A lateral meristem consisting of a layer of cells giving rise to secondary tissues, particularly xylem and phloem, in many roots and stems.

Campylotropous. Having the ovule turned so that the base and apex are close together.

Capillitium. A network of delicate threads, as in the sporangium of a myxomycete.

Capsule. In bryophytes, any closed vessel containing spores; in angiosperms, a dry, dehiscent, many-seeded fruit derived from a compound pistil.

Carinal canal. In the Equisetinae, one of the canals in the stele of the stem lying beneath a ridge on the surface.

Carotin. Any of a group of mainly deep yellow to orange-red pigments found in various plants, either alone or associated with others, particularly chlorophyll; they differ from the xanthophylls in containing only carbon and hydrogen.

Carotinoid. Any of a group of pigments that includes the carotins and xanthophylls.

Carpel. The megasporophyll or ovule-bearing organ of seed plants; in angiosperms, forming a simple pistil or part of a compound pistil.

Carpogonium. In the red algae, the basal portion of the procarp where the egg is formed, or sometimes comprising the entire female sex organ.

Carpospore. In the red algae, one of a group of nonmotile spores produced either by the zygote directly or budded off from the tips of short filaments arising from the carpogonium after fertilization.

Cauline. Growing on, or belonging to, a stem.

Cellulose. A carbohydrate constituting the chief substance in the cell wall of plants.

Chalaza. The portion of an ovule below where the integuments are united to the nucellus.

Chalazogamy. Fertilization of an egg by means of a pollen tube entering the ovule through the chalaza.

Chlamydospore. A thick-walled resting spore produced in certain fungi, particularly the smuts, and representing a transformed vegetative cell.

Chlorophyll. The green coloring matter of plants, occurring in two associated forms, chlorophyll a and chlorophyll b.

Chloroplast. A plastid containing chlorophyll.

Choripetalous. Having separate petals.

Chromatin. A deeply staining, granular, protoplasmic material occurring in the nucleus of cells.

Chromosome. One of the organized bodies, of definite number, into which the chromatin of a nucleus resolves itself in connection with mitotic division.

Cilium. A hair-like protoplasmic process capable of vibratory or lashing movement.

Circinate. Coiled; rolled up on the axis with the apex at the center.

Cleistothecium. A closed ascocarp.

Coccus. A spherical bacterium.

Coenocyte. A plant body, as in some algae and fungi, the protoplasm of which is continuous and multinucleate and not divided into separate cells.

Coleorhiza. In some seed plants, a sheath covering the root tip of an embryo.

Collateral. Side by side, as the arrangement of xylem and phloem in the vein of a leaf.

Colony. A group of unicellular plants of the same kind held together by a common investment or stalk.

Columella. A sterile central portion of the sporangium of certain molds; a sterile central axis in the capsule of certain liverworts and mosses.

Companion cell. A cell associated with a sieve tube in the phloem of angiosperms and of common origin with it.

Conceptacle. In certain algae, as in the Fucales, a cavity with an external opening containing reproductive cells.

Conidiophore. In certain fungi, a specialized hypha that produces conidia by abstriction.

Conidium. An aerial spore produced by abstriction from the tip of a conidiophore.

Conjugation. The fusion of two similar gametes.

Corolla. The petals of a flower, collectively; the inner whorl of perianth parts.

Corpus. The central growth zone in a stem tip.

Cortex. The region of a root or stem that lies between the epidermis and the stele.

Cotyledon. The first leaf, or one of the first pair or whorl of leaves, formed on the embryo of seed plants.

Cuneate. Wedge-shaped, as an apical cell with four cutting faces.

Cupule. A small cup-shaped structure, especially in certain liverworts, in which gemmae are produced.

Cystocarp. A kind of sporocarp, in the red algae, produced after fertilization and consisting of the carpogonium, gonimoblasts, carpospores, and often other associated structures.

Cytoplasm. The protoplasm of a cell exclusive of the nucleus.

Deciduous. Falling off at the end of the growing season, as some leaves; said of plants having leaves of this type.

Dehiscence. Bursting open, at maturity, in some regular manner, of a sporangium to discharge its spores or of a fruit to liberate its seeds.

Dermatogen. A layer of embryonic cells, in a root tip or stem tip, that gives rise to the epidermis.

Dichotomy. A type of branching in which the main axis forks repeatedly into two branches of equal length.

Dicotyledonous. Having two cotyledons.

Dictyostele. A dissected stele; a stele consisting of a wide-meshed network of vascular strands.

Dimorphic. Occurring in two distinct forms upon the same plant or upon other plants of the same species.

Dioecious. Having the male organs on one plant and the female on another; having staminate and pistillate flowers on separate plants.

Diploid. Having twice the basic or haploid number of chromosomes.

Dolabrate. Hatchet-shaped, as an apical cell with two cutting faces.

Dorsal. Pertaining to the back or outer side of an organ; designating the surface turned away from the axis, as the underside of a leaf; in liverworts and ferns, pertaining to the upper side of the prothallium.

Dorsiventral. Having distinct dorsal and ventral surfaces.

Ectophloic. A siphonostele with phloem external but not internal to the xylem.

Egg. A female gamete.

Egg apparatus. In angiosperms, a group of three cells at the micropylar end of the embryo sac, consisting of the egg and two synergids.

Elater. A filament or filamentous appendage for dispersing spores, as in the capsule of a liverwort.

Elaterophore. A structure to which a group of elaters is attached.

Embryo. A young sporophyte, ordinarily derived from a fertilized egg.

Embryo sac. In angiosperms, a large cell within the nucellus of the ovule in which the egg is produced and, following fertilization, the embryo develops; the female gametophyte of angiosperms.

Endarch. Development of primary xylem in a centrifugal direction.

Endodermis. The innermost layer of cortical cells in a root or stem.

Endogenous. Arising from within; growing from or on the inside.

Endophyte. A plant that grows inside another plant of a different species, but not parasitically.

Endosperm. Nutritive tissue in a young or mature seed, formed within the embryo sac and lying outside the embryo.

Endothecium. In bryophytes, the central mass of cells developed in the young sporophyte; in an anther, a specialized layer of cells lying beneath the epidermis and assisting in dehiscence.

Epidermis. A superficial layer of cells on leaves, young stems and roots, etc.

Epigynous. Said of flowers whose ovary is sunken in the receptacle so that the perianth seems to arise from its summit.

Epiphyte. A plant that grows upon another plant, but not parasitically.

Eusporangiate. A type of sporangial development occurring in spermatophytes and most pteridophytes in which the sporogenous tissue arises from the inner segment of the initial cell.

Exarch. Development of primary xylem in a centripetal direction.

Excurrent. Having a prolonged main stem extending to the top, as in some trees.

Exine. The outer layer of the cell wall of a pollen grain.

Eyespot. An eye-like spot of pigment in certain motile unicellular algae and reproductive cells.

Fertilization. The fusion of a sperm and an egg or of a male nucleus and a female nucleus to form a new individual (zygote).

Fiber. A thread or thread-like structure; a long, slender, thick-walled cell, as in sclerenchyma.

Filament. A thread-like series of cells or a very long, cylindrical, single cell, as in certain algae and fungi; the part of the stamen that supports the anther.

Fission. Reproduction of a unicellular plant by division into two equal cells.

Flagellum. A long, whip-like, protoplasmic process or appendage of a cell capable of lashing movement.

Flower. In angiosperms, a group of sporophylls usually surrounded by a perianth.

Foliar. Pertaining to, or consisting of, leaves.

Foot. The basal portion of the sporophyte in mosses and most liverworts; a part of the embryo of pteridophytes that is embedded in the gametophyte and acts as an absorbing organ.

Fruit. In angiosperms, a ripened ovary with any external parts that ripen in association with it.

Fucoxanthin. A brown pigment associated with chlorophyll in the brown algae.

Funiculus. The stalk of an ovule.

Fusion nucleus. The nucleus, in an embryo sac, typically formed by the union of two polar nuclei.

Gametangium. A cell or organ in which gametes are formed; a sex organ.

Gamete. A mature sex cell; a cell capable of uniting with another of opposite sex to form a zygote.

Gametophore. A branch bearing sex organs or gametangia, as in mosses.

Gametophyte. In plants with an alternation of generations, the individual that bears gametes and has the haploid number of chromosomes.

Gemma. A detachable bud or bud-like body capable of developing into a new plant, as in bryophytes and pteridophytes.

Generative cell. In gymnosperms, the cell in the pollen grain that gives rise to the stalk and body cells, in angiosperms to the two male cells.

Gill. One of the plates on the under surface of the pileus of a mushroom.

Gleba. The inner portion of the basidiocarp in the Gasteromycetales.

Glycogen. A carbohydrate related to starch and dextrin, very common in animal tissues.

Gonimoblast.   In many red algae, one of the many short filaments arising from the fertilized carpogonium and giving rise to carpospores.

Gullet.   A tube leading into the interior of the cell in such organisms as *Euglena*.

Haematochrome.   An orange-red pigment in the cell sap of certain green algae, such as *Sphaerella*.

Haploid.   Having the single or basic chromosome number.

Haustorium.   In parasitic plants, a specialized outgrowth that serves to absorb food from the host.

Heterocyst.   In certain blue-green algae, an enlarged cell differing from the other cells in a filament in being clear, colorless, and thick-walled.

Heteroecious.   Requiring two different hosts to complete the life cycle, as certain rust fungi.

Heterogamous.   Having a union of unlike gametes, one (the egg) considerably larger than the other (the sperm).

Heteromorphic.   Of unlike form; a type of alternation of generations in which the gametophyte and sporophyte are dissimilar vegetatively.

Heterosporous.   Producing two kinds of spores, usually of different size, the small ones (microspores) producing male and the large ones (megaspores) female gametophytes.

Heterothallic.   Having two kinds of mycelia, distinct physiologically and representing opposite sexes.

Heterotrophic.   Obtaining nourishment from organic matter, either living or dead, as all plants lacking chlorophyll.

Histogen.   A group of embryonic cells that gives rise to a particular kind of permanent tissue.

Homosporous.   Producing spores of only one kind.

Homothallic.   Having two kinds of structures representing opposite sexes borne on the same mycelium.

Hormogonium.   In the blue-green algae, a portion of a filament, usually marked off by heterocysts, that may become detached and produce a new filament.

Host.   The organism from which a parasite secures its food.

Hymenium.   In the higher fungi, a layer of cells from which asci or basidia arise.

Hypha.   One of the filaments comprising the mycelium of a fungus.

Hypocotyl.   In seed plants, the portion of the stem below the cotyledons in an embryo or a seedling.

Hypodermal.   Situated immediately beneath the epidermis.

Hypogynous.   With the perianth and stamens attached to the receptacle below the ovary and free from it.

Imbricate.   Overlapping in regular order, like shingles on a roof.

Imperfect flower.   Having either stamens or a pistil but not both, these being in separate flowers.

Indusium.   In many ferns, a membrane that covers or invests a sorus.

Inflorescence.   A flower cluster.

Integument.   The covering of an ovule.

Intercalary.   Inserted or occurring between cells or regions of a different kind; growth occurring between the apex and base.

Intine.   The inner layer of the cell wall of a pollen grain.

Involucre.   In some bryophytes, an envelope partially or completely enclosing a sporophyte and arising from the surrounding tissue of the gametophyte. In angiosperms, a whorl or set of bracts surrounding a flower or flower cluster.

Irregular flower. One showing lack of uniformity among members of the same whorl of perianth parts.

Isocarpic. Flowers in which the number of carpels is equal to that of each of the other cycles.

Isogamete. A gamete without apparent sexual differentiation.

Isogamous. Characterized by the union of gametes of equal size.

Isomorphic. Of like form; a type of alternation of generations in which the gametophyte and sporophyte are similar vegetatively.

Isthmus. A contracted part or passage connecting two similar structures or cavities, as in desmids.

Lamarin. A dextrin-like carbohydrate constituting a form of reserve food in many brown algae.

Leaf gap. A break or interruption in the continuity of a siphonostele caused by the departure of a leaf trace from it.

Leaf trace. A strand of vascular tissue passing through the cortex of a stem and connecting the stele with a leaf base.

Leaflet. One of the parts of a divided ("compound") leaf.

Lenticel. A pore in the corky bark of a woody stem through which gases pass.

Leptosporangiate. A type of sporangial development, occurring in the higher ferns, in which the sporogenous tissue arises from the outer segment of the initial cell.

Leucosin. A protein-like substance constituting a form of reserve food in certain algae.

Lignin. A substance related to cellulose and with it forming the cell walls of woody tissue, stone cells, and most fibers.

Ligule. A single scale-like appendage near the base of some leaves on the adaxial surface, as in *Selaginella* and *Isoetes*.

Linear. Long and narrow with parallel sides.

Locule. A compartment or cavity, as in a sporangium or ovary.

Megaphyllous. Having large leaves.

Megasporangium. A sporangium producing only megaspores.

Megaspore. In heterosporous plants, a spore that gives rise to a female gametophyte and generally is larger than a microspore.

Megasporophyll. A sporophyll that bears only megasporangia.

Meiosis. The two nuclear divisions that result in a reduction in chromosome number from the diploid to the haploid condition.

Meiospore. A spore formed as a result of meiosis.

Meristem. Embryonic tissue, the cells of which are capable of active division.

Mesarch. Development of primary xylem in both centripetal and centrifugal directions.

Mesophyll. Green parenchyma occurring between the epidermal layers of a leaf and forming the internal ground tissue.

Metaxylem. Primary xylem formed later than the protoxylem.

Microphyllous. Having small leaves.

Micropyle. A minute opening in the integument of an ovule through which the pollen tube ordinarily enters.

Microsporangium. A sporangium producing only microspores.

Microspore. In heterosporous plants, a spore that gives rise to a male gametophyte and is generally smaller than a megaspore.

Microsporophyll. A sporophyll that bears only microsporangia.

Mitosis. The series of complex changes through which a nucleus ordinarily passes when it divides.

Monocotyledonous. Having a single cotyledon.

Monoecious. Having the male and female organs on the same plant; having stamens and pistils in separate flowers on the same plant.

Monophylletic. Developed from a single stock or from a common ancestry.

Monopodium. A main stem that continues its original line of growth, giving off lateral branches.

Monosiphonous. Consisting of a single filament.

Monosporangiate. With microsporangia and megasporangia borne in separate strobili or flowers.

Multicellular. Many-celled.

Multiciliate. Having many cilia.

Multilocular. Having many locules or cavities.

Mycelium. The mass of hyphae forming the vegetative body of most fungi.

Myxamoeba. A uninucleate, amoeboid, reproductive cell in the myxomycetes.

Naked flower. A flower without a perianth.

Nucellus. The main body of an ovule, constituting the megasporangium, and surrounded by the integument or integuments.

Nucleus. A rounded protoplasmic body, enclosed by a membrane, embedded in the cytoplasm of nearly all cells, and controlling their metabolism, growth, reproduction, and inheritance.

Ontogeny. The development of an individual organism throughout its successive growth stages.

Oögonium. The female sex organ of thallophytes.

Operculum. A lid formed at the top of a capsule, as in mosses.

Orbicular. Flat and circular, or nearly circular, in outline; disk-shaped.

Orthotropous. Having the ovule erect, with the micropyle and chalaza at opposite ends.

Ovary. In angiosperms, the part of the pistil that contains the ovules.

Ovule. The megasporangium of a seed plant with its integument or integuments; an immature seed.

Palisade tissue. The portion of the mesophyll that is composed of elongated cells lying directly below and at right angles to the upper epidermis of a leaf.

Palmate. Having lobes, divisions, or leaflets radiating from a common center.

Papilla. A small protuberance or projection.

Paramylon. A starch-like carbohydrate constituting a form of reserve food in the Euglenophyceae.

Paraphysis. One of the sterile filaments commonly accompanying the sporangia or gametangia in many thallophytes and bryophytes.

Parasite. An organism living on or in another organism and getting its food at the other's expense.

Parenchyma. A soft, loose tissue composed of living, thin-walled cells that are not greatly differentiated.

Parietal. Pertaining or belonging to the walls of a part or cavity.

Parthenocarpy. The development of a fruit without fertilization.

Parthenogenesis. The development of an embryo from an unfertilized egg.

Pellicle. A thin, firm, outer membrane on certain unicellular organisms that lack a cell wall, such as *Euglena*.

Peltate. Shield-shaped, with the support attached to the lower surface instead of at the base or margin.

Pentacyclic. Having five cycles or whorls of floral parts.

Pentamerous. Having the floral parts in sets of five or multiples of five.

Perfect flower. Having both stamens and pistil in the same flower.

Perianth. The floral envelope; the calyx and corolla collectively. In the leafy liverworts, a group of specialized united leaves surrounding the archegonia.

Periblem. A group of embryonic cells, in a root tip or stem tip, that gives rise to the cortex.

Pericarp. The ripened wall of an ovary.

Perichaetium. A sheath or rosette of modified leaves surrounding the sex organs of many mosses.

Periclinal. Parallel to the outer surface, as a cell wall.

Pericycle. One or more layers of cells forming the outermost part of the stele in most vascular plants.

Peridium. The outer covering of the basidiocarp in the Gasteromycetales.

Perigynous. With the perianth and stamens borne on a disk or cup formed by the receptacle.

Perisperm. Nutritive tissue in a seed formed outside the embryo sac, mainly in the nucellus.

Peristome. A ring of teeth surrounding the open rim of a moss capsule.

Perithecium. A spherical or flask-shaped ascocarp opening by a small terminal pore.

Petal. One of the leaf-like parts of the corolla.

Petiole. A leafstalk.

Phellogen. The cambium that produces cork tissue.

Phloem. In vascular plants, a complex tissue consisting of sieve tubes and often also of companion cells, parenchyma, and fibers, and serving for the conduction of food.

Phycocyanin. A blue pigment associated with chlorophyll in the blue-green algae.

Phycoerythrin. A red pigment associated with chlorophyll in the red algae.

Phylogeny. The evolutionary development of the race or group to which an organism belongs.

Pileus. The expanded or cap-like part of a mushroom.

Pinna. A leaflet or primary division of a pinnate leaf.

Pinnate. Feather-like; with the leaflets or primary divisions arranged on each side of a common axis or rachis.

Pinnule. One of the ultimate divisions of a bipinnate leaf.

Pistil. In angiosperms, a carpel or an organization of two or more carpels.

Pith. The central portion of a siphonostelic stem, generally consisting of parenchyma.

Placenta. The place within an ovary to which the ovules are attached.

Plasma membrane. A thin membrane that encloses the cytoplasm of all living cells.

Plasmodium. A mass of naked, multinucleate protoplasm usually showing amoeboid movement.

Plastid. An organized protoplasmic body, other than the nucleus, occurring in some plant cells and concerned with some special metabolic activity.

Plerome. A group of embryonic cells, in a root tip or stem tip, that gives rise to the stele.

Plumule. The primary bud of the embryo of a seed plant.

Polar nucleus. One of two free nuclei in an embryo sac, one coming from each pole, that eventually unite to form the fusion nucleus.

Pollen chamber. A cavity developed at the apex of the nucellus, as in cycads.

Pollen sac. One of the pollen-containing cavities in an anther.

Pollen tube.   The tube produced by a pollen grain when it germinates.

Pollination.   In angiosperms, the transfer of pollen from a stamen to a pistil or, in gymnosperms, to an ovule.

Pollinium.   A mass of coherent pollen grains, as in milkweeds and orchids.

Polycotyledonous.   Having many cotyledons, at least more than two.

Polyembryonous.   Having several embryos in the same seed.

Polymerous.   Having many floral parts in each set.

Polyphyletic.   Derived from more than one ancestral stock.

Polyploid.   Having several or many times the basic or haploid chromosome number.

Polysiphonous.   Consisting of several or many united filaments, as the plant body of certain brown and red algae.

Primary xylem.   Wood differentiated directly from a terminal meristem and consisting of protoxylem and metaxylem.

Primordium.   A rudiment or first-formed part of an organ or member.

Procarp.   The female sex organ of the red algae, consisting of a carpogonium and a trichogyne.

Proembryo.   In pteridophytes and spermatophytes, a group of cells derived from the fertilized egg and later differentiating into a suspensor and embryo.

Prothallium.   The reduced, thalloid gametophyte of the pteridophytes.

Protonema.   The primary or filamentous stage in the development of a moss gametophyte.

Protostele.   A solid stele, without a central pith.

Protoxylem.   The first xylem to be formed in an organ.

Pseudopodium.   A temporary foot-like protrusion of an amoeboid cell, used in locomotion and in the procuring of food.   In *Sphagnum* and *Andreaea*, a leafless stalk developed from the stem of the gametophyte in which the foot of the sporophyte is embedded.

Pyrenoid.   A starch-forming body in the chloroplast of many algae.

Pyriform.   Pear-shaped.

Rachis.   In divided ("compound") leaves, the extension of the petiole bearing the leaflets.

Radial.   Occupying alternate radii, as the arrangement of primary xylem and phloem in a root.

Radicle.   The rudimentary root in the embryo of a seed plant.

Ramentum.   A woolly covering of scales on the stem, as in many ferns.

Raphe.   In anatropous ovules, the portion of the funiculus that is united to the integument, forming a ridge along the body of the ovule.   In diatoms, a longitudinal slit extending along the median line of a valve.

Receptacle.   In liverworts, a special branch or portion of the thallus that bears the sex organs.   In angiosperms, the portion of the axis that bears the floral parts.

Regular flower.   One in which the members of each whorl of perianth parts are uniform in size and form.

Reticulate.   Forming or resembling a network.

Rhizoid.   In the lower plants, one of the root-like filaments that attaches the gametophyte to the substratum.

Rhizome.   An elongated underground stem; a rootstock.

Rhizophore.   A special root-bearing organ.

Rootcap.   A cellular sheath at the end of a root tip.

Saprophyte.   A plant living on dead organic matter.

Scalariform.   Ladder-like; having bars or markings like the rungs of a ladder.

Sclerenchyma. A hard tissue with thickened, generally lignified cell walls and non-conductive in function.

Sclerotium. In myxomycetes, a resting stage in which the plasmodium becomes a hard waxy mass. In certain higher fungi, a hard compact mass of mycelium containing reserve food material.

Secondary xylem. Wood formed by a cambium.

Sepal. One of the leaf-like parts of the calyx.

Septate. Divided by walls or partitions.

Sessile. Without a stalk; attached directly by the base.

Seta. A slender, bristle-like organ or part, especially the stalk that supports the capsule of bryophytes.

Sieve tube. An elongated living cell in which at least the end walls are perforated, characteristic of phloem tissue.

Siphonostele. A tubular stele containing a central core of pith.

Soredium. A special reproductive body of lichens, consisting of a few algal cells surrounded by fungal hyphae.

Sorus. A group or cluster of sporangia, as in ferns.

Spatulate. Spoon-shaped; gradually narrowed downward from a rounded apex.

Sperm. A male gamete, generally motile by means of cilia.

Spermatium. In red algae, a naked, nonmotile male gamete; in certain fungi and lichens, a cell apparently functioning as a male gamete.

Spermatogenous. Sperm-producing.

Spermogonium. In certain fungi and lichens, a flask-shaped, sunken receptacle in which spermatia are produced.

Spike. An inflorescence consisting of sessile flowers borne on a common elongated axis.

Spirillum. A bacterium that is curved or spiral in form.

Spongy tissue. The loose parenchyma in a leaf, forming all the mesophyll except the palisade tissue.

Sporangiophore. A stalk or branch bearing one or more sporangia.

Sporangium. A cell or organ containing spores.

Spore. A reproductive body, typically unicellular, capable of direct development into a new individual.

Sporocarp. A special structure enclosing the sporangia in the water ferns.

Sporogenous. Capable of producing spores.

Sporophyll. A spore-bearing leaf, usually more or less modified in form and structure.

Sporophyte. In plants with an alternation of generations, the individual that bears spores and has the diploid number of chromosomes.

Stamen. The microsporophyll or pollen-bearing organ of seed plants.

Stele. The central cylinder in the roots and stems of vascular plants, containing the vascular tissues.

Sterigma. A slender tip arising from a basidium and bearing a basidiospore.

Stigma. The portion of a pistil that receives pollen grains and on which they germinate.

Stipule. One of a pair of appendages borne at the base of some leaves.

Stoma. A small mouth-like opening in the epidermis of a leaf or young stem, bounded by a pair of guard cells, and through which gases pass.

Strobilus. A compact group of sporophylls borne on a more or less elongated axis; a cone.

Stroma. A compact, cushion-like mass of mycelium on or in which perithecia are borne.

Style. The usually attenuated portion of a pistil situated above the ovary.

Suspensor. In many pteridophytes and spermatophytes, an appendage to the embryo, both derived from the zygote.

Symbiosis. The living together, in intimate association, of two dissimilar organisms to their mutual advantage.

Sympetalous. Having petals more or less united.

Sympodium. An apparent main axis composed of successive secondary axes, each representing one fork of a dichotomy, the other being weaker or entirely suppressed.

Synangium. A group of sporangia developed as a single structure, as in some ferns.

Syncarpous. With united carpels.

Synergid. In angiosperms, one of a pair of cells accompanying the egg and with it forming the egg apparatus.

Tapetum. In pteridophytes and spermatophytes, one or several layers of nutritive cells investing the sporogenous tissue in a young sporangium.

Teliospore. In the rust fungi, a thick-walled spore, commonly bilocular and stalked, that produces a basidium when it germinates, generally after a period of dormancy.

Telium. A group of teliospores.

Tetracyclic. Having four cycles or whorls of floral parts.

Tetrad. A group of four cells formed by two successive divisions of a spore mother cell.

Tetramerous. Having the floral parts in sets of four or multiples of four.

Tetraspore. In certain red algae, one of the nonmotile spores produced in a group of four in a sporangium.

Thallus. A vegetative body without differentiation into true roots, stems, and leaves.

Trabecula. A plate of cells bridging an intercellular space or extending partially or completely across the cavity of a sporangium.

Tracheid. A slender, elongated, nonliving, water-conducting cell with tapered, closed ends and thickened, lignified walls.

Trichogyne. In the red algae, a thread-like extension of the carpogonium; in the ascomycetes, a tubular outgrowth of the ascogonium.

Trilocular. Having three locules or cavities.

Trimerous. Having the floral parts in sets of three or multiples of three.

Triploid. Having three times the basic or haploid chromosome number.

Tunica. The outer growth zone in a stem tip, consisting of one or several superficial layers of embryonic cells.

Undulate. Having a wavy surface or margin.

Unicellular. One-celled.

Uniciliate. Having a single cilium.

Unilocular. Having a single locule or cavity.

Uredinium. A group of uredospores.

Uredospore. In the rust fungi, a unicellular spore, commonly borne singly on a stalk, and generally capable of producing a mycelium at once.

Vacuole. A cavity or vesicle in the protoplasm of a cell, containing a watery fluid, the cell sap.

Vallecular canal. In the Equisetinae, one of the canals in the cortex of the stem and lying beneath a groove on the surface.

Vascular bundle. A strand composed primarily of vascular tissue traversing some part of the plant.

Velum. A membranous partition or covering resembling a veil or curtain, especially the membrane covering the gills in an immature mushroom.

Venation. The arrangement or system of veins or vascular bundles in a leaf blade.

Venter. The enlarged basal portion of an archegonium enclosing the egg.

Ventral. Pertaining to the front or inner side of an organ; designating the surface toward the axis, as the upper side of a leaf; in liverworts and ferns, pertaining to the lower side of the prothallium.

Vermiform. Worm-like.

Vernation. The arrangement of foliage leaves within a bud.

Vessel. A water-conveying duct composed of a row of thick-walled, nonliving cells that have lost their end walls; one of the cells forming such a duct.

Volva. A cup at the base of the stipe in certain mushrooms.

Whorl. A circle of similar parts about the same point on an axis.

Xanthophyll. Any of a group of mainly light yellow pigments found in various plants, either alone or associated with others, particularly chlorophyll; they differ from carotins in containing oxygen as well as carbon and hydrogen.

Xylem. In vascular plants, a complex tissue consisting of tracheids, vessels, or both, and often also of wood fibers and parenchyma, and serving for the conduction of water and for mechanical support; woody tissue.

Zoospore. A naked spore with cilia, by the vibration of which it moves.

Zygomorphic. Having bilateral symmetry, the parts arranged symmetrically on either side of a median longitudinal axis.

Zygote. A cell formed by the fusion of two gametes.

INDEX

Numbers in **boldface** type indicate pages on which illustrations appear

A

Abietaceae, 340
Acetabularia, **57**
Achlya, 113, 114
Acorus, vascular bundle, **372**
Acrasieae, 107
Actaea, root, **366**
Actinostele, 220
Adiantum, leaflet, **285**
Adoxa, embryo sac, **388**, 389
Aeciospore, **144**
Aecium, **144**
Aethalium, 105
Agapanthus, embryo, 396
Agaricaceae, 149
Agaricus, **148**, 149
Air chamber, **162**, **163**
Air pore, **162**, **163**
Akinete, **12**, 19
Albugo, 114, **115**
Algae, 7
 alternation of generations, 98
 asexual reproduction, 96
 blue-green, 8
 brown, 66
 classes, 7
  comparison, 93
 evolutionary tendencies, 415
 general conclusions, 94
 golden-brown, 16, **17**
 green, 25
 interrelationships, 98
 multicellular bodies, 95
 red, 85
 sexual reproduction, 96
 yellow-green, 18
Allium, embryo sac, 387, **388**
 root tip, **365**
Alternation of generations, 42, 422
 Algae, 98
 Bryophyta, 160
 Cladophora, 55
 Cutleria, 70
 Dictyota, 72
 Ectocarpus, 68

Alternation of generations, heteromorphic, 70
 isomorphic, 42
 Laminaria, 76
 origin, 423
 Polysiphonia, 92
 Pteridophyta, 209
 Ulva, 42
Amanita, 149
Amphigastrium, 183, **184**
Amphipleura, **22**
Amphithecium, **169**, 171, 181, 189, 196, 202
Anabaena, **10**, **12**
Andreaea, **198**
Andreaeales, 197
 gametophyte, 197
 sex organs, 197
 sporophyte, 197
 summary, 198
Androspore, 47
Anemia, sporangium, **287**
Anemone, development of embryo sac, **385**, **386**
 megasporogenesis, **385**
 ovule, **385**, **386**
Angiopteris, **271**
 antheridium, **274**
 archegonium, **275**
 leaflet, **272**
 sporangium, **272**
Angiospermae, 362
 apomixis, 397
 chief orders, 399
 embryo, 394
 endosperm, 393
 female gametophyte, 384
 fertilization, 391
 flower, 372
 male gametophyte, 389
 subclasses, 362
 summary, 409
 vegetative organs, 363
Annulus, *Agaricus*, **148**
 fern sporangium, 284, **286**, **287**
 moss capsule, 204

Anther, 378
  Iochroma, **380**
  Lilium, **379**
  Trillium, **373**
Antheridium, *Albugo,* **115**
  Angiopteris, **274**
  Anthoceros, **188**
  Azolla, **303**
  Batrachospermum, **90**
  Botrychium, **268, 269**
  Bryales, 201
  Bryophyta, 160
  Chara, **65, 66**
  Claviceps, 135
  Coleochaete, **43**
  Cutleria, **71**
  Dictyota, **74**
  Equisetum, **256**
  Filicales, 289
  Fucus, **82, 83**
  Isoetes, **245**
  Laminaria, **77**
  Lycopodium, **226–228**
  Marchantia, **165, 167**
  Marsilea, **297**
  Mnium, **201**
  Monoblepharis, **111**
  Nemalion, **88**
  Nephrolepis, **290**
  Oedogonium, **47**
  Ophioglossum, **268, 269**
  Pellia, **180**
  Perisporiales, 128
  Polysiphonia, **91**
  Porella, **184**
  Porphyra, **86**
  Psilotum, **216**
  Pyronema, **130**
  Saprolegnia, **113**
  Selaginella, **236**
  Sphaerocarpus, **175**
  Sphaeroplea, **56**
  Sphaerotheca, **129**
  Sphagnum, **193**
  Vaucheria, **58, 59**
  Zonaria, **75**
Anthoceros, **187**
  antheridium, **188**
  archegonium, **188**
  embryo, **189**
  gametophyte, **187**
  plan of, 207
  sporophyte, **187, 190**
Anthocerotales, 186
  gametophyte, 186
  sex organs, 187
  sporophyte, 189

Anthocerotales, summary, 190
Antibiotics, 125
Antipodal cell, **386, 390**
Apical cell, Anthocerotales, 187
  Bryales, 199
  Chara, **64**
  Dictyota, **73**
  Equisetum, **252**
  Filicales, 278
  Fossombronia, **178**
  Fucus, 18
  Jungermanniales, acrogynae, 183
    anacrogynae, 178
  Marchantiales, 162
  Ophioglossales, 263
  Porella, **184**
  Psilotales, 215
  Pteris, **279**
  Reboulia, **162**
  Selaginella, **231**
  Sphacelaria, **70**
  Sphaerocarpales, 174
  Sphagnales, 194
Aplanospore, 19
Apogamy, 398
Apomixis, 397
Apophysis, **203, 204**
Apothecium, 130
  Helvella, **133**
  Morchella, **133**
  Peziza, **132**
  Physcia, **156**
  Sclerotinia, 133
Apple scab, 137
Arales, 407
Araucariaceae, 340
Archaeocalamites, **258,** 259
Archegoniatae, 2
Archegonium, *Angiopteris,* **275**
  Anthoceros, **188**
  Azolla, **303**
  Bryales, 201
  Bryophyta, 161
  Dioon, **327**
  Dryopteris, **291**
  Ephedra, **359**
  Equisetum, **256**
  Filicales, 289
  Ginkgo, **338**
  Isoetes, **246**
  Lycopodium, **226, 227, 229**
  Marchantia, **166, 168**
  Marsilea, **298**
  Mnium, **202**
  Ophioglossum, **269**
  Pellia, **181**
  Pinus, **347**

Archegonium, *Porella,* **184**
  Psilotum, **216**
  Selaginella, **237**
  Sphaerocarpus, **176**
  Sphagnum, **195**
  Zamia, **326**
Archichlamydeae, 362, 399
Arcyria, **105**
Aristolochiales, 400
Armillaria, **150**
Ascocarp, 121
  Aspergillus, **126**
  Claviceps, **136**
  Helvella, **133**
  Microsphaera, **128**
  Morchella, **133**
  Nectria, **135**
  Peziza, **132**
  Physcia, **156**
  Plowrightia, **138**
  Pyronema, **130**
  Sclerotinia, 133
  Tuber, 134
  Venturia, **138**
  Xylaria, **138**
Ascogonium, *Claviceps,* 135
  Laboulbeniales, 140
  Lichenes, 155
  Neurospora, 139
  Pyronema, **130**
  Sphaerotheca, **129**
  Venturia, **138**
Ascogynous hyphae, *Claviceps,* 136
  Lichenes, 155
  Plectascales, 126
  Pyronema, **130**
  Venturia, 137
Ascomycetes, orders, 121
  summary, 157
Ascospore, 121
  Aspergillus, **126**
  Claviceps, 135
  Microsphaera, **128**
  Neurospora, **139**
  Peziza, **132**
  Pyronema, **130**
  Schizosaccharomyces, **123**
  Taphrina, **124**
  Venturia, **138**
  Xylaria, **139**
Ascus, 121
  Aspergillus, **126**
  Claviceps, **136**
  Microsphaera, **128**
  Nectria, **135**
  origin, 130, **131**
  Peziza, **132**

Ascus, *Physcia,* **156**
  Plowrightia, **138**
  Pyronema, **130**
  Sphaerotheca, **129**
  Taphrina, **124**
  Venturia, **138**
  Xylaria, **139**
Aspergillus, **125, 126**
Asterella, 163, 165, 166, 168, 169
Asteroxylon, 212, **213**
Aulocodiscus, **22**
Auricularia, 146
Auriculariales, 146
Autotrophic, definition, 7, 103
Auxospore, 24
Azolla, **299**
  antheridium, **303**
  gametophytes, **303**
  massula, **303**
  sporangia, **301**
  sporocarps, **301**
Azotobacter, 102

B

Bacillariophyceae, 21, **22**
  cell structure, 23
  orders, 23
  reproduction, 24
  summary, 94
Bacillus, **101**
Bacteria, 100
  aerobic, 102
  anaerobic, 102
  autotrophic, 103
  denitrifying, 103
  nitrifying, 103
  nitrogen-fixing, 102
Basidiocarp, 140
  Agaricus, **148**
  Auriculariales, 146
  Clavaria, **147**
  Gasteromycetales, 151
  Hymenomycetales, 147
  Phallus, **152**
  Tremellales, 146
Basidiomycetes, orders, 140
  summary, 157
Basidiospore, 140
  Coprinus, **149**
  Gasteromycetales, 151
  Hymenomycetales, 147
  Puccinia, **144**
  Ustilago, **141**
Basidium, 140
  Auriculariales, 146
  Coprinus, **149**

Basidium, development, **150**
    Exobasidiales, 147
    Gasteromycetales, 151
    Hymenomycetales, 147
    Puccinia, **144**
    Tremellales, 146
    Ustilago, **141**
Batrachospermum, **89, 90**
Beggiatoa, 101, 103
Bennettitales, 315
    sporophyte, 315
    strobilus, 316
    summary, 318
Black knot, 136, **137**
Botrychium, 262, **263**
    antheridium, **268, 269**
    archegonium, **268, 269**
    embryo, **269**
    gametophyte, **268**
    petiole, **266**
    rhizome, **265**
    root, **264**
Botrydium, 19, **20**
Branch trace, 212, 222
Bread mold, 117
Bryales, 198
    gametophyte, 199
    sex organs, 200
    sporophyte, 201
    summary, 204
Bryophyta, classes, 160
        comparison, 205
    evolutionary tendencies, 416
    gametophyte, 206
    general conclusions, 205
    sporophyte, 206
Bryopsis, **60**
Budding, **122**
Bulbochaete, 48

C

Calamitales, cones, **258**
Calamites, **257**
Calamophyton, **248**
Calyptra, 161, 168, **171, 172**, 290, **292**
Calyptrogen, 364, **365**
Calyx, 373
Campanulales, 406
Capillitium, 105, **106,** 152
Capsella, development of embryo, 394,
    395
    floral development, **377**
Capsule, 161, 169, **170, 172, 177, 182, 186,**
    194, **203, 204**
Carboniferous swamp forest, **239, 257,**
    312
Carinal canal, 252, **253**

Carotin, 19
Carpel, 309, 381
Carpogonium, 87
    Batrachospermum, **90**
    Nemalion, **88**
    Polysiphonia, **92**
    Porphyra, **86**
Carpospore, 87
    Batrachospermum, **90**
    Nemalion, **88**
    Polysiphonia, **91**
    Porphyra, **86**
Caulerpa, 60, **61**
Cell division, *Anabaena*, **10**
    Oedogonium, 43, **44**
    Surirella, **24**
Centrospermales, 400
Ceratium, **18**
Chaetophora, 39
Chalaza, 383
Chamaesiphon, 12
Chara, **64, 65, 66**
Charophyceae, 63
    reproduction, 64
    summary, 66, 94
    vegetative body, 63
Chlamydomonas, 26, **27**
Chlamydospore, **141**
Chlorella, 32
Chlorochromonas, **19**
Chlorococcales, 32
    summary, 38
Chlorococcum, 32, **33**
Chlorophyceae, 25
    orders, 26
    summary, 61, 94
Chromulina, 16, **17**
Chroococcus, 9
Chrysamoeba, 16, **17**
Chrysophyceae, 16, **17**
    summary, 93
Chytridiales, 108
    summary, 111
Chytridium, 108, **109**
Cilium, 14
Cladophora, 54, **55**
Cladothrix, 101
Classification, Embryophyta, 2–4
    plants, 1
    Thallophyta, 2, 3
Clavaria, **147**
Clavariaceae, 147
Claviceps, 135, **136**
Cleistothecium, *Aspergillus*, **126**
    Microsphaera, **128**
Closterium, 48, **49**
Clostridium, 102

Cocconeis, **25**
Codium, **59**
Codonotheca, **313**
Coelosphaerium, 9
Coenocyte, 20, 34, 36, 54, 57
Coenopteridales, 260
Colacium, 15
Coleochaete, 42, **43, 44**
Coleus, stem tip, **368**
Columella, *Anthoceros*, 189
  Funaria, **203**
  Rhizopus, 117, **118, 119**
  Sphagnum, 196
Conceptacle, **82**
Conducting tissues, **369**
Cone (*see* Strobilus)
Conidiophore, 125
  Aspergillus, **125,** 126
  Claviceps, 135
  Erysiphe, **127**
  Nectria, 135
  Penicillium, **125,** 126
  Plowrightia, 136
  Sclerotinia, 132
  Venturia, 137, **138**
  Xylaria, 139
Conidium, 124, 125
  Aspergillus, **125**
  Claviceps, 135
  Erysiphe, **127**
  Nectria, 135
  Neurospora, 139
  Penicillium, **125**
  Plowrightia, 136
  Sclerotinia, 132
  Taphrina, 124
  Venturia, **138**
  Xylaria, 139
Coniferales, 340
  embryo, 349
  families, 340
  female gametophyte, 346
  male gametophyte, 348
  ovulate strobilus, 345
  sporophyte, 342
  staminate strobilus, 345
  summary, 353
Conjugales, 48
  summary, 54
Conjugation, 27
  Closterium, **49**
  Cocconeis, **25**
  Mougeotia, **50**
  Rhizopus, **118**
  Schizosaccharomyces, **123**
  Spirogyra, **51, 53**
  Zygnema, **54**

Conocephalum, 163, 165, 166, 169
Contractile vacuole, 15
Coprinus, **149**
Cordaianthus, **333**
Cordaitales, 330
  gametophytes, 332
  sporophyte, 330
  strobili, 331
  summary, 333
Cordaites, **332**
Cormophyta, 2
Corn smut, 141
Corolla, 373
Corpus, 367
Cortex, 211
Cosmarium, **50**
Cotyledon, 327, **353**
Craterum, **105**
Crossotheca, **313**
Cryptogam, 1
Cryptogamia, 1
Cryptomitrium, embryo, **170**
Cryptophyceae, 17
Cupressaceae, 340
Cupressus, **343**
Cutleria, 70, **71**
Cutleriales, 70
  summary, 72
Cyanophyceae, 8
  branching, 12
  cell structure, **10**
  distribution and habitat, 8
  false branching, **13**
  orders, 8
  plant body, 9
  reproduction, 11
  resting spores, **12**
  simple colonial, **9**
  summary, 13, 93
Cyanophycin, 10
Cyatheaceae, 277
Cycadales, 319
  embryo, 326
  female gametophyte, 323
  male gametophyte, 325
  ovulate strobilus, 323
  sporophyte, 319
  staminate strobilus, 321
  summary, 328
Cycadeoidea, stem, **315**
  strobilus, **316–318**
Cycadofilicales, 311, **312**
  gametophytes, 313
  megasporangium, 311
  microsporangium, 311, **313**
  sporophyte, 311
  summary, 314

Cycas, female cone, **322**
  megasporophylls, **325**
  microsporophylls, **323**
  vernation, **320**
Cyrtomium, sporangium, **288**
Cyst, 15, 16, 57
Cystocarp, 88
  Nemalion, **88**
  Polysiphonia, **91**

D

Danaea, **272**–274
Dendroceros, 186, 187, 190
Dennstaedtia, stele, **281**
Dermatogen, 364, **365**, 394, **395**
Dermocarpa, **12**
Desmids, 48, **49, 50**
Diachea, **105**
Dianthus, pistil, **382**
Diatoms (*see* Bacillariophyceae)
Dicksonia, **277**
Dicksoniaceae, 277
Dicotyledoneae, 362, 399
Dictyostele, 211, 283
Dictyostelium, **107**
Dictyota, 72, **73, 74**
Dictyotales, 72
  summary, 76
Didymium, **104**
Dinobryon, 16, **17**
Dinocladium, **18**
Dinoflagellate, **18**
Dinophyceae, 18
  summary, 93
Dinothrix, 18
Dioecious, 30
Dioon, **319**
  archegonium, **327**
  male gametophyte, **328**
  ovule, **329**
Docidium, **50**
Dorycordaites, **331**
Dothideales, 139
Draparnaldia, 39, **40**
Dryopteris, archegonium, **291**
  leaflet, **285**
  sperm, **290**

E

Ebenales, 404
Ectocarpales, 67
  summary, 68
Ectocarpus, **67**
Egg, 29
  Anemone, **386**
  Angiopteris, **275**

Egg, *Anthoceros*, **188**
  Chara, **66**
  Coleochaete, **43, 44**
  Cutleria, **71**
  Dictyota, **74**
  Dioon, **329**
  Dryopteris, **291**
  Equisetum, **256**
  Eudorina, **30**
  Fritillaria, **390, 392**
  Fucus, **83**
  Isoetes, **246**
  Laminaria, **77**
  Lycopodium, **229**
  Marchantia, **168**
  Marsilea, **298**
  Mnium, **202**
  Monoblepharis, **111**
  Oedogonium, **47**
  Ophioglossum, **269**
  Pellia, **181**
  Pinus, **347, 350**
  Porella, **184**
  Saprolegnia, **113**
  Sphaerocarpus, **176**
  Sphaeroplea, **56**
  Sphagnum, **195**
  Vaucheria, **58**
  Volvox, **31**
Egregia, 79
Elater, 171, **172**, 190
Elaterophore, 181, **182**
Embryo, Angiospermae, 394
  Anthoceros, **189**
  Botrychium, **269**
  Capsella, **395**
  Coniferales, 349
  Cryptomitrium, **170**
  Cycadales, 326
  Equisetales, 256
  Filicales, 290
  Fossombronia, **182**
  Funaria, **203**
  Ginkgo, **339**
  Ginkgoales, 339
  Gnetales, 360
  Hydropteridales, 297, 302
  Isoetales, 247
  Isoetes, **246**
  Lycopodiales, 229
  Lycopodium, **227, 230**
  Marattiales, 274
  Marchantia, **166, 171**
  Marsilea, **298**
  Megaceros, **189**
  Ophioglossales, 269
  Pinus, **351, 353**

Embryo, Polypodiaceae, **292**
  Psilotales, 217
  Riccia, **169**
  Sagittaria, **397**
  Selaginella, **238**
  Selaginellales, 237
  Sphagnum, **196**
  Zamia, **330**
Embryo sac, 384
  Anemone, **385, 386**
  Fritillaria, **390**
  ordinary type, **388**
  variation in development, 386, **388**
Embryophyta, 2
  classification, 2–4
Empusa, 120, **121**
Endarch, 210
Endodermis, 211
Endosperm, 327, **353, 393**
Endospore, **12**, 102
Endothecium, **169**, 171, 181, 189, 196, 202, **379, 380**, 381
Entomophthorales, 120
Ephedra, 354, **355**
  archegonium, **359**
  female gametophyte, **359**
  male gametophyte, **360**
  ovule, **359**
  proembryo, **361**
  strobili, **355**
Epidermis, 211
Epigyny, 375, **376**
Equisetales, 250
  gametophyte, 254
  sporangium, 253
  sporophyte, 250
  summary, 256
  vascular anatomy, 252
Equisetinae, orders, 247
  summary, 304
Equisetum, 250, **251**
  embryo, 256
  gametophyte, **256**
  sporangium, **254, 255**
  stem structure, **253**
Ergot, 135
Ergotine, 135
Ericales, 404
Erigeron, floral development, **378**
Erysiphe, **127**
Etapteris, **261**
Eudorina, 28, **29**
Euglena, **14**
Euglenophyceae, cell structure, 14
  relationships, 15
  reproduction, 15
  summary, 16, 93

Eusporangiate, 226
Evolution, plant kingdom, 412
  sex, 417
    organs, 419
Evolutionary tendencies, algae, 415
  bryophytes, 416
  prominent, 415
  pteridophytes, 416
  spermatophytes, 417
Exarch, 210
Exobasidiales, 146
Exobasidium, 146
Eyespot, **14**, 26, 27, 39

F

Fagales, 399
Families, Coniferales, 340
  Filicales, 276
  Gasteromycetales, 151
  Hymenomycetales, 147
Farinales, 407
Fertile spike, 265
Fertilization, 30
  Angiospermae, 391
  Fritillaria, **392**
  Pinus, **350**
Fiber, 210, **369**
Filicales, embryo, 290
  families, 276
  gametophyte, 287
  sorus, 284
  sporangium, 286
  sporophyte, 278
  summary, 291
  vascular anatomy, 278
Filicinae, orders, 260
  summary, 304
Fission, 11
Flagellates, 14
Flagellum, 14
Floral development, 376
  Capsella, **377**
  Erigeron, **378**
  Ranunculus, **377**
Flower, 372, 410
  actinomorphic, 374
  apetalous, 373
  apocarpous, 375, 381
  carpel, 381
  choripetalous, 375
  establishment of whorls and definite numbers, 374
  hypogyny, perigyny, and epigyny, 375
  Magnolia, **374**
  naked, 374
  ovule, 383

Flower, pentacyclic, 375
   perianth, 373
   stamen, 378
   sympetalous, 375
   syncarpous, 375, 381
   tetracyclic, 375
   Trillium, **373**
   zonal development, 375
   zygomorphic, 374
Foot, 161, 169, **171, 172, 230**, 238, **246, 292**
Fossombronia, apical cell, **178**
   embryo, **182**
Fritillaria, embryo sac, **388**, 389, **390**
   endosperm, **393**
   fertilization, **392**
Frond, 278
Fruit, 398
Fucales, 80
   summary, 84
Fucoxanthin, 66
Fucus, 80, **81–83**
Fuligo, **105**
Funaria, **200, 203**
Fungi, 100
   alga-like, 108
   bird's-nest, 152
   classes, 100
     comparison, 156
   club, 140
   coral, 147
   ear, 146
   gametic reproduction, 158
   general conclusions, 157
   gill, 149
   Imperfecti, 153
   pore, 147
   sac, 121
   spore reproduction, 158
   stinkhorn, **152**
   tooth, 147
   trembling, 146
   vegetative body, 157
Funiculus, 383

G

Gametangium, *Bryopsis*, 60
   Codium, 59
   Ectocarpus, **67**
   Pylaiella, **68**
Gametes, 27
   differentiation, 418
Gametophore, 199
Gametophyte, 42
   Andreaea, **198**
   Andreaeales, 197

Gametophyte, *Anthoceros*, **187**
   Anthocerotales, 186
   Botrychium, **268**
   Bryales, 199
   Bryophyta, 206
   Cutleria, **71**
   Cycadofilicales, 313
   Equisetales, 254
   Equisetum, **256**
   female, Angiospermae, 384
     Azolla, **303**
     Coniferales, 346
     Cordaitales, 332
     Cycadales, 323
     Ephedra, **359**
     Ginkgoales, 338
     Gnetales, 356
     Isoetes, **246**
     Marsilea, **298**
     Pinus, **347**
     Selaginella, **237**
     Zamia, **326**
   Filicales, 287
   Isoetales, 245
   Jungermanniales, acrogynae, 183
     anacrogynae, 178
   Laminaria, **77**
   Lycopodiales, 226
   Lycopodium, **226, 227**
   male, Angiospermae, 389
     Azolla, **303**
     Coniferales, 348
     Cordaitales, 332
     Cycadales, 325
     Dioon, **328**
     Ephedra, **360**
     Ginkgoales, 339
     Gnetales, 358
     Isoetes, **245**
     Marsilea, **297**
     Pinus, **348**
     Selaginella, **236**
   Marattiales, 273
   Marchantia, **164**
   Marchantiales, 162
   Marsileaceae, 296
   Ophioglossales, 267
   Ophioglossum, **268**
   Pallavicinia, **179**
   Pellia, **179**
   Polypodiaceae, **289**
   Porella, **184**
   Psilotales, 216, 217
   Psilotum, **216**
   Pteridophyta, 306
   Riccia, **162**
   Salviniaceae, 301

Gametophyte, Selaginellales, 234
  Sphaerocarpales, 173
  Sphaerocarpus, **174**
  Sphagnales, 192
  Sphagnum, **193, 194**
  Symphyogyna, **179**
Gap, 212
Gasteromycetales, families, 151
Gemma, 164, 179, 183, 199
Gentianales, 405
Geologic eras, 5, 6
Geologic periods, later, 6, 310
Geologic time, division, 5, 6
Geothallus, 173, 174
Geraniales, 402
Gill, **148, 149**
Ginkgo, 333, **334**
  archegonium, **338**
  embryo, **339**
  leaf blade, **335**
  megaspores, **337**
  ovulate strobili, **337**
  ovule, **337**
  staminate strobili, **336**
  stem, **335**
Ginkgoales, 333
  embryo, 339
  female gametophyte, 338
  male gametophyte, 339
  ovulate strobilus, 337
  sporophyte, 334
  staminate strobilus, 336
  summary, 340
Girdle, 21
Gleba, 151
Gleichenia, **276**
  sporangium, **287**
  stele, **280**
Gleicheniaceae, 277
Glochidium, 310, **303**
Gloeocapsa, **9**
Gloeodinium, 18
Gloeotrichia, **12**
Glumales, 407
Glycogen, 10
Gnetales, 354
  embryo, 360
  female gametophyte, 356
  male gametophyte, 358
  ovulate strobilus, 356
  sporophyte, 354
  staminate strobilus, 355
  summary, 360
Gnetum, 354
  strobili, **357**
Gonimoblast, **88, 90**
Gonium, **28**

Gullet, 15
Gymnospermae, 301
  geologic distribution, **310**
  orders, 311
  summary, 409

H

Haematochrome, 28
Haplostele, 220
Haustorium, *Albugo*, 115
  Erysiphe, **127**
  Rhizopus, **118**
Helminthostachys, 262, 264–267, 269, 270
Helobiales, 406
Helvella, **133,** 134
Helvellales, 133
Hemitrichia, **105**
Hepaticae, orders, 161
  summary, 205
Heterocyst, 11, **12**
Heterogamy, 30
Heterospory, 209, 233, 306
Heterothallic, 120
Heterotrophic, 7, 100
Histogen, 364, **365**
Homologous structures, 414
Homospory, 161, 209
Homothallic, 120
Hormogonium, 11
Hornea, 214
Horsetails, 250
Hydnaceae, 147
Hydrodictyon, 34, **36**
Hydropteridales, families, 292
  summary, 302
  (*See also* Marsileaceae; Salviniaceae)
Hydrurus, 16, **17**
Hyenia, 248
Hyeniales, 247
Hymenium, 124
  Agaricaceae, 149
  Auriculariales, 146
  Claviceps, 135
  Gasteromycetales, 151
  Hymenomycetales, 147
  Peziza, 132
  Physcia, **156**
  Plowrightia, 136
  Pyronema, 130
  Taphrina, 124
  Tremellales, 146
  Xylaria, 139
Hymenogastraceae, 151
Hymenomycetales, families, 147
Hymenophyllaceae, 277
Hymenophyllum, sporangium, **287**

Hypha, 108
Hypocotyl, 327, **353**
Hypocreales, 139
Hypogyny, 375, **376**
Hypophysis, **395**

I

Indusium, 284, **285, 295, 301**
    false, **285**
Integument, 312, 323, **326, 347, 359, 386**
Interrelationships, Algae, 98
    Pteridophyta, 307
    Spermatophyta, 410
Iochroma, microsporangium, **380**
Isoetales, 241
    embryo, 247
    gametophytes, 245
    sporangia, 243
    sporophyte, 241
    summary, 248
    vascular anatomy, 242
Isoetes, **241**
    embryo, **246**
    female gametophyte, **246**
    male gametophyte, **245**
    megasporangium, **244**
    microsporangium, **244, 245**
    sporangia, **244**
    stele, **243**
    stem tip, **242**
Isogamete, 27
    Acetabularia, 57
    Caulerpa, 61
    Chlamydomonas, **27**
    Chlorococcum, 32
    Cladophora, 55
    Desmids, 49
    Ectocarpus, 67
    Gonium, 26
    Hydrodictyon, **36**
    Olpidium, 109
    Pandorina, **29**
    Pediastrum, **36**
    Plasmodiophora, 112
    Protosiphon, **37**
    Rhizopus, **118**
    Spirogyra, **51**
    Synchytrium, 111
    Ulothrix, **38**
    Ulva, 41
    Zygnema, 54
Isogamy, 27
Isthmia, **22**

J

Juglandales, 399
Jungermanniales, 177

Jungermanniales, Acrogynae, 183
    gametophyte, 183
    sex organs, 184
    sporophyte, 185
    Anacrogynae, 177
        gametophyte, 178, **179**
        sex organs, 179
        sporophyte, 180
        summary, 185

K

Kelps, 76
    other, 79

L

Laboulbeniales, 140
Labyrinthuleae, 108
Laminaria, **76, 77**
Laminariales, 76
    summary, 79
Land habit, establishment, 206
Leaf, gap, 212, 260
    structure, angiosperms, **363**
        Pinus, **343**
    trace, 212, 222
Lepidodendrales, 238
Lepidodendron, **240**
Lepidostrobus, **239**
Leptosporangiate, 286
Leucosin, 16
Lichenes, 153, **154, 155, 156**
    crustose, 153, **154**
    foliose, 153, **154**
    fruticose, 153, **154**
Life cycles, types, 422
Ligule, *Isoetes*, **242, 244**
    Selaginella, 231, 233, **234, 238**
Liliales, 408
Lilium, anther, **379**
    pollen grain, **391**
Liverworts, 161
Lunularia, 164
Lycogala, **105**
Lycoperdaceae, 152
Lycopodiales, 218
    embryo, 229
    gametophyte, 226
    sporangium, 223
    sporophyte, 219
    summary, 229
    vascular anatomy, 220
Lycopodiinae, orders, 218
    summary, 304
Lycopodium, **218, 223, 224**
    antheridium, **228**

Lycopodium, archegonium, **229**
  embryo, **230**
  gametophyte, **226, 227**
  sporangium, **225**
  stele, **221, 222**
  stem tip, **219**
Lycopsida, 3, 4, 218
Lyginopteris, **312–314**
Lyngbya, 11

M

Macrocystis, **78**
Macrozamia, megasporophyll, **325**
Magnolia, flower, **374**
  stem, **370**
Malvales, 403
Marattia, leaflet, **272**
  root, **271**
Marattiales, 270
  embryo, 274
  gametophyte, 273
  sporangium, 272
  sporophyte, 270
  summary, 274
  vascular anatomy, 270
Marchantia, air chamber, **163**
  air pore, **163**
  antheridium, **165, 167**
  archegonium, **166, 168**
  cupule, 164
  embryo, **166, 171**
  female receptacle, **166**
  gemma, 164
  male and female plants, **164**
  male receptacle, **165**
  sperm, **165**
  sporophyte, **172**
  thallus, **163**
Marchantiales, 161
  gametophyte, 162
  sex organs, 164
  sporophyte, 168
  summary, 172
Marsilea, **293**
  female gametophyte, **298**
  male gametophyte, **297**
  rhizome, **294**
  sporangia, **295**
  sporocarp, **296**
Marsileaceae, 293
  embryo, 297
  gametophytes, 296
  sporocarp, 294
  sporophyte, 293
Massula, 301, **303**
Megaceros, **189**, 190

Megasporangium, 233
  Anemone, **385**
  Azolla, **301**
  Cycadofilicales, 311
  Fritillaria, **390**
  Isoetes, **244**
  Marsilea, **295**
  Salix, **384**
  Salvinia, **302**
  Selaginella, **233, 235**
Megaspore, 233
  Anemone, **385**
  Azolla, **301**
  Ginkgo, **337**
  Isoetes, **244**
  Marsilea, **298**
  Pinus, **348**
  Salvinia, **302**
  Selaginella, **233, 235**
Megasporocarp, 300
  Azolla, **301**
  Salvinia, **302**
Megasporophyll, 233
  Cycadales, **325**
  Isoetes, **244**
  Selaginella, **233**
Merismopedia, **9**
Mesarch, 210
Metachlamydeae, 316, 404
Metaxylem, 210
Micrasterias, **50**
Micropyle, 312, 323, **326, 386**
Microsphaera, 127, **128**
Microsporangium, 233
  Angiospermae, 378
  Azolla, **301**
  Bennettitales, 317
  Cycadofilicales, 311, **313**
  Ginkgoales, 336
  Gnetales, 355
  Iochroma, **380**
  Isoetes, **244**
  Lilium, **379**
  Marsilea, **295**
  Pinus, **345**
  Salvinia, **302**
  Selaginella, **233–235**
  Zamia, **324**
Microspore, 233
  Azolla, **303**
  Dioon, **328**
  Isoetes, **244**
  Marsilea, **297**
  Pinus, **348**
  Selaginella, **233, 235**
Microsporocarp, 300
  Azolla, **301**

Microsporophyll, 233
  Cycadeoidea, **317**
  Cycas, **323**
  Ginkgo, **336**
  Isoetes, **244**
  Pinus, **345**
  Selaginella, **233**
Mildews, downy, 114
  other, 116
  powdery, 127
Mnium, 199
  antheridium, **201**
  archegonium, **202**
  capsule, **204**
Monoblepharidales, 111
Monoblepharis, **111**
Monocotyledoneae, 316, 406
Monosiphonous, 67
Monospore, 89
Morchella, **133**
Mosses, 192
  plan of, 207
Mougeotia, **50,** 51
Mucorales, 117
  summary, 120
Multicellular bodies, development of, 95
Musci, orders, 192
  summary, 205
Mushroom, 149
Mycelium, 108
Mycophyta, 2, 3, 7
Myrtales, 403
Myxamoeba, 106
Myxobacteria, 103
Myxomycetes, plant body, 104
  reproduction, 105
  summary, 106, 156

N

Navicula, **22**
Nectria, 134, **135**
Nemalion, 87, **88**
Nereocystis, **79**
Neuropteris, **239, 312**
Neurospora, **139**
Nidulariaceae, 152
Nitrifying bacteria, 103
Nitrobacter, 103
Nitrogen-fixing bacteria, 102
Nitrosomonas, 113
Nostoc, **9**
Notothylas, 187, 189, 190
Nucellus, 312, **313**, 323, **326, 347,** 383
Nucleus, fusion, 384, **386**
  generative, **348, 391**
  male, **350,** 391, **392**

Nucleus, polar, 384, **390**
  primary endosperm, 392
  tube, **328, 348, 350, 391**

O

Oedogoniales, 45
  summary, 48
Oedogonium, 45, **46–48**
Oenothera, embryo sac, 387, **388**
Olpidium, **109**
Ontogeny, 1, 414
Oögonium, *Albugo*, **115**
  Chara, **65, 66**
  Coleochaete, **44**
  Cutleria, **71**
  Dictyota, **73**
  Fucus, **82, 83**
  Laminaria, **77**
  Monoblepharis, **111**
  Oedogonium, **47, 48**
  Saprolegnia, **113**
  Sphaeroplea, **55**
  Vaucheria, **58, 59**
  Zonaria, **75**
Oöplasm, **115**, 116
Operculum, Bryales, **203, 204**
Ophioglossales, 261
  embryo, 269
  gametophyte, 267
  sporangium, 265
  sporophyte, 262
  summary, 270
  vascular anatomy, 263
Ophioglossum, **262**
  antheridium, **268, 269**
  archegonium, **269**
  gametophyte, **268**
  root, **264**
  sporangium, **267**
Opuntiales, 403
Orchidales, 408
Oscillatoria, **9**
Osmunda, sporangium, **287**
  stele, **282**
Osmundaceaea, 276
Ovary, 362, **373**, 381
  inferior, 376
  superior, 376
Ovule, 309, 312, 383
  anatropous, **383**
  Anemone, **385, 386**
  campylotropous, **383**
  Cycadeoidea, **318**
  development, **383**
  Dioon, **329**
  direction, **363**

Ovule, *Ephedra*, **359**
  Fritillaria, **390**
  Lyginopteris, **314**
  orthotropous, **383**
  Pinus, **345, 346**
  Welwitschia, **358**
  Zamia, **326**
Ovuliferous scale, **345, 346**

P

Palaeostachya, **258**, 259
Pallavicinia, thallus, **179**
Palmales, 407
Palmella, 26, **27**, 32, 39
Pandanales, 406
Pandorina, 28, **29**
Papaverales, 401
Parallel development, 413
Paramylon, 15
Paraphysis, Bryales, 200
  Claviceps, 135, **136**
  Cutleria, 72
  Fucus, **82**, 83
  Laminaria, **77**
  Nectria, **135**
  Physcia, **156**
  Plowrightia, 136, **138**
  Pyronema, **130**
  Zonaria, 76
Parasite, 100
Parietales, 403
Parthenocarpy, 398
Parthenogenesis, 114, 397
Pediastrum, 33, **34, 35**
Pelargonium, pistil, **382**
Pellia, antheridium, **180**
  archegonium, **181**
  capsule, **182**
  thallus, **179**
Pellicle, 14
Penaea, embryo sac, 387, **388**
Penicillium, 124, **125**
Peperomia, embryo sac, 387, **388**
Perianth, 373
Periblem, 364, **365, 394, 395**
Pericarp, 398
Perichaetium, 200
Peridium, 151
Perigyny, 375, **376**
Periplasm, 116
Perisperm, 393
Perisporiales, 127
Peristome, **203, 204**
Perithecium, 135
  Claviceps, **136**
  Laboulbeniales, 140

Perithecium, *Nectria*, **135**
  Neurospora, 139
  Plowrightia, **138**
  Venturia, **138**
  Xylaria, **139**
Peronosporales, 114
  summary, 117
Petal, **373**
Peziza, **132**
Pezizales, 129
  summary, 133
Phaeocystis, 16
Phaeophyceae, 66
  orders, 67
  summary, 85, 94
Phaeothamnion, 16, **17**
Phallaceae, 152
Phallus, **152**
Phanerogam, 1
Phanerogamia, 1
Phellogen, 369
Phloem, 210
  elements, **369**
Phycocyanin, 8
Phycoerythrin, 8, 85
Phycomycetes, orders, 108
  summary, 157
  Phycophyta, 2, 3, 7
Phyllactinia, 127
Phylloglossum, 219, **220,** 226
Phylogeny, 1, 144
Physcia, **155, 156**
Phytophthora, 116
Pileus, **148,** 149
Pilobolus, 120
Pilularia, 293, 294
Pinna, 278
Pinnularia, **21**
Pinnule, 278
Pinus, archegonium, **347**
  embryo, **351, 353**
  female gametophyte, **347**
  fertilization, **350**
  leaf, **343**
  male gametophyte, **348**
  ovulate strobilus, **341**
  ovule, **346, 347**
  staminate strobilus, **345**
  stem, **344**
Piperales, 399
Pistil, **373, 382**
Placenta, 383
Plant life of the past, 4
Plantaginales, 405
Plasmodiophora, **112**
Plasmodiophorales, 112
Plasmodium, 104, 254, **267,** 287, **295,** 381

Plasmopara, 116, **117**
Plectascales, 124
Plectostele, 220
Plerome, 364, **365**, 394, **395**
Pleurosigma, **22**
Plowrightia, 136, **137**, **138**
Plumbagella, embryo sac, **388**, 389
Plumbago, embryo sac, **388**, 389
Plumule, 327, **353**
Podocarpaceae, 340
Podosphaera, 127, 128
Pollen, grain, *Dioon*, **328**, 329
    Ephedra, **360**
    Lilium, **371**, **391**
    Pinus, **348**
  sac, **379**
  tube, Angiospermae, 391
    Dioon, **328**, **329**
    Ephedra, **360**
    Pinus, **348**, **349**
Pollinium, 381
Polyembryony, 352
Polygonales, 400
Polypodiaceae, 278
Polypodium, leaflet, **285**
Polyporaceae, 147
Polysiphonia, 89, **91**, **92**
Polysiphonous, definition, 67
Polytrichum, 199, 203
Porella, **184**, **186**
Porphyra, **86**
Porphyridium, 87
Postelsia, **80**
Primulales, 404
Procarp, *Batrachospermum*, **90**
  Nemalion, **88**
  Polysiphonia, **92**
Proembryo, 326
  Capsella, **395**
  Ephedra, **361**
  Ginkgo, **339**
  Pinus, **351**
  Sagittaria, **397**
  Zamia, **330**
Propagule, 69
Prothallium (*see* Gametophyte)
Protoascales, 122
Protococcus, 40, **41**
Protodiscales, 123
Protonema, 161
  moss, **199**
Protosiphon, 36, **37**
Protostele, 211, 280
Protoxylem, 210
Pseudopodium, 196, 198
Psilophytales, 212, **213**

Psilophytinae, orders, 212
  summary, 303
Psilophyton, 212
Psilopsida, 3, 4, 212
Psilotales, **214**
  embryo, 217
  gametophyte, 217
  sporangium, 216
  sporophyte, 215
  summary, 217
  vascular anatomy, 215
Psilotum, **214–216**, 217
Pteridium, leaflet, **285**
  rhizome, **283**
  vascular bundle, **284**
Pteridophyta, classes, 209, 260
  comparison, 303
  evolutionary tendencies, 416
  gametophyte, 306
  general conclusions, 304
  interrelationships, 307
  sporophyte, 304
  strobilus, 305
  vascular system, 210
Pteris, root tip, **279**
Pteropsida, 4, 260
Puccinia, **142–144**
Puffball, 152
Pylaiella, **68**
Pyrenoid, 26
Pyrenomycetales, 134
  summary, 139
Pyronema, 129, **130**, **131**
Pythium, 116

R

Radicle, 327, **353**
Ranales, 401
Ranunculus, floral development, **377**
Raphe, 23
Reboulia, 165, 166
  air chambers, **162**
  air pore, **162**
  apical cell, **162**
  embryo, 169
  thallus, **162**
Recapitulation, 414
Regnellidium, 293
Reproduction, asexual, 417
  in algae, 96
  in fungi, 158
  sexual, 418
  in algae, 96
  in fungi, 158
Reservoir, 15
Rhamnales, 403

Rhizobium, 102
Rhizoid, **163**
Rhizophore, 231, 240, 243
Rhizopus, 117, **118, 119**
Rhodophyceae, orders, 85
  summary, 93, 94
Rhynia, **213**
Riccardia, capsule, **182**
Riccia, gametophyte, **162**
  sporophyte, **170**
Riella, 173, 174
Rivularia, 12
Root, mature, 365, **366**
  tip, *Allium*, **365**
    Pteris, **279**
  trace, 212, 222
Rootcap, **365**
Rosales, 402
Rubiales, 406
Rusts, 142
  autoecious, 146
  heteroecious and other, 145

S

Saccharomyces, **122**
Sagittaria, development of embryo, 396, **397**
Salicales, 399
Salix, megasporangium, **384**
  root, **367**
Salvinia, **299**
  sporangia, **302**
  sporocarp, **302**
Salviniaceae, 299
  embryo, 302
  gametophytes, 301
  sporocarps, 300
  sporophyte, 299
Santalales, 400
Sapindales, 402
Saprolegnia, **113**
Saprolegniales, 113
  summary, 114
Saprophyte, 100
Sarcina, **101**
Sargassum, **84**
Sarraceniales, 402
Scenedesmus, 33, **34**
Schizaeaceae, 276
Schizomycetes, 100
  activities, 102
  structure and reproduction, 100
  summary, 103, 156
Schizosaccharomyces, **123**
Scitaminales, 408
Sclerodermaceae, 152
Sclerotinia, 132

Sclerotium, 135
  Claviceps, **136**
  Myxomycetes, 105
  Xylaria, 139
Scytonema, 12, **13**
Sedum, carpels, **382**
Seed, **353,** 409
Seedling, 398
Selaginella, 230
  embryo, **238**
  female gametophyte, **237**
  male gametophyte, **236**
  megasporangium, **233, 235**
  microsporangium, **233–235**
  stele, **232**
  stem tip, **231**
Selaginellales, 230
  embryo, 237
  gametophytes, 234
  sporangia, 231
  sporophyte, 231
  summary, 237
  vascular anatomy, 231
Sepal, **373**
Seta, 161, 169, 172
Sex, determination, 175
  evolution, 417
  organs, Andreaeales, 197
    Anthocerotales, 187
    Aspergillus, **126**
    Bryales, 200
    Claviceps, 135
    evolution, 149
    Jungermanniales, acrogynae, 184
      anacrogynae, 179
    Laboulbeniales, 140
    Lichenes, 155
    Marchantiales, 164
    Perisporiales, 128
    Plectascales, 127
    Pyronema, **130**
    Sphaerocarpales, 174
    Sphaerotheca, **129**
    Sphagnales, 193
    Venturia, 137
  origin, 418
  significance, 422
Sexuality, further expressions of, 421
Sieve tube, 210, **369**
Sigillaria, **239**
Silphium, endosperm, **393**
Siphonales, 57
  summary, 61
Siphonocladiales, 54
  summary, 57
Siphonostele, amphiphloic, 211, 281
  ectophloic, 211, 282

Slime fungi, other, 106
Slime molds, 104
Solanum, pistil, **382**
Soredium, 154
Sorus, *Angiopteris,* **272**
  Filicales, 284, **285**
  gradate, 286
  Marsilea, **295, 296**
  mixed, 287
  simple, 285
Specialization, 413
Sperm, *Chara,* **65**
  Coleochaete, **43**
  Cutleria, **71**
  Dictyota, **74**
  Dioon, **329**
  Dryopteris, 290
  Equisetum, **256**
  Eudorina, **30**
  Fucus, **83**
  Isoetes, **246**
  Laminaria, **77**
  Lycopodium, **288**
  Marchantia, **165**
  Marsilea, **297**
  Monoblepharis, **111**
  Oedogonium, **47**
  Ophioglossum, **269**
  Psilotum, **216**
  Selaginella, **236**
  Sphaeroplea, **56**
  Vaucheria, **58**
  Volvox, **31**
  Zamia, **328**
Spermatium, *Batrachospermum,* **90**
  Laboulbeniales, 140
  Lichenes, 155
  Nemalion, **88**
  Polysiphonia, **91**
  Porphyra, **86**
  Puccinia, **144**
Spermatophyta, classes, 309
    comparison, 408
  evolutionary tendencies, 417
  flower, 410
  general conclusions, 409
  interrelationships, 410
  seed, 409
Spermogonium, 143, **144,** 155
Sphacelaria, 69, **70**
Sphacelariales, summary, 69
Sphaerella, 28
Sphaeriales, 140
Sphaerocarpales, gametophyte, 173
  sex determination, 175
  sex organs, 174
  sporophyte, 174

Sphaerocarpales, summary, 176
Sphaerocarpus, antheridium, **175**
  archegonium, **176**
  sporophyte, **177**
Sphaeroplea, **56**
Sphaerotheca, 127–**129**
Sphagnales, 192
  gametophyte, 192
  sex organs, 193
  sporophyte, 194
  summary, 195
Sphagnum, antheridium, **193**
  archegonium, **195**
  embryo, **196**
  gametophyte, **193, 194**
  leaf, **194**
  sporophyte, **194**
Sphenophyllales, 248
Sphenophyllum, **249, 250, 257**
Sphenopsida, 4, 247
Spirillum, **101**
Spirogyra, **51–53**
Sporangiophore, *Albugo,* **115**
  Calamitales, **258**
  Empusa, **121**
  Equisetum, **254**
  Hyeniales, 248
  Plasmopara, **117**
  Psilotales, 216
  Rhizopus, **118**
  Sphenophyllales, 249
Sporangium, *Albugo,* **115**
  Angiopteris, **273**
  Azolla, **301**
  Chytridium, **109**
  Cladophora, **55**
  Cutleria, **71**
  Cyrtomium, **288**
  Dictyota, **74**
  Ectocarpus, **67**
  Empusa, **121**
  Equisetales, 253
  Equisetum, **254, 255**
  Filicales, 286
  Hyeniales, 248
  Isoetales, 243
  Laminaria, **77**
  Leptosporangiate ferns, **287**
  Lycopodiales, 223
  Lycopodium, **225**
  Marattiales, 270
  Marsilea, **295**
  Monoblepharis, 111
  Olpidium, **109**
  Ophioglossales, 265
  Ophioglossum, **267**
  Plasmopara, **117**

Sporangium, Polypodiaceae, **286**
  Psilophytales, 213
  Psilotales, 216
  Psilotum, **214**
  Pylaiella, **68**
  Rhizopus, **118, 119**
  Salvinia, **302**
  Saprolegnia, **113**
  Selaginellales, 231
  Sphenophyllales, 248, **249**
  Synchytrium, **110**
  Tmesipteris, **214**
  Vaucheria, **58**
  Zonaria, **75**
Spore, mature, *Dictyota*, **74**
    Equisetum, **254**
    Marchantia, **172**
    Polysiphonia, **91**
    Riccia, **170**
    Zonaria, **75**
  mother cell, 169
    Anemone, **385**
    Anthoceros, **191**
    Cyrtomium, **288**
    Fossombronia, **182**
    Fritillaria, **390**
    Isoetes, **245**
    Lycopodium, **225**
    Marchantia, **172**
    Ophioglossum, **267**
    Pinus, **346**
    Porella, **186**
    Riccia, **170**
    Selaginella, **235**
    Sphaerocarpus, **177**
  tetrad, 169
    Anemone, **385**
    Anthoceros, **191**
    Ginkgo, **337**
    Marchantia, **172**
    Riccia, **170**
Sporocarp, 294
  Azolla, **301**
  Marsilea, **295, 296**
  Marsileaceae, 294
  Salviniaceae, 300
Sporophyll, 223
  Lycopodium, **223**
  Sphenophyllum, **250**
  Tmesipteris, **214**
Sporophyte, 42
  Andreaea, **198**
  Andreaeales, 197
  Angiospermae, 363
  Anthoceros, **187, 191**
  Anthocerotales, 189
  Bennettitales, 315

Sporophyte, Bryales, 201
  Bryophyta, 206
  Coniferales, 342
  Cordaitales, 330
  Cutleria, **71**
  Cycadales, 319
  Cycadofilicales, 311
  Equisetales, 250
  Filicales, 276
  Funaria, **200**
  Ginkgoales, 334
  Gnetales, 354
  Gymnospermae, 309
  independent, 304
  Isoetales, 241
  Jungermanniales, acrogynae, 185
    anacrogynae, 180
  Lycopodiales, 219
  Marattiales, 270
  Marchantia, **172**
  Marchantiales, 168
  Marsileaceae, 293
  Ophioglossales, 262
  Porella, **184, 186**
  Psilotales, 215
  Pteridophyta, 304
  Riccia, **170**
  Salviniaceae, 299
  Selaginellales, 231
  Spermatophyta, 309
  Sphaerocarpales, 174
  Sphaerocarpus, **177**
  Sphagnales, 192
  Sphagnum, **194**
Sporophytic budding, 398
Stamen, 309, **373, 378**
Staurastrum, **50**
Stele, 211
  Actaea, **366**
  Botrychium, **264, 265**
  Dennstaedtia, **281**
  Equisetum, **253**
  Ginkgo, **335**
  Gleichenia, **280**
  Isoetes, **243**
  Lepidodendron, **240**
  Lycopodium, **221, 222**
  Lyginopteris, **313**
  Magnolia, **370**
  Marattia, **271**
  Marsilea, **294**
  Ophioglossum, **264**
  Osmunda, **282**
  Pinus, **344**
  Psilotum, **215**
  Pteridium, **283**
  Selaginella, **232**

Stele, types, 211, 279, 370
  Zamia, **321**
  Zea, **371**
Stem tip, 367
  Coleus, **368**
  Equisetum, **252**
  Isoetes, **242**
  Lycopodium, **219**
  Selaginella, **231**
Stemonitis, **105, 106**
Sterigma, 143, 149
Stigeoclonium, 39
Stigma, 382
Stigonema, **13**
Stoneworts, 63
Streptococcus, **101**
Strobilus, 224
  Bennettitales, 315
  Calamitales, **258**, 259
  Equisetum, **254, 256**
  Hyeniales, **248**
  Lycopodium, **224**
  ovulate, Coniferales, 345
    Cordaianthus, **333**
    Cordaitales, 332
    Cycadales, 323
    Cycas, **322**
    Dioon, **319**
    Ephedra, **355**
    Ginkgo, **337**
    Ginkgoales, 337
    Gnetales, 356
    Gnetum, **357**
    Pinus, **341**
    Welwitschia, **358**
    Zamia, **322**
  Phylloglossum, **220**
  Pteridophyta, 305
  Selaginella, **233**
  Sphenophyllales, **249**
  staminate, Coniferales, 345
    Cordaianthus, **333**
    Cordaitales, 331
    Cycadales, 321
    Ephedra, **355**
    Ginkgo, **336**
    Ginkgoales, 336
    Gnetales, 355
    Gnetum, **357**
    Pinus, **345**
    Welwitschia, **358**
    Zamia, **322**
Stroma, 134
  Claviceps, 135, **136**
  Nectria, 134, **135**
  Plowrightia, 136, **138**
  Xylaria, 139

Style, **373**, 382
Surirella, **22**
  cell division, **24**
Suspensor, 229
  Capsella, **395**
  Ginkgo, **339**
  Lycopodium, **230**
  Pinus, **351**
  Sagittaria, **397**
  Selaginella, **238**
  Zamia, **330**
Symphyogyna, thallus, **179**
Synangium, 273
  Danaea, **272**
  Marattia, **272**
Synchytrium, 109, **110**
Synergid, 385, **386, 390**
Synura, 16, **17**
Syringa, leaf, **363**

T

Tapetum, 226
  Angiopteris, **273**
  Bryales, 203
  Cyrtomium, **288**
  Equisetum, 254, **255**
  Iochroma, **380**
  Lilium, **379**
  Lycopodium, **225**, 226
  Marsilea, **295**
  Salvinia, **302**
  Selaginella, 232, **234**
  Sphagnum, 196
  Zamia, **324**
Taphrina, 123, **124**
Taxaceae, 341
Taxodiaceae, 340
Teliospore, **143**
Telium, **143**
Tetraspore, **91**
Thallophyta, 2, **7**
  classification, 2, 3
Thallus, 7
Thelephoraceae, 147
Tmesipteris, **214**, 216, **217**, 218
Tolypothrix, 12, **13**
Trabecula, 231, 244
Trace, 212
  branch, 212, 222
Tracheid, 210
Tracheophyta, 2–4
Tremella, 146
Tremellales, 146
Tribonema, 19, **20**
Triceratium, **22, 23**

Trichogyne, 87
  Batrachospermum, **90**
  Nemalion, **88**
  Polysiphonia, **92**
  Pyronema, **130**
  Venturia, **137**
Trillium, floral structure, **373**
Tuber, 134
Tuberales, 134
Tubiflorales, 405
Tunica, 367

U

Ulothrix, **38**
Ulotrichales, 38
  summary, 44
Ulva, 41, **42**
Umbellales, 404
Uncinula, 127
Uredinales, 142
Uredinium, **142,** 143
Uredospore, **142,** 143
Uroglena, 16
Urticales, 400
Ustilaginales, 140
Ustilago, **141**

V

Vallecular canal, 252, **253**
Vascular anatomy, Angiospermae, 363–
  372
  Coniferales, 344
  Cycadales, 320
  Equisetales, 252
  Filicales, 276
  Ginkgoales, 335
  Gnetales, 354
  Isoetales, 242
  Lycopodiales, 220
  Marattiales, 270
  Ophioglossales, 263
  Psilotales, 215
  Selaginellales, 231
Vascular bundle, *Acorus,* **372**
  Pteridium, **284**
Vascular system, development of xylem,
  210
  traces and gaps, 212
  types of steles, 211
Vascular tissues, arrangement, 211
Vaucheria, 57, **58, 59**
Vegetative body, algae, 95
  fungi, 157
Vegetative organs (Angiospermae), 363
  leaf structure, **363**

Vegetative organs (Angiospermae), ma-
  ture root, 364, **366**
  older stem, 368, **370**
  root tip, 364, **365**
  stelar types, 370
  stem tip, 367, **368**
Velum, *Agaricus,* **148,** 149
  Isoetes, 243, **244**
Venturia, 137, **138**
Vernation, circinate, 278, **320**
Vessel, 210, **369**
Volva, 149
Volvocales, 26
  summary, 32
Volvox, 30, **31**

W

Welwitschia, 354, **356**
  ovule, **358**
  strobili, **358**
Wheat rust, 142
Woodwardia, leaflet, **285**

X

Xanthophyceae, 18
  summary, 94
Xanthophyll, 19
Xylaria, **139**
Xylem, development, 210
  elements, **369**
  primary, 211
  secondary, 211

Z

Zamia, embryo, **330**
  female cone, **322**
  leaflets, **320**
  male cones, **322**
  megasporophyll, **325**
  microsporangium, **324**
  ovule, **326**
  sperm, **328**
  stem, **321**
Zanardinia, 72
Zea, stem, **371**
Zonal development, 375
Zonaria, **75**
Zoospore, 19
  Chlamydomonas, **27**
  Chlorococcum, **33**
  Chytridium, **108**
  Cladophora, **55**
  Coleochaete, **43**
  Cutleria, **71**

Zoospore, *Ectocarpus,* **67**
   Hydrodictyon, **36**
   Laminaria, 78
   Monoblepharis, **111**
   Oedogonium, **47**
   Olpidium, **109**
   Pediastrum, **35**
   Plasmodiophora, **112**
   Protosiphon, **37**
   Saprolegnia, **113**
   Synchytrium, 111
   Ulothrix, **38**
   Ulva, 41
   Vaucheria, **58**
Zygnema, 53, **54**

Zygote, *Chlamydomonas,* **27**
   Closterium, **49**
   Cocconeis, **25**
   Coleochaete, **43, 44**
   Hydrodictyon, **36**
   Monoblepharis, **111**
   Mougeotia, **50**
   Oedogonium, **47**
   Pandorina, **29**
   Protosiphon, **37**
   Rhizopus, **118**
   Spirogyra, **51–53**
   Ulothrix, **38**
   Volvox, **31**
   Zygnema, **54**
Zymase, 123